SPECTROMETRIC TECHNIQUES

VOLUME III

Contributors

RUDOLF A. HANEL

SAMUEL J. HOWARD

JYRKI K. KAUPPINEN

DAVID G. MURCRAY

FRANK J. MURCRAY

F. W. TAYLOR

SPECTROMETRIC TECHNIQUES

Edited by GEORGE A. VANASSE

Optical Physics Division
Air Force Geophysics Laboratory
Hanscom Air Force Base
Bedford, Massachusetts

VOLUME III

ACADEMIC PRESS   1983

A Subsidiary of Harcourt Brace Jovanovich, Publishers

New York   London
Paris   San Diego   San Francisco   São Paulo   Sydney   Tokyo   Toronto

7127-1570

PHYSICS

ACADEMIC PRESS, INC.
111 Fifth Avenue, New York, New York 10003

United Kingdom Edition published by
ACADEMIC PRESS, INC. (LONDON) LTD.
24/28 Oval Road, London NW1   7DX

 Library of Congress Cataloging in Publication Data
Main entry under title:

Spectrometric techniques.

   Includes bibliographies and indexes.
   1. Spectrum analysis. 2. Spectrum analysis--In-
struments. I. Vanasse, George A. II. Baker,
Doran J.
QC451.S619   535.8'4   76–13949
ISBN 0–12–710403–8 (v. 3 : alk. paper)

PRINTED IN THE UNITED STATES OF AMERICA

83 84 85 86   9 8 7 6 5 4 3 2 1

Contents

Chapter 1   **Experimental Atmospheric Spectroscopy**

David G. Murcray and Frank J. Murcray

Chapter 2   **Planetary Exploration with Spaceborne Michelson Interferometers in the Thermal Infrared**

Rudolf A. Hanel

Chapter 3   **Pressure Modulator Radiometry**

F. W. Taylor

Contributors

Numbers in parentheses indicate the pages on which the authors' contributions begin.

RUDOLF A. HANEL (43), Laboratory for Extraterrestrial Physics, NASA/Goddard Space Flight Center, Greenbelt, Maryland 20771

SAMUEL J. HOWARD* (233), Department of Physics, The Florida State University, Tallahassee, Florida 32306

JYRKI K. KAUPPINEN (199), Department of Physics, University of Oulu, SF-90570 Oulu 57, Finland

DAVID G. MURCRAY (1), Department of Physics, University of Denver, Denver, Colorado 80208

FRANK J. MURCRAY (1), Department of Physics, University of Denver, Denver, Colorado 80208

F. W. TAYLOR (137), Department of Atmospheric Physics, Oxford University, Oxford OX1 2JD, England

*Present address: Code 332, NORDA, NSTL Station, Mississippi 39529.

Preface

This volume, like the two previous volumes, consists of review articles on various areas of spectrometric techniques. Three chapters discuss application of these techniques to atmospheric and space studies, with results obtained described in detail. Remote temperature-sounding techniques are also described in detail in two of these chapters. The remaining two chapters review (with examples) spectral data processing and analysis techniques which are of broad applicability. It was intended that the specific techniques treated be self-contained and of sufficient depth to allow practitioners in spectroscopy to implement them for their use. The technique of Fourier spectroscopy, although mentioned in all chapters but one, is not described in detail because it has been amply covered in the first two volumes of this edited treatise. It is hoped that this volume will serve as a useful reference for spectrometric techniques.

Contents of Previous Volumes

Chapter **1**

Experimental Atmospheric Spectroscopy

DAVID G. MURCRAY
FRANK J. MURCRAY

DEPARTMENT OF PHYSICS
UNIVERSITY OF DENVER
DENVER, COLORADO

1.1. Introduction

The sun is the primordial source of most of the energy present in the earth's atmosphere and surface layers. With negligible exceptions (i.e., solar events), this energy is transmitted to the earth in the form of electromagnetic radiation. Electromagnetic radiation arriving at the outer layers of the earth's atmosphere is modified in intensity and spectral distribution by several processes before some fraction of it reaches the earth's surface where it is absorbed to produce heat or reflected back through the atmosphere.

SPECTROMETRIC TECHNIQUES, VOL. III

In general, the relative importance of various interacting processes between incoming solar radiation and atmospheric gases and particles changes with the wavelength of the radiation. The far ultraviolet (UV) wavelengths are depleted by scattering and absorption, which result in molecular dissociation or atomic ionization. Near UV is also scattered and absorbed, and the absorptions produce electronic transitions in atmospheric gases. As a result of these effects, most of the far- and mid-UV energy is deposited in the mesosphere and upper stratosphere. Scattering by molecules and particles is the primary energy depletion process in the visible region of the spectrum and is small enough that most of the energy in these wavelengths reaches the surface to be absorbed and produces warming or reflection. In the infrared (IR) region photon energies correspond to vibration–rotation and pure rotational transitions in most molecules, and hence attenuation in this region is strongly wavelength dependent.

Strictly speaking, the topic of atmospheric spectroscopy covers all these processes, but this discussion emphasizes mainly the IR region where molecular vibration–rotation or pure rotation transitions are the prime factors in influencing radiative transfer. Under this limitation, atmospheric spectroscopy becomes a study of molecular spectroscopy with a fundamental difference in objectives. The major objective of molecular spectroscopy has been the determination of molecular structure, energy levels, etc., from the spectrum of the molecule. Atmospheric spectroscopy utilizes knowledge of molecular parameters, from whatever source, to predict the spectrum of a molecular species so that its atmospheric presence and/or concentration can be derived from measured spectra or to predict the species' influence on radiative transfer in the atmosphere. Input from these aspects of atmospheric spectroscopy is directly applicable to two questions that have strong implications for society as a whole. These are briefly discussed in the following to illustrate the practical importance of the topic.

A black sphere placed at the mean Earth–sun distance would reach a temperature at which the net radiation flow would be zero. Calculation of this temperature results in a much lower value than the mean temperature of the earth. This difference is primarily due to absorption of the outgoing long-wave radiation by the earth's atmosphere, that is, the so-called greenhouse effect. The absorption of the outgoing IR is strongly dependent on atmospheric parameters such as the concentrations of CO_2, oxides of nitrogen, and hydrocarbons. This has led to concerns about climatic changes due to the increases in concentrations of these gases as a result of man's activities. Although the effect is qualitatively understood, quantitatively it is a very complex problem requiring more accurate information on radiative transfer in the atmosphere than is currently available. The process of deriving this information fits precisely the above definition of atmospheric spectroscopy.

The role of solar radiation (either directly by absorption of solar radiation, or indirectly through the coupling of surface warming into the atmosphere) as the driving engine for atmospheric motions, as well as for the temperature structure of the atmosphere, has been studied for some time and is qualitatively understood. But the role of the solar UV radiation as a factor in the chemistry of the stratosphere has, with the single exception of ozone production, received little attention. There is, however, a growing awareness of the complexity of stratospheric photochemistry and the possible adverse effects of perturbations of these processes by man-made pollutants.

Under the narrow definition given above, the actual photochemical processes lie outside the scope of this discussion. However, as a result of these reactions certain molecular species should exist in the stratosphere, and atmospheric spectroscopy provides a powerful tool for the detection and determination of concentration levels for these species. The accuracy of many theoretical photochemical models can be tested in this manner.

The two examples cited, that is, climatic change as a result of pollutant buildup in the atmosphere, and the photochemistry of the ozone layer, have been the subject of studies by the National Academy of Sciences (National Research Council, 1979, 1980, 1982). These and other questions of a similar nature point up the importance of atmospheric spectroscopy as a tool in the assessment of man's impact on atmospheric processes.

1.2. Experimental Requirements

A. THEORETICAL CONSIDERATIONS

1. *Origin of Spectral Lines*

The frequency of a spectral line is determined by the difference in the energy states of an atom or molecule before and after the absorption or emission of a photon. Electronic transitions in atoms result in individual lines at UV or visible frequencies. Molecular electronic transitions are accompanied by changes in vibrational and rotational states resulting in groupings of lines which are designated as bands. These again absorb in the UV and visible frequency ranges. Lines in the far IR are produced by transitions in the rotational states of molecules. When these rotational transitions are associated with changes in the vibrational state of the molecule, the result is a group of lines at mid-IR frequencies which constitute a vibration – rotation band.

The study of the selection rules, transition probabilities, and molecular energy states which govern the frequencies and intensities of these bands fall (under our definitions) in the province of molecular spectroscopy, and the reader is referred to works on this subject, such as the excellent three-volume treatise by Herzberg (1945), for details.

2. Calculation of Transmittance

The parameters listed in the preceding permit the calculation of the positions and strengths of spectral lines. Calculation of atmospheric transmissions also requires expressions for the variation in apparent strength over the width of the line (i.e., the line shape). Various line shapes have been employed in calculations, most of which are empirical or theoretical modifications of the Lorentz line. The monochromatic transmittance of a Lorentz line spectrum is given by

$$T(v) = \exp\left[-\sum_i \frac{s_i^0}{\pi} \frac{\gamma_i}{(v - v_{0i})^2 + \gamma_i^2} u\right] \tag{1.1}$$

where the summation is over all lines that contribute to the absorption at the frequency v, v_0 is the frequency of the line center (cm^{-1}), s^0 is the line intensity (cm^{-2} atm), γ is the half-width (cm^{-1}), and u is the amount of gas (atm cm) in the optical path. For binary gas mixtures, γ is proportional to the effective broadening pressure P_e (atm): $\gamma = \gamma^0 P_e$ where $P_e = P_t + (B - 1)P$. Here B is the self-broadening coefficient, P_t is the total pressure of the gas mixture, P is the pressure of the absorbing gas, and γ^0 is the half-width at standard conditions.

The line intensities are generally assumed to depend on temperature T according to

$$S^0(T) = S^0(T_0)(T_0/T)^{3/2} \exp\left[-1.439E''\left(\frac{1}{T} - \frac{1}{T_0}\right)\right] \tag{1.2}$$

where E'' (cm^{-1}) is the lower state energy.

From these expressions it is evident that when calculating the transmission for a slant path in the atmosphere, the variation of temperature and pressure along the path must be taken into account. With today's large computers, the absorption spectra of many IR absorption bands can be calculated using the expression given in Eq. (1.1). For calculating the atmospheric transmission, the pressure and temperature dependence is taken into account by performing the calculation for thin layers of constant pressure and temperature. Given the large number of lines present in the absorption bands of many of the species found in the atmosphere, performance of such calculations is not a trivial matter. Computer programs for performing such calculations have been developed by several groups, the most notable being a group of investigators at the Air Force Geophysics Laboratory (AFGL). The programs they have assembled are given in several reports (McClatchey, 1970; McClatchey and Selby, 1972, 1974; McClatchey *et al.*, 1972; Smith *et al.*, 1978).

In order to use the various line-by-line computer programs, it is necessary that the individual line parameters — positions, strengths, halfwidths, and lower state energy — for all the lines that contribute to the absorption in the region of interest be known. Compiling a list of such parameters for the molecular species of atmospheric interest is also a very large task. Most of these represent elaborations from a list compiled at AFGL (McClatchey *et al.*, 1973; Rothman, 1981). The most recent version of this compilation contains several hundred thousand lines.

Given the temperature, pressure, and composition along an atmospheric slant path, it is then possible with these programs and compilations to calculate in great detail the atmospheric transmission over the slant path. Figure 1.1 shows the result of several such calculations. These were performed to show the relative transparency of the atmosphere above the observing platform in various wavelength regions as a function of the altitude of the observing platform. The 4-km altitude represented a high-altitude ground observing site, 14-km altitude a typical aircraft platform, and 30-km altitude a balloon platform. These calculations assumed an instrument resolution of 0.1 cm^{-1} and are taken from a report of Kyle and Goldman (1975).

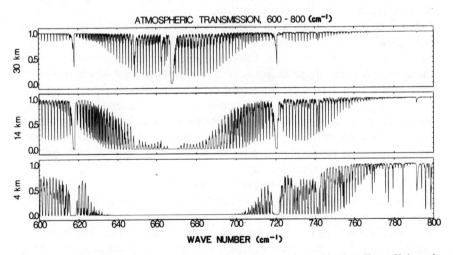

FIG. 1.1. Calculated atmospheric transmission above various altitudes. (From Kyle and Goldman, 1975, p. 53.)

B. ROLE OF EXPERIMENTAL STUDIES

If it is possible to perform calculations of the sort discussed in Section 1.2.A, what are the implications for experimental atmospheric spectroscopy? One of the major tasks of the experimental studies is to provide data for checking the accuracy of the theoretical calculations. Since the calculations can be performed for infinite resolution, this implies that the experimental studies should also be obtained at as high a resolution as possible. As already noted, the calculations depend on a number of factors, that is, the molecular parameters, the atmospheric composition, the shape of the absorption line, and the accuracy with which the variable pressure path can be replaced with discrete layers. Thus comparisons between experimental atmospheric spectra and theoretical spectra can be used to check the accuracy of the computer program and the line parameter data used in the calculations. In many cases comparisons of this type have resulted in the use of atmospheric data to correct the molecular line parameters' data tape. This occurs because most atmospheric data are obtained over optical paths that are difficult to duplicate in the laboratory. In most cases, where possible, the corrections are verified by further laboratory data or theoretical calculations.

Given molecular line parameters and an accurate computer program, the accuracy of the calculations then depends on the accuracy with which the state of the atmosphere is known. Conversely, the experimental data can be used to obtain information on the state of the atmosphere. Spectral resolution is particularly important in this type of investigation, and some aspects of these studies require high resolution.

The final parameter in these calculations, and one which is not discussed in Section 1.2.A, is the shape of the absorption line. The expression given in Eq. (1.1) is for a Lorentz line. Laboratory studies and theoretical analysis show that this line shape is not correct for low pressure where molecular collisions are no longer the dominant broadening mechanism. Laboratory and atmospheric studies have also shown that this line shape is not correct for the wings of the lines. Most calculations employ modifications to the line shapes which affect the wings of the lines. Some aspects of the line-shape problem are best studied in the atmosphere. For these studies high absolute accuracy in transmission is required.

The preceding discussion has been limited to atmospheric transmission measurements and calculations. An additional problem area, quite closely related, concerns the flow of IR radiation in the atmosphere. The theoretical analysis follows directly from the transmission calculations but is complicated by the fact that each atmospheric layer both absorbs and emits radiation. Experimental investigations of radiative transfer in the atmosphere place requirements on the instrumentation which are quite different from those placed on it by transmission measurements. This difference is mainly due to the weak intensity of the source (the earth and its atmosphere) which must be used in the emission studies. Thus, the major requirement for emission studies is sensitivity.

The various points raised in the foregoing discussion are treated in more detail in the following sections, which also include examples as illustrations.

1.3. Instrumentation

A. ABSORPTION STUDIES

As noted in previous sections, atmospheric spectroscopy is strongly dependent on molecular spectroscopy. This reliance also requires a close association between the instrumentation used in molecular spectroscopy laboratories and that used in atmospheric spectroscopy experiments. A great deal of the laboratory work needed in atmospheric spectroscopy can be performed in molecular spectroscopy laboratories. It should be noted, however, that much of the data required in atmospheric spectroscopy differs sufficiently from those of interest to the molecular spectroscopist, so only a few laboratories concentrate on obtaining data of interest for atmospheric spectroscopy. The instrumentation employed in these studies is the same as that used in molecular spectroscopy laboratories and has been discussed in other volumes of this series. In view of this, the major emphasis of this chapter is placed on the instrumentation used for obtaining field data.

1. *Sources*

Major emphasis in most field programs is placed on getting data concerning the transmission over fairly long atmospheric paths, that is, on the order of several kilometers. This imposes very stringent conditions on the sources for such measurements. Most studies using artificial sources have employed carbon arcs and searchlight optics. Several studies have been performed using such sources over path lengths up to 10 km since Taylor and Yates (1957) pioneered work in this area. The early studies were limited in resolution by the technology available at the time they were made. However, they were more than adequate for checking the theoretical models available at that time. The studies have been repeated by Dowling and Haught (1977) at higher resolution, as the technology for making the measurements became available and theoretical models grew more detailed. Several pollutants in urban areas have been monitored using long atmospheric paths

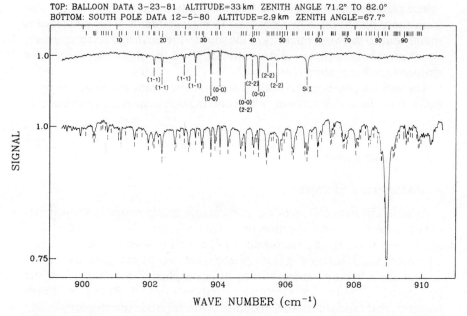

TOP: BALLOON DATA 3-23-81 ALTITUDE=33 km ZENITH ANGLE 71.2° TO 82.0°
BOTTOM: SOUTH POLE DATA 12-5-80 ALTITUDE=2.9 km ZENITH ANGLE=67.7°

FIG. 1.2. Solar spectra in the 900–910-cm⁻¹ region as observed from the ground and 33 km showing numerous OH lines. (From Goldman *et al.*, 1981.)

achieved by using many traversal absorption cells filled with ambient air. These also employ carbon-arc sources (Pitts *et al.*, 1977).

The development of tunable lasers promises to add a significant new source for use in such studies. Current available power levels and the wavelength range over which they can be tuned have limited their use to date to shorter atmospheric paths, with emphasis placed on measuring pollutants or trace constituents (Hinkley, 1976).

The difficulty of using these sources and the need for data taken where the pressure varies over the absorption path led to the use of the sun as the source of IR radiation for absorption studies. The sun is a very good source, particularly at the longer wavelengths. At the shorter wavelengths many of the absorption features are due to molecules and atoms present in the solar atmosphere. The solar lines diminish in number at the longer wavelengths. However, at the resolution achieved in current studies (Goldman *et al.*, 1981, 1983b), a number of solar OH lines are visible in the 10-μm region (Fig. 1.2). A recently noted characteristic of the sun is the presence of narrow emission lines in the mid-IR (Fig. 1.3). When the sun is used as the source for detecting trace constituents and pollutants in the atmosphere, care must be taken to make sure that the line used originates in the earth's atmosphere and not in the sun. Since the solar lines are of interest to the solar physicist, they have been the topic of investigation at the Kitt Peak National Observatory, and an atlas listing various solar lines has been prepared (Hall, 1974). One problem with using the sun as a source is the determination of the intensity outside the atmosphere. This is particularly troublesome in attempting to study continuum absorption and atmospheric line shapes. Other celestial objects have been used as sources for atmospheric spectroscopy studies, particularly at the shorter wavelengths. Their use has been limited, since in most cases they are weak sources in comparison to the sun.

2. Spectral Information

a. Radiative Transfer Studies. It has been pointed out in Section 1.2 that one requirement of experimental atmospheric spectroscopy is to obtain data that can be used to check the accuracy of the theoretical transmittance calculations. For these studies high-resolution spectral data covering a relatively broad spectral region are required. Early experimental investigations performed to obtain data pertinent to this objective generally employed grating spectrometers as the means of obtaining the spectral information. In most cases the spectrometers used in these studies were constructed specifically for field use, since in many cases the units were required to operate automatically. In addition, getting a laboratory unit to operate properly in the field environment required such extensive modifications that it was simpler and less expensive to construct a custom unit. As the resolution needed in the experimental studies increased, the physical size of

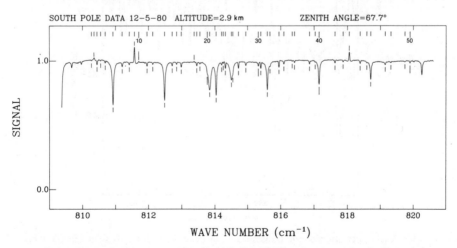

FIG. 1.3. IR solar spectrum obtained from the South Pole. Note presence of solar emission lines (9, 43) near 811 and 818 cm⁻¹. (From Blatherwick *et al.*, 1982.)

the grating spectrometer required to achieve the desired resolution became too large for field use. At this time, several Fourier transform spectrometer (FTS) systems became available commercially, and several special units were constructed for taking astronomical data. The combination of relatively small size and high signal to noise offered by the FTS systems led to their being incorporated into the majority of systems used to obtain the data needed in transmission studies. In most cases the units used in the field program have been constructed specifically for field work. For some ground-based measurements, excellent results have been obtained at relatively low cost using slightly modified commercial units. The resolution that can be achieved in the field data with FTS systems now appears to be adequate to meet most experimental needs insofar as checking the accuracy of theoretical transmission calculations is concerned. Considerable work remains to be done in the area of "continuum" studies, but an FTS system may not be the best instrument to use. "Continuum" studies are concerned with atmospheric transmission in spectral regions several wave numbers away from absorption line centers. For these studies resolution is not so

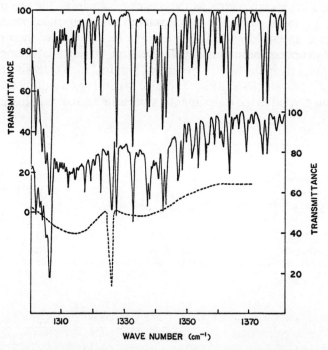

FIG. 1.4. Upper atmospheric transmittance as determined from IR solar spectra. Upper curve, 11.0 km, solar zenith angle 58.7°. Lower curve, 30 km, solar zenith angle 92.4°. Dashed line indicates absorption due to HNO_3. (From Murcray et al., 1968, p. 79.)

important as radiometric accuracy, and grating spectrometers are often used.

b. Constituent Measurements. The fact that absorption features present in IR solar spectra obtained from 30 km during sunset are due to HNO_3 (Fig. 1.4) and NO_2 (Fig. 1.5) emphasized the capability of atmospheric spectroscopy for obtaining data on atmospheric composition. Detection of these species, coupled with the controversy over possible perturbation of the stratospheric ozone layer by operation of aircraft in the stratosphere or by continued release of chlorofluoromethanes, has led to the use of IR techniques to obtain data on the distribution of many constituents of interest in atmospheric chemistry. The instruments used in these studies have run the range from low-resolution filter radiometers to high-resolution laser heterodyne spectrometer systems. In addition, radiometers employing gas cells have been used to obtain data on particular species. The use of gas cells to obtain spectral information is one area in which atmospheric spectroscopy employs systems that were not initially developed for laboratory investigations. The unique aspects of these instruments is discussed in more detail in Section 1.5.B on atmospheric remote sensing.

B. ATMOSPHERIC EMISSION STUDIES

The source of the radiation in these studies is the earth's atmosphere. In many cases, data are sought concerning the composition or physical state of the atmosphere in spectral regions where the atmospheric emissivity may be considerably less than 1% and the temperature 200 K or less. This is obviously not a very intense source of radiation, and the instrumentation used in these studies must be sensitive. For ultimate sensitivity IR detectors should be operated in a background-limited condition. For many instruments the limiting radiation can arise from radiation emitted by the instrument itself. In these cases increased sensitivity can be achieved by cooling the instrument. The problems associated with cooling various instruments has been discussed in detail in a chapter in the first volume of this series (Huppi, 1977). Almost all types of spectral instruments used as room-temperature instruments have been operated at cryogenic temperatures with the exception of the large grating spectrometers. The problems associated with cooling such large instruments have generally precluded using them cold. On the other hand, small grating spectrometers, high- and low-resolution interferometers, and a number of radiometers that employ cold optics have been used to obtain atmospheric emission data. Several novel spectroscopic instruments have been constructed specifically to obtain atmospheric emission data. One of these is the cold etalon spectrometer system which will be

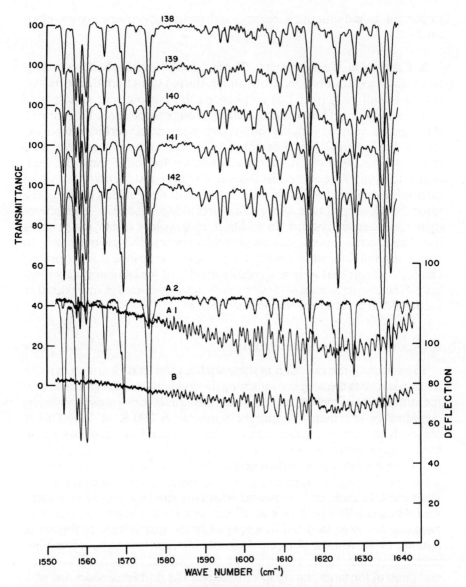

FIG. 1.5. Identification of the v_3 NO_2 band. Records 138–142, sunset balloon spectra. Curve A1, spectrum of NO_2 obtained from reagent-grade red fuming nitric acid supplied by Baker Co. and curve A2, the corresponding portion of the v_2 H_2O spectrum. Curve B, spectrum of CP grade NO_2 from Matheson Co., at a pressure of 2.5 mm Hg. (From Goldman *et al.,* 1970, p. 444.)

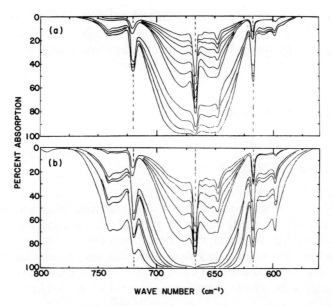

FIG. 1.6. Absorption curves of CO_2 in the 500–800-cm⁻¹ region (from Burch *et al.*, 1961, p. 44):

(a)		(b)	
w (atm cm)	P_e (mm Hg)	w (atm cm)	P_e (mm Hg)
0.386	33.2	0.748	60.5
	67		116
	116		218
	208		436
	416		884
	832		1675
	1680	6.15	529
	269		984
3.14	468		1780
	900	12.1	1055
	1715		1905
		24.3	2110

flown on the Upper Atmosphere Research satellite (UARS). This instrument has the advantage of large throughput, moderate resolution, and simple spectral scanning. It is subsequently discussed in more detail, since it has been developed specifically for atmospheric spectroscopic studies.

1.4. Experimental Studies

A. LONG-PATH TRANSMISSION

1. *Absorption Cell Studies*

Elsasser, in a series of classic monographs (Elsasser, 1942; Elsasser and Culbertson, 1960) on heat transfer by IR radiation in the atmosphere, pointed out that for many studies of atmospheric radiative transfer, high-resolution spectra contained more detail than the atmospheric modelers could handle. He emphasized that what was needed at that time was low-resolution data for the major absorbing species (H_2O, CO_2, and O_3) taken under atmospheric conditions. Howard *et al.* (1956) undertook a

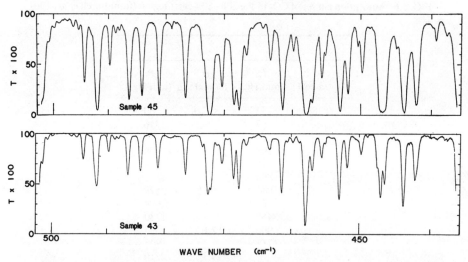

FIG. 1.7. Spectral transmittance curves of pure H_2O between 437 and 502 cm^{-1}. Spectral slit width $\cong 6$ cm^{-1} (from Burch *et al.*, 1973, p. 3-3):

Sample	Temp. (K)	p (atm)	u (molecules cm^{-2})
43	425	0.0198	1.42×10^{20}
45	425	0.0684	4.92×10^{20}

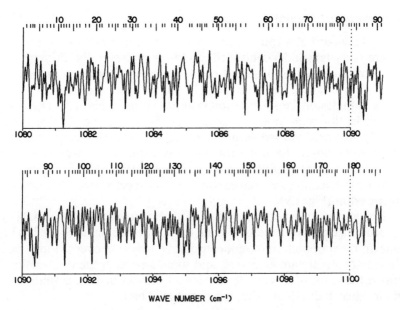

FIG. 1.8. Portion of a laboratory spectrum of ozone obtained by Damon. (From Damon *et al.*, 1981.)

series of measurements which they used to obtain transmission data that would meet these requirements. The measurements were taken over long absorption paths, under carefully controlled conditions with respect to amount, temperature, and pressure of any broadening gas in the cell. Sample spectra obtained in this study are shown in Fig. 1.6. Burch *et al.* (1973) have continued to conduct investigations using long-path absorption cells with increased resolution as spectroscopic technology has improved. Figure 1.7 shows a recent spectrum obtained by this group. It is characteristic of the resolution which can be achieved in broadband transmission studies of this sort.

Shaw and co-workers (Damon *et al.*, 1981) also have been using long-path cells to obtain spectroscopic data for several compounds of interest in atmospheric transmission studies, as well as for some species of interest in atmospheric composition measurements. Figure 1.8 shows a portion of an ozone spectrum obtained recently by this group. The long-path length in the cell makes it possible to simulate the amounts and pressure environments of ozone in the stratosphere. Several other long-path absorption cell facilities have been developed. However, most of these are used to obtain constituent data and are discussed subsequently.

2. Atmospheric Studies

The long-path absorption cells offer an excellent method of obtaining transmission data under controlled conditions; however, the ultimate test of the theoretical calculations must be made against data taken in the atmosphere. Taylor and Yates (1957) conducted such an experiment in the late 1950s. Samples of the spectra obtained are given in Fig. 1.9. The Navy's interest in this topic has continued over the years, and data have been recently obtained by Dowling and Haught (1977) over similar paths at much higher resolution. These spectra have been compared with one of the computer programs (LOWTRAN) developed at the AFGL (Selby *et al.,* 1978) for calculating the transmission to be expected over various atmospheric paths (Fig. 1.9).

These studies have been concerned with obtaining transmission data over a broad range of wavelengths. During the last decade, much work has been done on the propagation of monochromatic radiation over the long paths. These laser studies are extensive, and some aspects of the propagation lie outside the scope of this article. In view of the fact that these studies are a major research discipline, they are not treated here.

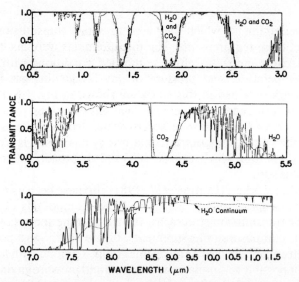

FIG. 1.9. Atmospheric transmittance over a 0.3-km path in the Chesapeake Bay area compared with LOWTRAN 2 calculations (· · ·); (—) Taylor and Yates (1957). (From Taylor and Yates, 1957.)

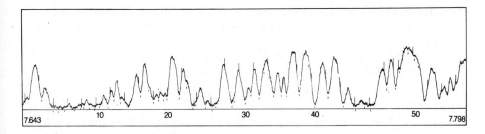

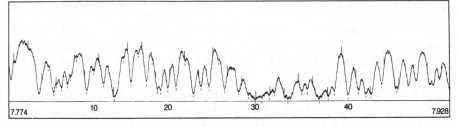

WAVELENGTH (μm)

FIG. 1.10. Portion of the IR solar spectrum obtained from the Jungfraujock by Migeotte. (From Migeotte *et al.*, 1956.)

B. SOLAR SPECTRAL INVESTIGATIONS

1. *Ground-Based Experiments*

As noted in the previous section, long-path transmission studies using conventional IR sources are difficult to perform and do not yield any data relative to the slant-path problem. It has long been recognized that the sun is an excellent source for IR studies of the atmosphere. It is relatively easy, experimentally, to obtain solar spectra; hence atmospheric studies using the sun as the source can be undertaken at relatively low cost. The large atmospheric absorptions in many spectral regions due to absorption by atmospheric water vapor and carbon dioxide represent one difficulty encountered when the sun is used as a source. In order to reduce these absorptions, several investigators have made their observations from high-altitude sites. The classic study of this sort is that of Migeotte *et al.* (1956) who obtained solar spectra from the Jungfraujoch in the spectral region from 2 to 25 μm. These spectra were published in the form of an atlas, along with identification of the various atmospheric absorption features present in the spectra. Figure 1.10 shows a portion of this atlas. This work has been continued by Delbouille *et al.* (1973) with emphasis on the shorter wavelengths and, in particular, on solar absorption features for solar physics studies. Farmer and Key (1965) went to Mt. Chacaltaya, Bolivia, to obtain spectra at an even higher altitude in order to extend the wavelength region covered.

The strong water vapor rotational band almost completely absorbs the solar radiation before it reaches the ground even at Mt. Chacaltaya. Farmer and Key were able to obtain data in several long-wavelength windows, particularly at 345 μm.

Ground-based solar spectra have also been obtained over the years by other investigators. However, no systematic investigation utilizing the high-resolution currently available was undertaken until our group at the University of Denver started a new atlas based on higher resolution data, obtained using an interferometer system (Goldman *et al.*, 1980). Sample spectra from this atlas are given in Fig. 1.11, and Table 1.1 lists the identification of the observed absorption features.

These atlases have played a very significant role in atmospheric spectroscopy. The identification of the various absorption features in the Jungfraujoch spectra formed a significant portion of the data that comprised the first AFGL tape of atmospheric absorption line parameters. The interplay between the identification of absorption features present in atmospheric spectra and the data contained on the AFGL tape started with this atlas and has continued through the years. Particular examples of this interplay are discussed in the following.

The major objective of the various atlases has been to improve our theoretical understanding of the interaction of IR radiation with the atmo-

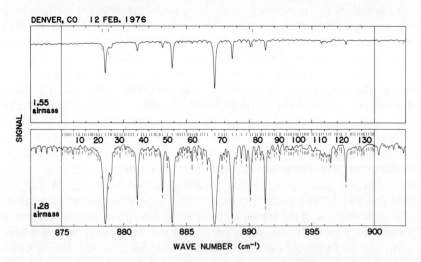

FIG. 1.11. Portion of the IR solar spectrum obtained from Denver. Identification of the observed features is in Table 1.1. (From Goldman *et al.*, 1980.)

TABLE 1.1

IDENTIFICATION OF SOME SPECTRAL FEATURES IN FIGURE 1.11

No.	Sequence v (observed) (cm^{-1})	Identification	No.	Sequence v (observed) (cm^{-1})	Identification
1	875.094	HNO_3	31	879.868	HNO_3
2	875.282	HNO_3	32	880.069	?
3	875.428	HNO_3	33	880.180	HNO_3
4	875.525	HNO_3, CO_2	34	880.364	HNO_3, CO_2
5	875.621	HNO_3	35	880.509	HNO_3
6	875.765	HNO_3	36	880.651	HNO_3
7	875.960	H_2O, HNO_3	37	880.797	HNO_3
8	876.209	HNO_3	38	881.094	H_2O
9	876.371	HNO_3	39	881.400	HNO_3
10	876.476	HNO_3, CO_2	40	881.592	HNO_3
11	876.710	HNO_3	41	881.795	HNO_3
12	876.867	HNO_3	42	882.057	HNO_3
13	876.994	HNO_3	43	882.217	HNO_3
14	877.193	HNO_3	44	882.417	HNO_3
15	877.345	HNO_3	45	882.523	HNO_3
16	877.430	HNO_3	46	882.624	HNO_3
17	877.519	HNO_3	47	882.791	HNO_3
18	877.651	HNO_3	48	882.880	Cal?
19	877.832	HNO_3	49	883.095	H_2O
20	877.939	HNO_3	50	883.449	HNO_3
21	878.081	HNO_3	51	883.860	H_2O
22	878.282	HNO_3	52	884.235	HNO_3, CO_2
23	878.547	H_2O	53	884.369	HNO_3
24	878.781	HNO_3	54	884.485	HNO_3
25	878.941	HNO_3	55	884.646	HNO_3, H_2O
26	879.032	HNO_3	56	884.835	HNO_3
27	879.228	HNO_3	57	885.046	HNO_3
28	879.359	HNO_3	58	885.166	HNO_3, H_2O
29	879.488	HNO_3	59	885.297	HNO_3
30	879.709	HNO_3	60	885.440	HNO_3

sphere. Ground-based solar spectroscopy has also been used to study the composition of the atmosphere. Once a particular absorption feature has been identified as the result of a constituent of interest in atmospheric chemistry, then solar spectra obtained at various times and locations can be used to study the constituents' variability. This technique is particularly valuable for studies of stratospheric constituents or constituents that cannot be measured from the ground using *in situ* techniques. Quantitative studies generally require moderately high resolution, and it is only in recent years that this technique has been used extensively for such objectives. The

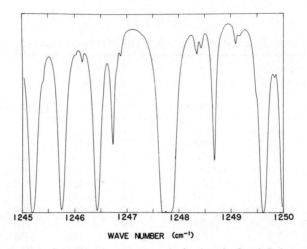

WAVE NUMBER (cm⁻¹)

FIG. 1.12. Portion of the IR solar spectrum obtained at the South Pole on 5 December 1980. (From Goldman *et al.*, 1983a. Copyright © 1983 Pergamon Press, Ltd., reprinted with permission.)

technique becomes a more valuable experimental tool as the resolution obtainable is increased. This is due not only to the increase in sensitivity of the technique for detection and measurement of these species, but also to the fact that with sufficient resolution the data can be used to obtain information on the altitude distribution of the constituent. An example of this is given in Fig. 1.12, which shows a portion of a solar spectrum obtained from the South Pole (Blatherwick *et al.*, 1982). Figure 1.13 shows a comparison between this spectrum and one calculated using a nonlinear least-squares technique. In the theoretical calculations, the altitude profile for N_2O, which is responsible for the absorption line at 1248.7 cm⁻¹, is adjusted to provide the best fit possible for the total line profile. The profile determined by this technique gives excellent agreement with groundbased *in situ* techniques and other observations of the variation of N_2O with altitude. Hoell *et al.* (1980) have used laser heterodyne techniques to study the absorption due to ammonia at 927.323 cm⁻¹ with a resolution of 0.007 cm⁻¹. As laboratory studies of the shapes of absorption lines yield better information on the pressure dependence of such lines, information concerning the altitude distribution of the constituent should become even better defined. The improved sensitivity that can be achieved with laser heterodyne techniques has been used by Mumma and co-workers (Rogers *et al.*, 1982) in an attempt to detect stratospheric ClO. The results to date have been negative, which is surprising as calculations indicate that the absorption should be observable.

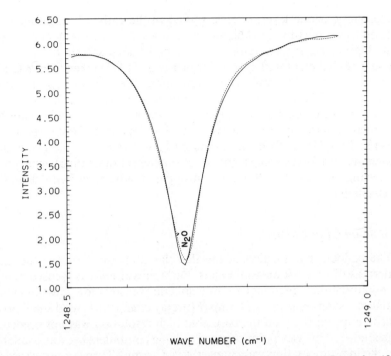

FIG. 1.13. A comparison between observed (dashed line, South Pole, 5 December 1980) and calculated (solid line) spectra for the 1248.5-cm^{-1} region. (From Goldman *et al.*, 1983a. Copyright © 1983 Pergamon Press, Ltd.; reprinted with permission.)

2. Aircraft Observations

Since the total column amounts of H_2O, CO_2, CH_4, and N_2O fall off, at least linearly, with pressure (exponentially with altitude), there is considerable advantage when attempting to measure stratospheric trace constituents in obtaining spectra from a high-altitude platform. In addition, most studies concerned with the flow of radiation in the earth's atmosphere require experimental data taken at various altitudes. Aircraft provide an excellent means of obtaining data at altitudes up to 15 km (operator attended) and up to 20 km (unattended U-2 operation). Early atmospheric transmission measurements from aircraft generally were performed to obtain data in the 2- to 4-μm region. Houghton *et al.* (1961) performed one of the first studies of this type from a Canberra aircraft. A large number of solar spectra covering the region from 2 to 5 μm were obtained by a group at the Canadian Armament Research and Development Establishment (Cumming *et al.*, 1965). The objective of these studies was to obtain data on atmospheric transmission at high altitudes.

With the controversy that arose owing to the possible perturbation of the stratospheric ozone layer, interest shifted in the early 1970s to obtaining data on trace constituents. This gave rise to several measurement programs that obtained constituent data by analyzing IR solar spectra from aircraft. These included measurements by Farmer *et al.* (1975) taken from KC 135, Concorde, and U-2 aircraft. They were among the first solar spectral measurements made using a moving mirror interferometer system. (The earlier aircraft measurements used grating spectrometers.) Girard and co-workers also made aircraft measurements from the Concorde (Fontanella *et al.*, 1974) and the NASA Convair 990 (Girard and Besson, 1977). These measurements were made using a grill spectrometer (Girard, 1963), which is an interesting method for obtaining throughput advantage with a grating spectrometer.

3. *Balloon Observations*

The balloon investigation of the IR solar spectrum followed the same pattern as the aircraft measurements. Early measurements focused mainly on obtaining data pertinent to atmospheric transmission measurements. Initial measurements by our group (Murcray *et al.*, 1961) used small prism instruments, partially on the basis that high resolution was not needed in such studies. This viewpoint changed as large computers became available, and the instrumentation was changed to a Czerny–Turner grating system, which aimed at achieving increased resolution in the balloon studies. Several flights were made with this system, the results of which were summarized in an article in *Applied Optics* (Murcray *et al.*, 1969). One objective of this program was to study transmission over very long stratospheric paths. In order to achieve such paths, data were taken during sunset. Examination of these spectra revealed absorptions that were identified as being due to HNO_3 and NO_2. This detection, coupled with the interest in the stratospheric ozone layer, led several groups to use solar spectra obtained from balloon platforms to compile data on many compounds of atmospheric interest. Farmer and Raper (1977) and Girard (Ackerman *et al.*, 1976) flew instruments similar to those used in their aircraft measurement programs on balloons. Zander *et al.* (1977), who had been studying the sun by obtaining solar spectra in regions that could not be observed from the ground, also used the instrument to obtain data on stratospheric constituents.

Resolution is important in constituent studies, and, in view of this, our group at the University of Denver also changed instrumentation again in order to achieve better resolution. We decided to use an interferometer, with which it was possible to obtain a resolution of 0.01 cm^{-1} (unapodized) in a small package. With computers now capable of processing large amounts of data at relatively low cost, FTSs have been replacing grating spectrometers

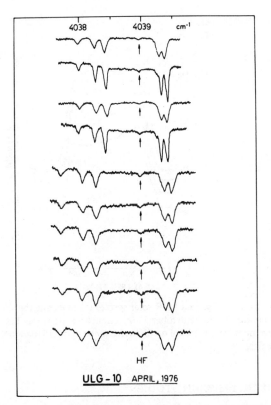

FIG. 1.14. Solar spectra near 4039 cm⁻¹, taken from 27.9-km altitude, at various solar zenith angles (linear ordinate deflections). (From Zander *et al.*, 1977, p. 118.)

as standard spectroscopic instruments. The Zander *et al.* (1977) results illustrate that very excellent spectra can be obtained with a grating spectrometer (see Fig. 1.14). However, as noted above, the grating instrument will be much larger. The ultimate resolution in balloon-borne spectral studies is that achieved by Menzies (1979), using a laser heterodyne technique. Figure 1.15 shows sunset solar spectra obtained by Menzies. This absorption feature, which was thought to be due to ClO, may be due to ozone. This is one of the current problems of atmospheric spectroscopy that is addressed in the next chapter.

4. *Satellite Observations*

Several satellite experiments have been accepted by NASA for shuttle and other vehicles. None of these have flown to date, and their discussion is included in the next chapter.

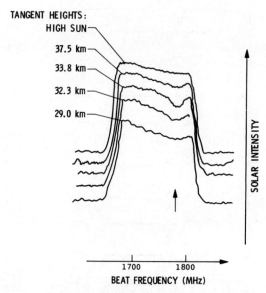

FIG. 1.15. An overlay of several LHR solar spectra taken during the sunset period from a float altitude of 40 km, on 20 September 1978. Launch location was Palestine, Texas. The frequency displacement from the local oscillator frequency, 853.18104 cm⁻¹, is the horizontal axis. (From Menzies, 1979, p. 152.)

C. ATMOSPHERIC EMISSION STUDIES

1. Atmospheric Temperature Measurements

From a theoretical standpoint, atmospheric emission calculations are an almost trivial extension of the atmospheric transmission calculations involving convolutions of the change in transmission with the Planck function for blackbody radiation. Kaplan (1959) pointed out that since CO_2 was uniformly mixed at a known concentration in the atmosphere, atmospheric transmission in regions where CO_2 was the dominant absorber could be accurately determined. The observed atmospheric emission in these regions can then be used to obtain information on atmospheric temperature. In particular, a satellite instrument measuring the upwelling radiation in the 15-μm region could be used to obtain atmospheric temperature profiles under the satellite. Information concerning the altitude dependence of the temperature in such a measurement arises from the fact that the atmospheric transmission over a vertical atmospheric path varies significantly with wavelength over the band. As a result, the emission observed by the satellite is strongly weighted by the atmospheric temperature at particular altitudes. Examples of the weighting functions associated with various spectral intervals are given in Fig. 1.16. The concept has progressed through the various required stages to become incorporated into operational satellite systems. In fact this area has been the subject of considerable research, in addition to the operational aspects of retrieving temperature profile from the radiation data. Too much work has been done in this area to treat it in detail in this chapter; however, in spite of this work, there are still some areas where additional research is needed. One major concern is the question of what sort of instrumentation should be used on the next generation of meteorological satellites. There is no agreement on what spectral intervals to include in the instrument in order to obtain the best temperature profile data. Part of the lack of agreement is the result of our lack of understanding of atmospheric spectroscopy.

Current operational satellite inversion schemes use statistical methods rather than calculations based on atmospheric transmission. Thus, the

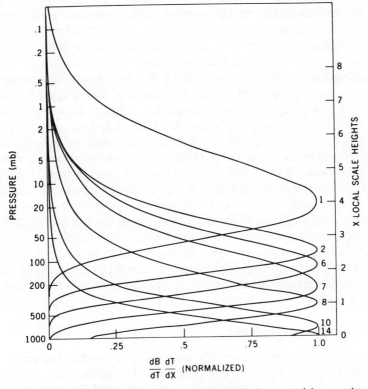

FIG. 1.16. Kernel functions for the 15-μm CO_2 band in the terrestrial atmosphere. The labels 1, 2, 6, 7, 8, 10, and 14 refer to frequencies 667.5, 677.5, 697.5, 702.5, 707.5, 727.5, and 747.5 cm^{-1}, respectively. (From Conrath, 1977, p. 170.)

results of studies which show improved temperature retrieval based on additional spectral channels or changes in spectral regions covered by the proposed instruments may be accepted with some reservation. The reader interested in this area can find many references to the original articles in the papers presented at the Workshop on Inversion Methods in Atmospheric Remote Sounding (Deepak, 1977).

2. *Atmospheric Emission Measurements for Comparison with Theoretical Calculations*

The ultimate lower limit of detectable power for an IR sensor is the statistical fluctuation in photons on the detector. Given proper cold shielding of the detector, the source of these photons will be the sensor optics, as well as all emitters within the sensor's field of view. The emissivities of good reflecting optics can be of the order of 1%. Even so, the noise contribution from this source may swamp the signal from weak sources such as the stratosphere, particularly in wavelength regions where there are no emission bands of the major atmospheric gases. The emissivity of a vertical atmospheric path above 15 km at 11 μm was estimated in the early 1960s to be less than 10^{-6}, well below the noise level generated by warm optics. This led to the development of several instruments in which the optics were cooled to cryogenic temperatures for aircraft, balloon, and rocket applications. Descriptions of several of these instruments and samples of data obtained with them are given in a chapter by Huppi (1977) in the first volume of this series.

It should be noted that the theoretical results were in error by several orders of magnitude due to the fact that HNO_3 emission was not included in the calculations. HNO_3 has a strong absorption band in the 11-μm region and is present in the stratosphere at levels that give emission in the few tenths of a percent range from aircraft altitudes even looking at relatively high elevation angles. The need for measurements to test the calculated atmospheric emission under conditions under which the emission is expected to be very low has resulted in a continuation of these studies with improved instruments. In many cases these have been or will be used to obtain data on atmospheric composition at the higher altitudes, and they are discussed in the next section.

3. *Constituent Measurements*

If atmospheric temperature data are available, measured spectral emission levels can be converted to emissivities. The emissivities can then be utilized to calculate the atmospheric concentration of the emitting species. Many of the constituents of interest in stratospheric chemistry are present in the atmosphere at very low concentration. As a result, long atmospheric

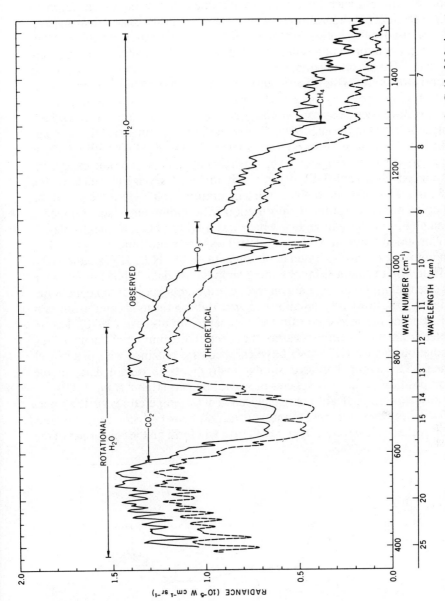

FIG. 1.17. Comparison of the observed and theoretical radiances for a clear atmosphere over the Gulf of Mexico at 1734 GMT, 22 April 1969. The observed spectrum is displaced upward 0.2×10^{-5} W cm^{-1} sr^{-1} for clarity. (From Conrath *et al.,* 1970.)

paths are required in order to obtain measurable effects. In cases of stratospheric interest, such long paths are obtained by viewing the atmosphere
close to disk from high altitude. This is also true for the case of solar spectra.
A major advantage of using atmospheric emission measurements to obtain
constituent information is that such data can be obtained at any time of day
or night. On the other hand, long-path solar spectra can only be obtained at
sunrise or sunset. This is particularly important for satellite experiments for
which global coverage is desired. Several satellite IR limb-viewing instruments have been flown on Nimbus satellites, and several others are scheduled for flights in the late 1980s. One of the first experiments of this sort was
the Limb Radiance Emission Radiometer (Gille *et al.*, 1980) with J. Gille as
the principal investigator. The instrument was a radiometer system
equipped with cooled IR detectors. It included several channels in the
15-μm region in order to obtain the temperature profile needed to invert the
data to obtain constituent information. The radiometer data included a
channel in the 9.6-μm region, which was used to obtain ozone profiles. A
follow-on instrument (Gille *et al.*, 1980) was flown on Nimbus 7, which had
radiometric channels chosen to obtain data on O_3, H_2O, HNO_3, and NO_2,
in addition to channels for obtaining temperature data. While limb viewing
is essential for obtaining data on trace constituents, spectroscopic measurements of the upwelling radiation can yield data on the total column amount
of some of the minor constituents. Hanel (Conrath *et al.*, 1970) flew an
interferometer system to measure the spectral distribution of the upwelling
radiation. Figure 1.17 shows a typical spectrum obtained with this instrument. This group has used similar instruments to obtain data on the
composition of the atmospheres of several planets (Hanel *et al.*, 1980).

Instruments that are completely cooled to temperatures in the range
10–100 K have been used to measure atmospheric emission from balloons
and rockets. However, CO_2 and H_2O frost will form on the cold optics of the

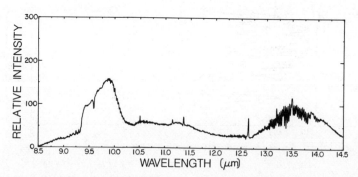

FIG. 1.18. Atmospheric emission spectrum covering the wavelength region from 8.5 to
14.5 μm obtained from 27,300 ft at a latitude of 87° S. (From Murcray *et al.*, 1980a, p. 45.)

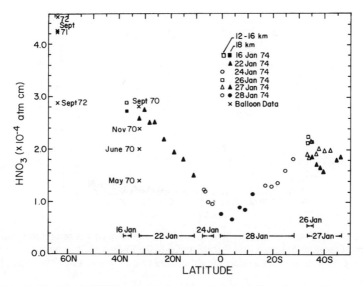

FIG. 1.19. Variation of HNO₃ column density with latitude from January airstream series. (From Barker *et al.*, 1976; © 1976 IEEE.)

balloon-borne instruments at the atmospheric pressure present at balloon altitudes. Such instruments must employ windows that will also frost unless they are kept frost free by a suitable antifrost system. A small (0.4-m Littrow) grating spectrometer that can be cooled at 10 K with liquid helium has been constructed by the University of Denver and flown on balloons and aircraft (U-2, RB-57, and the Antarctic Programs LC 130). For balloon use the window on the instrument is cooled to 77 K with liquid nitrogen and kept frost free with the nitrogen boil-off gas. The antifrost problem is more severe for aircraft use, and the unit has been used with ambient temperature windows. Figure 1.18 gives an emission spectrum taken over the South Pole (Murcray *et al.*, 1980a) with this instrument showing the emission due to stratospheric HNO₃. Aircraft measurements are particularly valuable for obtaining data on the geographic variability of various constituents, as illustrated in Fig. 1.19, which shows the latitudinal variability of the total column of HNO₃ (Barker *et al.*, 1976). Operation of the instrument within the earth's atmosphere requires the use of a window on liquid-helium-cooled units. It is generally impractical to cool the window sufficiently to achieve full sensitivity. This is not the case for rocket operation, as such instruments can function without windows. Stair (1978) has been particularly active in this area, and several of the instruments constructed by his group are described by Huppi (1977). An illustration of the wide dynamic range that can be achieved by such instruments is given in Fig. 1.20, and

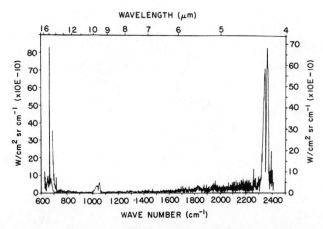

FIG. 1.20. Atmospheric spectra obtained by HIRIS on the upleg. For presentation purposes there is a split scale at 700 cm^{-1}; the left scale applies to the 15-μm CO_2; the right scale applies to the rest of the spectrum: scan number 26; altitude, 99 km; elevation, 45°. (From Stair, 1978.)

points up the major advantage of this technique for probing the atmosphere over a wide altitude range. Windowless operation is also possible from space, and several systems have been proposed for use of satellites. The major technological problem such systems must address is the achievement of a long cryogen hold time. Cooling for at least two weeks is required even for shuttle missions. For free flyers, satellite lifetimes of one to two years is desirable. In addition, limb viewing of the earth requires moderate aperture telescopes with very high off-axis rejection. Systems that can achieve these objectives have been proposed; some of those which have a high probability of flying in the 1980s are discussed in the next section.

1.5. Current Status and Future Research

A. LINE-BY-LINE CALCULATIONS

The heart of any line-by-line calculation lies in the input data (line strengths, positions, half-widths, energy state assignments, etc.) used in making the calculation. In most cases, these data are taken from one of the versions of the AFGL tapes. These tapes contain data on several hundred thousand absorption lines. Since they are an area of current research at AFGL, the data are continually being updated as the result of input from various experimental and theoretical groups. An illustration of the process showing the care that must be exercised in using any particular version of the tape is given in Fig. 1.21. At the time these spectra were obtained, they were compared with the latest version of the tape, and it was found that few of the observed lines were present on the tape. Since it was known that HNO_3 had a band in this spectral region, it was suspected that the majority of the lines were due to HNO_3. Maki and Wells (1980) had recently completed an analysis of this band. Their results, coupled with laboratory data taken with the interferometer employed to obtain the solar spectra, were used to verify that the lines are due to HNO_3. Line parameters were generated for the band, and they have now been included in the latest AFGL tape of line parameters for trace constituents.

Figure 1.22 shows another example of the difficulties encountered in using the tape. The lines in the 1234-cm^{-1} region are obviously part of the rotational structure of a molecular band. After considerable effort, the lines were identified as belonging to N_2O. The lines were present on the AFGL tape; however, their positions were incorrect (several wave numbers in error). It should be emphasized that these cases represent extreme conditions insofar as atmospheric paths are concerned. The initial objective of the AFGL listing was to be able to calculate transmission over reasonable atmospheric paths in spectral regions where the major atmospheric absorption bands occur. It is only in the last few years, as emphasis has been placed on predicting radiance and transmission close to the earth's limb, that many of these absorptions have become important. A great deal of the data on the early versions of the tape were based on low-resolution laboratory data, and as a result, the line positions could not be accurately determined.

This points up another aspect of the data on the tape. The tape is based on

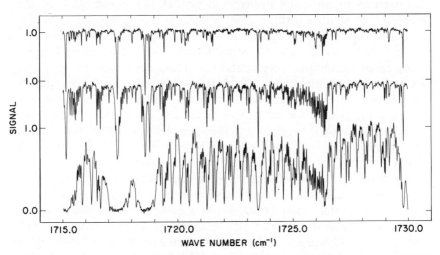

FIG. 1.21. IR solar spectra obtained from 33 km during sunset. The spectra were obtained at solar zenith angles of 85.9°, 91.4°, and 94.2°. (From Murcray et al., 1980b.)

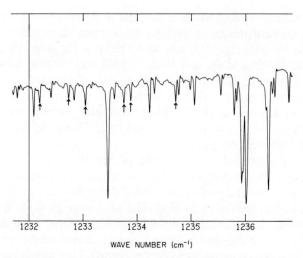

WAVE NUMBER (cm⁻¹)

FIG. 1.22. Portion of an IR solar spectrum obtained with a balloon-borne interferometer system from an altitude of 39 km and solar zenith of 93.6°. The lines indicated by the arrows are due to N_2O and are displaced by 0.15 cm⁻¹ from the positions given on the AFGL tape. (From Murcray *et al.*, 1979.)

the best laboratory data available at the time the tape is generated. It is also based on the best estimate of the use that will be made of the tape. On the early tape many weak absorption lines were not included, since it was felt that they would not be important over most atmospheric paths. When investigators began using the tape to predict the transmission in limb geometry, these lines became observable, and recent versions of the tape have included them. A similar problem currently exists with respect to the center frequencies of many of the weak lines. Current values are based, in many cases, on moderate-resolution laboratory data. With the increasing use in the field measurements of high-resolution techniques (laser spectroscopy, laser heterodyne spectroscopy, etc.), the position of these lines must be known with greater accuracy than is currently available. Considerable experimental work is required to achieve this increased accuracy, since the data are needed not only for the species being measured by the high-resolution techniques, but also for possible interfering species.

The situation is much the same when one considers the current status concerning the calculation of transmission in spectral regions away from the line centers. Current model calculations use a spectral line-shape function which depends on the pressure and temperature. In most cases, the Voigt profile is used. This profile combines the Lorentz profile, which is thought to be applicable in the lower atmosphere (higher pressure), and the Doppler profile, which is applicable at the higher altitude. As noted in the earlier discussion, it is known that the Lorentz line shape is incorrect in the wings, and the question of line shape is receiving considerable attention. For many spectral regions and atmospheric paths, the current calculations yield absolute accuracies of a few percent. Many studies of current and future interest will require a higher degree of accuracy than can now be achieved. While part of the problem of accuracy is due to the uncertainty in line shape, there still remain a number of so-called continuum effects which have not been properly explained. In addition, continuum effects due to O_2 and N_2 quadrupole transitions have recently been observed in experimental spectra. Figure 1.23, from the paper by Rinsland *et al.* (1982), shows solar spectra taken at sunset from 33 km in the 1600-cm^{-1} region illustrating the effect of the O_2 quadrupole absorption in this region. These effects are particularly important at the lower altitudes.

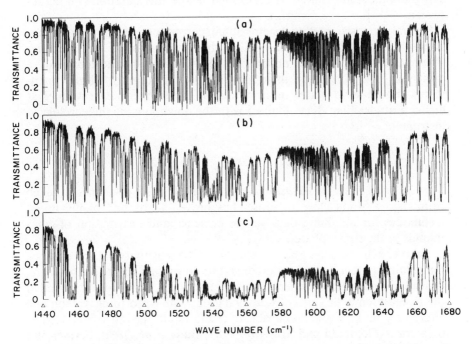

FIG. 1.23. Stratospheric transmittance spectra derived from scans obtained at 0.02-cm^{-1} resolution with the University of Denver balloon-borne interferometer near Alamogordo, New Mexico on 10 October 1979. Each transmittance spectrum was determined from the point-by-point ratio of a low-sun scan to a high-sun scan. All the scans were obtained from a float altitude of 33 km. The astronomical zenith angles of the scans and corresponding tangent altitudes are as follows: (a) 93.9°/85.9°, 19.2 km; (b) 94.2°/85.9°, 16.8 km; (c) 94.6°/85.9°; 14.4 km. (From Rinsland *et al.*, 1982.)

B. Atmospheric Remote Sensing

1. *Physical Properties*

Meteorological satellites continue to play an ever-increasing role in day-to-day operations of the weather bureau while providing data for atmospheric research. Current systems use multichannel radiometers as the basic IR instrument. As noted in the previous section, there is considerable disagreement as to how much temperature retrieval can be improved by obtaining additional spectral radiometric data. Proposed instruments include an advanced radiometer with an increased number of spectral channels and an interferometer system in which the instrument is only partially scanned. Since use of either instrument is more costly than the continued use of the current instrument, the question of what additional information the proposed systems can obtain becomes a point of controversy. Additional experimental studies must be performed before this question can be answered.

Several proposed satellite systems obtain constituent data by scanning the atmosphere just above the disk or through solar occultation measurement. These satellites must also obtain data on the atmospheric temperature profile in order to retrieve their constituent data properly. These experiments should yield better information on the temperature structure at higher altitudes than data obtained with the down-looking meteorological instrument.

2. *Constituent Measurements*

a. Solar Occultation Measurements. The use of IR solar spectra taken from high altitude close to sunset has proved to be one of the major techniques for obtaining data on the presence and distribution of compounds in the stratosphere.

Since resolution plays a significant role in the sensitivity of the technique for obtaining data on species predicted to be present in the stratosphere, instruments capable of higher and higher resolution have been employed in these measurements. Currently, several groups are performing balloon and aircraft flights with systems capable of resolution in the range from 0.01 to 0.15 cm^{-1} (Goldman and Murcray, 1981; Buijs *et al.*, 1980; Farmer and Raper, 1977; Ackerman *et al.*, 1976; Zander *et al.*, 1977). Samples of the spectra obtained with these instruments have been given previously. Laser heterodyne techniques have been used both from the ground (Hoell *et al.*, 1980; Rogers *et al.*, 1982), and from balloon altitudes (Menzies, 1979). The resolution achieved with laser heterodyne spectrometer systems is greater than the spectral linewidth of most atmospheric absorption lines. Major emphasis in future experiments using this technique will be concentrated on increasing the spectral coverage and signal to noise that can be achieved with the technique. Interferometer systems capable of resolutions in the range 0.001 cm^{-1} are now becoming available commercially, and it is reasonable to expect them to be adapted for use on aircraft and balloons in the next few years.

Several solar occultation satellite experiments are also planned in the next few years. The most ambitious, from the standpoint of spectral resolution and breadth of wavelength coverage, is the ATMOS instrument (Farmer, 1982), which will be flown as a Spacelab experiment. The instrument will be capable of obtaining data over the region from 600 to 2000 cm^{-1} with a maximum resolution of 0.01 cm^{-1}. A satellite version of the Girard grill spectrometer is also scheduled for flight as a Spacelab experiment. Another solar occultation satellite experiment that is of interest from the atmospheric spectroscopy standpoint is the HALOE (HALogen Occultation Experiment) (Russell, 1979). This experiment uses gas cells as filters to obtain data on the altitude distribution of HCl and other species. This type of measurement relies strongly on our knowledge of atmospheric spectroscopy since the HCl spectral region used in the experiment lies in the region where CH$_4$ and H$_2$O give rise to interfering absorption features. Thus, choosing the optical blocking filters and the amount and pressure of the HCl in the gas cell, and developing data reduction algorithms for removing interference effects all depend on a knowledge of atmospheric spectroscopy. Several other constituents will be measured using standard optical filters. Choice of filter spectral regions and data reduction algorithms again depend strongly on our knowledge of atmospheric spectroscopy. Conversely, the satellite observations will also add to our knowledge of atmospheric spectroscopy.

b. Atmospheric Emission Measurements. As noted earlier, atmospheric emission measurements are especially advantageous for obtaining data on constituents that exhibit large diurnal changes, in particular, those that are only present at night. The measurements also serve as an advantage for satellite experiments since the instrument can be used to obtain data on a continuous basis, whereas the solar occultation technique only obtains data over a small portion of each orbit. In view of these advantages, the technique has been used to obtain data on the stratospheric distribution of several constituents from aircraft, balloons, and satellites.

As noted in the instrumentation discussion, atmospheric emission measurements require high sensitivity in the measuring instrument. This requires that for many applications the total instrument be cryogenically cooled. In many cases, particularly at the longer wavelengths, a significant increase in system sensitivity can be obtained by cooling the system below the 77 K which is achieved with liquid nitrogen. Owing to the thermal and physical properties and, in some cases, cost of the various cryogens, early systems were only cooled to 77 K, with detectors alone cooled to 10 K or below. As system requirements continued to call for greater sensitivity, systems were constructed whereby the total instrument could be cooled to temperatures of 10 K or less.

The University of Denver group has been using grating spectrometers cooled to liquid helium temperatures to measure atmospheric emission at high altitudes from balloons and U-2 aircraft. Figure 1.24 shows some atmospheric emission data obtained with one of these units during a recent balloon flight. For comparison, Fig. 1.25 includes an IR solar spectrum obtained during sunset with a small grating spectrometer several years ago. The two spectra were obtained with approximately the same geometric optical path. The resolution and spectral scan times are comparable in the two cases. In both cases a 0.4-m grating spectrometer was used as the spectra dispersing unit.

As already noted, most investigators using solar spectroscopy for atmospheric constituent studies now use FTSs to obtain spectral data. One of the reasons for the change is the physical size of the instruments. For comparable resolution, the grating spectrometer is significantly larger than a comparable FTS system. This trend is also seen in the case of atmospheric emission measuring instruments. The decreased size is particularly important, since it is easier to cool the instrument if the unit is not too large.

Development of cryogenically cooled FTS systems for use on rockets has been a major program of A. T. Stair of the AFGL. As mentioned earlier, these units have been described in detail in the first volume (Huppi, 1977) of this series. Construction of a higher resolution system (0.1 cm^{-1}) for use on a balloon has been performed for George Vanasse of AFGL. This unit uses two cats-eye systems in the arms of the interferometer and maintains alignment at liquid nitrogen temperatures. The HIRIS system described in Volume I has been adapted to satellite use and will be flown as a shuttle payload.

Cryogenically cooled systems have been proposed for use on the free-flying Upper Atmospheric Research Satellite (UARS). The main technological problem for such systems involves achieving an 18-month cryogen hold time. For long missions the hold-time problem and the data-handling problem have limited the accepted instruments to small instruments with

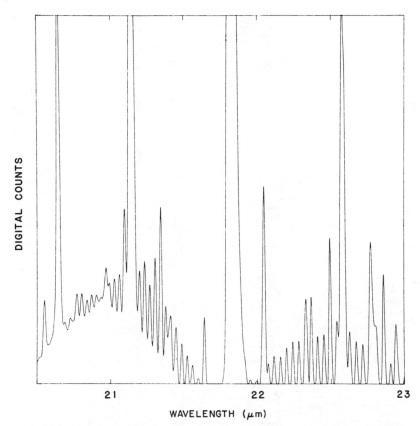

FIG. 1.24. Experimental spectrum recorded at 36 km and zenith angle 95°, showing the ν_9, $2\nu_9 - \nu_9$, and $3\nu_9 - 2\nu_9$ bands of HNO_3 with H_2O lines superimposed. (From Murcray, 1982.)

limited spectral scanning. Two cryogenically cooled spectrometer systems were chosen in the initial selection for the UARS. Owing to budget constraints, only one was chosen for the final payload. The instrument that has been accepted for the UARS is a cryogenically cooled etalon system which is scanned spectrally by angular rotation of the etalon. This is an interesting technique for obtaining spectral information at moderate resolution (0.25 cm^{-1}) over a limited spectral range. The system is identified by the acronym CLAES (for cold limb atmospheric etalon spectrometer). The principal investigator on this instrument is A. Roche of Lockheed. The system which will operate in the limb-scanning mode will be used to obtain data on a number of stratospheric species.

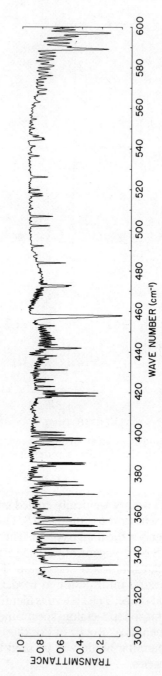

FIG. 1.25. IR solar spectrum as observed from 97,000 ft, solar zenith angle 93°, optical path 3.5 air mass. (From Murcray *et al.*, 1971.)

1.6. Summary and Conclusions

The preceding discussion points out the significant role played by experimental atmospheric spectroscopy in enhancing our knowledge of the chemistry and physics of the atmosphere. The instrumentation used in these studies has followed quite closely and, in some cases, preceded the state of the art of instrumentation used for laboratory studies of molecular spectroscopy.

The awareness of the possible environmental effects of small concentrations of some compounds has resulted in an ever-increasing need for greater measurement sensitivity in atmospheric constituent measurements. This, in turn, has placed a corresponding requirement on the experimental atmospheric spectroscopist. In addition to sensitivity, these studies are calling for greater absolute accuracy in the experimental measurements.

Lasers have played a significant role in recent advances in atmospheric spectroscopy, not only as sources, but also as a means of achieving optical performance with other instruments that would not be possible without them. As tunable lasers with greater power and the capability of operating over a wider range of wavelengths become available, they will play an increasing role in atmospheric spectroscopy. This role will not only include use as high-intensity sources, but also as local oscillators for laser heterodyne techniques. Interferometers have nearly replaced grating spectrometers in most molecular spectroscopy laboratories. Interferometers capable of resolution in the 0.001-cm^{-1} range are being used in laboratory studies and are expected to be used for atmospheric measurements within the year. Other techniques for obtaining high resolution will undoubtedly be used for atmospheric measurements as they are developed.

As noted in the preceding discussion, one of the major concerns of atmospheric physics is the possible climatic effect of an increase in the atmosphere concentration of a number of pollutants (CO_2, CH_4, etc.), which have strong absorption bands in the $6-20$-μm region. While higher resolution is certainly one way to obtain increased sensitivity for constituent studies, the need for higher resolution in radiative transfer studies is not so obvious. The major uncertainty in this area occurs from predicting the transmission well away from line centers, that is, the factors giving rise to the so-called continuum absorption. Line-shape studies require high resolution and high absolute radiometric accuracy. Resolution is not so important in atmospheric studies of continuum absorption; rather radiometric accuracy is the major requirement. New techniques for obtaining stable high-intensity continuous sources are needed. Instrument stability is also required.

It is interesting to note that in spite of the tremendous advance in our knowledge in atmospheric spectroscopy over the last few years, a great deal remains to be done. Experimental atmospheric spectroscopy will continue to play an active role in atmospheric chemistry and physics.

REFERENCES

Ackerman, M., Frimout, D., Girard, A., Gottignies, M., and Muller, C. (1976). *Geophys. Res. Lett.* **3,** 81.

Barker, D. B., Brooks, J. N., Goldman, A., Kosters, J. J., Murcray, D. G., Murcray, F. H., Van Allen, J., and Williams, W. J. (1976). Annals No. 75CH1004-1, 16-6. Institute of Electrical and Electronics Engineers, Inc., New York.

Blatherwick, R. D., Murcray, F. J., Murcray, F. H., Goldman, A., and Murcray, D. G. (1982). "Atlas of South Pole IR Solar Spectra." Department of Physics, University of Denver, Denver, Colorado.

Buijs, H. L., Vail, G. L., Tremblay, G., and Kendall, D. J. W. (1980). *Geophys. Res. Lett.* **7,** 205.

Burch, D. E., Gryvnak, D., and Williams, D. (1961). Scientific Report No. II, Contract No. AF 19(604)-2633. Ohio State University Research Foundation, Columbus.

Burch, D. E., Gryvnak, D. A., and Piper, G. H. (1973). "Infrared Absorption by H_2O and N_2O." Air Force Cambridge Research Laboratories (AFGRL) Final Report, Contract No. F19628-73-C-0011.

Conrath, B. J. (1977). *In* "Inversion Methods in Atmospheric Remote Sounding" (A. Deepak, ed.), pp. 155–193. Academic Press, New York.

Conrath, B. J., Hanel, R. A., Kunde, V. G., and Prabhakara, C. (1970). *J. Geophys. Res.* **75,** 5831.

Cumming, C., Hawkins, G. R., McKinnon, D. J. G., Rollins, J., and Stephenson, W. R. (1965). "Quantitative Atlas of Infrared Stratospheric Transmission in the 2.7 micron Region," Canadian Armament Research and Development Establishment (CARDE) Rep. 546/65.

Damon, E., Hawkins, R. L., and Shaw, J. H. (1981). *NASA Tech. Rep.* Proj. 761420/711626. (Grant No. NASA 7479.)

Deepak, A., ed. (1977). "Inversion Methods in Atmospheric Remote Sounding." Academic Press, New York.

Delbouille, L., Roland, G., and Neven, L. (1973). "Photometric Atlas of the Solar Spectrum from 3000 Å to 10,000 Å." Institute d'Astrophysique de l'Université de Liege.

Dowling, J. A., and Haught, K. M. (1977). *Opt. Lett.* **1,** 121.

Elsasser, W. M. (1942). "Heat Transfer by Infrared Radiation in the Atmosphere," Harvard Meteor. Stud. No. 6. Harvard Univ. Press, Cambridge, Massachusetts.

Elsasser, W. M., and Culbertson, M. F. (1960). "Atmospheric Radiation Tables," AFCRL-TR-60-236.

Farmer, C. B., principal investigator (1982). "Atmospheric Trace Molecule Spectroscopy," NASA Upper Atmos. Res. Summ. (1980–1981), p. 235. NASA, Washington, D.C.

Farmer, C. B., and Key, P. J. (1965). *EMI Electron. LTD Rep.* **DMP 2160.**

Farmer, C. B., and Raper, O. F. (1977). *Geophys. Res. Lett.* **4,** 527.

Farmer, C. B., Raper, O. F., and Norton, R. H. (1975). "Spectroscopic Detection and Vertical Distribution of HCl in the Atomosphere." *Climatic Impact Assessment Program (CIAP) Conf., 4th, 1975* DOT-TSC-OST-75-38.

Fontanella, J., Girard, A., Gramont, L., and Louisnard, N. (1974). "Vertical Distribution of NO, NO_2, and HNO_3 as Derived from Stratospheric Absorption Infrared Spectra." *CIAP Conf., 3rd, 1974* DOT-TSC-OST-74-15.

Gille, J. C., Bailey, P. L., Craig, R. A., House, F. B., and Anderson, G. P. (1980). *Science* **208**, 397.

Girard, A. (1963). *Appl. Opt.* **2**, 79.

Girard, A., and Besson, J. (1977). *NASA Tech. Memo.* **NASA TM-X-73630**.

Goldman, A., and Murcray, D. G. (1981). *SPIE, Atmos. Transm.* **277**, 69.

Goldman, A., Murcray, D. G., Murcray, F. H., and Williams, W. J. (1970). *Nature (London)* **225**, 443.

Goldman, A., Blatherwick, R. D., Murcray, F. H., Van Allen, J. W., Bradford, C. M., Cook, G. R., and Murcray, D. G. (1980). "New Atlas of IR Solar Spectra," Vols. I and II. Department of Physics, University of Denver, Denver, Colorado.

Goldman, A., Murcray, F. J., Gillis, J., and Murcray, D. G. (1981). *Astrophys. J.* **248**, L133.

Goldman, A., Fernald, F. G., Murcray, F. J., Murcray, F. H., and Murcray, D. G. (1983a). *J. Quant. Spectrosc. Radiat. Transfer* **29**, 189–204.

Goldman, A., Murcray, D. G., Lambert, D. L., and Dominy, J. F. (1983b). *Mon. Not. R. Astron. Soc.* **203**, 767–776.

Hall, D. N. B. (1974). "An Atlas of Infrared Spectra of the Solar Photosphere and Sunspot Umbra in the Spectral Intervals 4040-5095, 5550-6700, 7400-8790 cm^{-1}." Kitt Peak Natural Observatory, Tucson, Arizona.

Hanel, R., Crosby, D., Herath, L., Vanous, D., Collins, D., Creswick, H., Harris, C., and Rhodes, M. (1980). *Appl. Opt.* **19**, 1391.

Herzberg, G. (1945). "Molecular Spectra and Molecular Structure," Vol. II. Van Nostrand-Reinhold, Princeton, New Jersey.

Hinkley, E. D. (1976). "Laser Monitoring of the Atmosphere." Springer-Verlag, Berlin and New York.

Hoell, J. M., Harward, C. N., and Williams, B. S. (1980). *Geophys. Res. Lett.* **7**, 313.

Houghton, J. T., Hughes, N. D. P., Moss, T. S., and Seeley, J. S. (1961). *Philos. Trans. R. Soc. London* **254**, 47.

Howard, J. N., Burch, D. E., and Williams, D. (1956). *J. Opt. Soc. Am.* **46**, 237.

Huppi, E. R. (1977). *In* "Spectrometric Techniques" (G. A. Vanasse, ed.), pp. 153–188. Academic Press, New York.

Kaplan, L. D. (1959). *J. Opt. Soc. Am.* **49**, 1004.

Kyle, T. G., and Goldman, A. (1975). "Atlas of Computed Infrared Atmospheric Absorption Spectra," National Center for Atmospheric Research (NCAR) Tech. Note TN/STR 112, p. 53.

McClatchey, R. A. (1970). "Atmospheric Attenuation of CO Laser Radiation." AFCRL Rep. 71-0370.

McClatchey, R. A., and Selby, J. E. A. (1972). "Optical Properties of the Atmosphere." AFCRL Rep. 72-0312.

McClatchey, R. A., and Selby, J. E. A. (1974). "Atmospheric Attenuation of HF and DF Laser Radiation." AFCRL Rep. 74-0003.

McClatchey, R. A., Fenn, R. W., Selby, J. E. A., Volz, F. E., and Garing, J. S. (1972). "AFCRL Line Parameters Compilation." AFCRL Rep. 72-0497.

McClatchey, R. A., Benedict, W. S., Clough, S. A., Burch, D. E., Calfee, R. F., Fox, K., Rothman, L. S., and Garing, J. S. (1973). "Atmospheric Attenuations of Laser Radiation from 0.76 to 31.25 μm." AFCRL Rep. TR-0096.

Maki, A. G., and Wells, J. S. (1980). J. Mol. Spectrosc. 82, 427.

Menzies, R. T. (1979). *Geophys. Res. Lett.* **6**, 151.

Migeotte, M., Neven, L., and Swenson, J. (1956). AFCRC Final Rep. Contract AF61(514)-432.

Murcray, D. G. (1982). Final Report on Federal Aviation Administration (FAA) Contract DFTA 01-80-C-10039.

Murcray, D. G., Murcray, F. H., and Williams, W. J. (1961). *J. Opt. Soc. Am.* **51**, 186.

Murcray, D. G., Kyle, T. G., Murcray, F. H., and Williams, W. J. (1968). *Nature (London)* **218**, 78.

Murcray, D. G., Murcray, F. H., Williams, W. J., Kyle, T. G., and Goldman, A. (1969). *Appl. Opt.* **8**, 2519.

Murcray, D. G., Brooks, J. N., Hummer, S., Kosters, J. J., and Williams, W. J. (1971). "Atmospheric Transmission in the 16 μ to 18 μ Region at Various Altitudes." AFCRL Contract Rep. F 19628-71-C-0171.

Murcray, D. G., Cook, G., Goldman, A., Murcray, F. H., and Murcray, F. J. (1979). *SPIE Atmos. Eff. Radiat. Transfers* **195**, 7.

Murcray, D. G., Williams, W. J., and Kosters, J. J. (1980a). *SPIE Cryogenically Cooled Sensor Technol.* **245**, 43.

Murcray, D. G., Goldman, A., Cook, G., Murcray, F. H., and Murcray, F. J. (1980b). "Experimental Investigations of Atmospheric Transmission at Balloon Altitudes." *Infrared Data Symposium (IRDS) Paper* pp. 5.5-1 – 5.5.11.

National Research Council (1979). "Stratospheric Ozone Depletion by Halocarbons: Chemistry and Transport." Natl. Acad. Sci., Washington, D.C.

National Research Council (1980). "The Atmospheric Sciences: National Objectives for the 1980's." Natl. Acad. Sci., Washington, D.C.

National Research Council (1982). "Causes and Effects of Stratospheric Ozone Reduction: An Update." Natl. Acad. Press, Washington, D.C.

Pitts, J. N., Jr., Pitts, B. J., and Winer, A. M. (1977). *Environ. Sci. Technol.* **11**, 568.

Rinsland, C. P., Smith, M. A. H., Seals, R. K., Jr., Goldman, A., Murcray, F. J., Murcray, D. G., Larsen, J. C., and Rarig, P. L. (1982). *J. Geophys. Res.* **87**, 3119.

Roche, A. E., and Forney, P. B. (1982). "Cryogenic Etalon Spectrometer for Upper Atmospheric Research Satellite." SPIE International Technical Symposium and Exhibit.

Rogers, J. D., Mumma, M. J., Kostiuk, T., Deming, D., Hillman, J. J., Faris, J., and Zipoy, D. (1982). *Science* (in press).

Rothman, L. S. (1981). *Appl. Opt.* **20**, 791.

Russell, J. M., III (1979). *Pure Appl. Geophys.* **60**, 118.

Selby, J. E. A., Kneizys, F. X., Chetwynd, J. H., Jr., and McClatchey, R. A. (1978). "LOWTRAN4." Air Force Geophysis Laboratory (AFGL) AFGL-TR-78-0053.

Smith, H. J. P., Dube, D. J., Gardner, M. E., Clough, S. A., Kneizys, F. X., and Rothman, L. S. (1978). "FASCODE—Fast Atmospheric Signature Code (Spectral Transmittance and Radiance)." AFGL-TR-78-0081.

Stair, A. T., Jr. (1978). "Infrared Auroral Spectra (HIRIS). Topical Meeting on Atmospheric Spectroscopy (Technical Digest)." Opt. Soc. Am.

Taylor, J. H., and Yates, H. W. (1957). *J. Opt. Soc. Am.* **47**, 223.

Zander, R., Roland, G., and Delbouille, L. (1977). *Geophys. Res. Lett.* **4**, 117.

Chapter **2**

Planetary Exploration with Spaceborne Michelson Interferometers in the Thermal Infrared

RUDOLF A. HANEL

LABORATORY FOR EXTRATERRESTRIAL PHYSICS
NASA/GODDARD SPACE FLIGHT CENTER
GREENBELT, MARYLAND

2.1. Introduction

History books to be written two hundred years from now will probably devote considerable attention to the birth of the space age. In particular, three events will be recalled and recognized for their significance: the launching of the first artificial Earth satellite in 1957; the landing of man on an extraterrestrial body, the moon, in 1969; and the beginning of the

43

exploration of the solar system by spacecraft. Within the planetary program, imaging systems have been the most striking observing tools. Man is a visual creature, and the sharp pictures taken of the surface of the moon, the craters of Mercury, the volcanoes and canyons of Mars, the ever-changing clouds of Jupiter, the sulfurous eruptions of Io, the rings and smaller satellites of Saturn, and especially the pictures, taken by the landers, of the surrounding landscapes of the moon, Mars, and Venus are direct extensions of man's senses. While viewing the stony Martian surface photographed by Viking, one almost feels present, overlooking this desolate panorama. For such reasons the pictures appeal equally to the layman and the geologist or atmospheric scientist. In several scientific areas, however, nonimaging instruments carried on planetary missions have contributed even more than the pictures to the dramatic increase in knowledge about the planets that occurred throughout this period. This is especially true in obtaining quantitative understanding of physical and chemical conditions. It is not surprising that the analysis of reflected and emitted electromagnetic radiation by spectrometers plays the same important role in spaceborne investigations as it has in the more conventional astronomical observations from the earth.

If one ignores for a moment the information obtained from pictures taken with different color filters, which provide limited amounts of spectral information, true spectroscopic observations in the visible part of the spectrum have not been made by spacecraft. Ground-based measurements are frequently adequate because our own atmosphere is fairly transparent in this spectral range. However, this is not the case in the ultraviolet (UV) and infrared (IR), although partially transparent spectral windows may be found in the latter region. Because of this inaccessibility of large portions of the spectrum from the earth's surface, spectroscopic observations from spacecraft are especially useful. Most atomic and molecular species have electronic resonances in the UV; consequently, spectroscopic measurements in that range permit studies of the composition and energetics of planetary exospheres where molecules are often excited and sometimes dissociated by shortwave solar radiation and high-energy particles. Many complex molecules, which exist in planetary atmospheres, have vibrational and rotational transitions in the IR. Infrared measurements are more pertinent to deeper atmospheric levels than the UV measurements. Moreover, thermal emission from matter at temperatures typically found on surfaces and in atmospheres of planetary objects occurs predominantly in the IR. Spectroscopy in the thermal emission region has therefore been particularly successful because atmospheric and surface temperatures, as well as information on atmospheric composition, may be extracted from the spectra.

Figure 2.1 shows in a highly stylized way the magnitudes of emitted thermal and reflected solar radiation as a function of wave number. Of

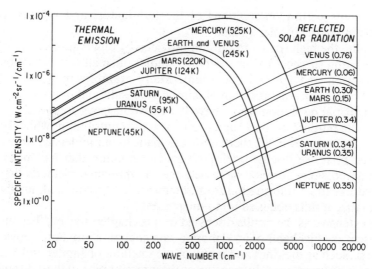

FIG. 2.1. Specific intensity of emitted and reflected planetary radiation. The thermal emission was calculated assuming the blackbody temperature shown in parentheses for each planet. The reflected solar radiation was calculated assuming the Bond albedo shown in parentheses and the solar flux at a distance appropriate for each planet.

course, the spectra are in reality not smooth blackbody curves but show complex structure due to many molecular absorption and emission features, as is shown later. However, the radiances plotted in Fig. 2.1 give the overall levels that spaceborne spectrometers must be able to detect. It is apparent that the difficulties in making spectral measurements increase substantially as one moves from the inner planets to the dimmer and cooler regions of the outer solar system. It is also apparent that emission spectroscopy, if used as an exploratory tool, should cover a large portion of the IR, say to about 2000 cm^{-1}, depending on the object. Between about 2000 and 3000 cm^{-1} reflected solar radiation becomes more and more dominant. In the near IR, above about 3000 cm^{-1}, reflected solar radiation completely preponderates and thermal emission can be neglected.

Another reason why radiometric measurements from space vehicles are advantageous is the wide range of phase angles which can be achieved from a spacecraft in a fly-by trajectory or in orbit around a planet in comparison to those achieved from Earth-based observations. The inner planets Mercury and Venus may be observed from Earth over a wide range of phase angles, but this range is severely limited for objects in the outer solar system. Mars may be observed over ±47°, Jupiter over ±11°, Saturn over ±6°, Uranus over ±3°, Neptune and Pluto only over less than ±2°. Only space-based instruments permit observations of the terminators and night sides of objects in the outer solar system.

Finally, the high spatial resolution provided by observations from fly-by and orbiting spacecraft allows detailed studies of small-scale variations in composition and thermal conditions. Many examples in which a high spatial resolution was crucial in obtaining the results and in which an even higher spatial resolution would have been advantageous are given.

It is the purpose of this chapter to review the contribution which space-borne spectroscopy in the thermal IR has made to our understanding of the planets. First, we discuss briefly the instrumentation that has made this progress possible. Second, we review the interpretative methods that are needed to extract information from the measured spectra, and, finally, we summarize results obtained up to the present time.

As extensive as the results discussed in this chapter may be, they merely represent the highlights of an elaborate data analysis effort. Some objects of interest, such as the rings and many of the satellites of Jupiter and Saturn, are not even mentioned. In many areas the interpretation of the data and the incorporation of the individual results into a comprehensive picture are just beginning. The existing data set will be the foundation of many individual research tasks for years to come. Magnetic tapes containing the infrared interferometer spectrometer (IRIS) data, together with appropriate documentation, are available from the National Space Science Data Center, Mail Code 601, Goddard Space Flight Center, Greenbelt, MD 20771.

2.2. Instrumentation

The team which was primarily responsible for the exploration of the thermal emission spectra shown in this chapter was originally engaged in observations of our own atmosphere from satellites in Earth orbit. The early meteorological investigations in this field, reaching back to the late 1950s, involved broadband radiometric measurements designed to obtain information on the degree of cloud cover, effective cloud height, the energy balance of the earth on a regional scale, and other related research tasks. The weight and power available for instrumentation on these early space missions (Vanguard, TIROS) were rather limited, as was experience with the construction of instruments for space flight. Mechanical, electrical, and thermal design practices had to be developed, in-flight calibration techniques had to be devised, and efficient processing methods for large quantities of data had to be found.

In analyzing the broadband data it became evident that spectroscopic measurements with higher spectral resolution and a trustworthy absolute calibration were badly needed in the thermal IR. Such spectroscopic measurements promised to be equally useful for meteorological research on Earth and for exploratory investigations of the planets. At that time Kaplan (1959) proposed to derive the temperature profile in the earth's atmosphere from remote measurements of the specific intensity within the 667-cm^{-1} (15-μm) band of CO_2. A spectral resolution of about 5 to 10 cm^{-1} appeared to be adequate, but the measurements had to be accurate to within a few percent. Even in the laboratory such accuracy (on an absolute scale) was difficult to achieve. Naturally, researchers in meteorology at the Environmental Science Service Administration (U.S. Weather Bureau) and at NASA were quite excited about the possibility of probing the atmosphere on a global scale. Ocean areas are insufficiently monitored by conventional radiosondes, and data are sparse and expensive to obtain. Great improvements in the quality of forecasts were expected by feeding global temperature data into computer models of the general circulation.

In preparation for the larger and more sophisticated Nimbus meteorological satellite series, the U.S. Weather Bureau developed a grating instrument with a single entrance slit and a set of detectors, each one forming an exit slit (Dreyfus, 1962). The positions of the detectors in the spectrometer were chosen so that each recorded a preselected spectral interval, about 5 cm^{-1} wide, within the 667-cm^{-1} CO_2 band (Wark and Hilleary, 1969; Wark, 1970). Another detector was placed so that it was sensitive to a transparent spectral interval at about 900 cm^{-1}. This channel was designed to observe the surface and cloud tops. SIRS, an acronym for satellite infrared spectrometer, was not a spectrometer in the true sense of the word, but a multichannel radiometer. At that time the choice of a grating instrument was the logical and conservative approach to this difficult problem. Narrow-band interference filters were not yet available with high efficiency and good out-of-band rejection ratios. Furthermore, a long tradition could be brought to bear on the construction of grating spectrometers. The main problem was to make the design more rugged and achieve the necessary signal-to-noise ratio (SNR) with thermistor bolometers, the best available uncooled detectors that could operate at the desired chopping rate.

The group at the Goddard Space Flight Center followed another path. Being primarily concerned with the geophysical aspects of measurements from space, including the retrieval of atmospheric composition, as well as the retrieval of atmospheric temperatures, it became apparent that the recording of a large portion of the thermal emission spectrum was most desirable. The choice of the wave-number intervals for optimum retrieval of the temperature profile or of other parameters could then be made *after* the spectra were in hand and after potentially disturbing effects of clouds in various spectral regions were better understood. A wide spectral range could also provide redundancy and flexibility in the interpretation. From the beginning, the Goddard group was interested in applying these remote sensing techniques to planetary exploration. There, with rather limited *a priori* information available, the recording of a wide spectral range was mandatory.

By that time the merits of the Michelson interferometer as a spectral analyzer had been discovered. Fellgett (1951, 1958) recognized the multiplex advantage and used the interferometer for astronomical observations. Jacquinot and Dufour (1948) called attention to the high-energy gathering efficiency available owing to the large area-times-solid-angle product (étendue). Janine Connes (1961) and Pierre Connes (Connes and Connes, 1966) had worked out much of the theoretical background and many practical details in the construction of large laboratory instruments. The first book (Mertz, 1965) to treat the subject in a modern way appeared. Loewenstein (1966), Vanasse and Sakai (1967), and others published important papers on the subject (Vanasse *et al.,* 1970). Some of these newly discovered properties of the Michelson interferometer must have been known to Michelson in the 1890s; however, he could not exploit the spectroscopic aspect of his interferometer in the absence of electronic capabilities and digital computers. Therefore, he was limited to observing the "visibility function." Nevertheless, he was probably aware of the potential, since he tried very hard to construct a mechanical Fourier analyzer (Michelson and Stratton, 1898).

The instruments which have recorded the planetary emission spectra shown in this chapter evolved from a prototype designed jointly in the mid 1960s by L. Chaney from the University of Michigan and the author. The optical and mechanical elements were constructed at Michigan, and the electronics required to operate the interferometer and extract the data were built at Goddard. Two working interferometers were assembled. The Michigan group flew one of these instruments on a balloon and obtained good atmospheric spectra (Chaney *et al.,* 1967), while the Goddard team used the other instrument in the laboratory to learn about its properties and to improve and adapt the design for use in space (Hanel and Chaney, 1966).

These prototypes demonstrated that a Michelson interferometer can indeed be built to operate in the desired range ($400-1600$ cm^{-1}), with the desired resolution (5 cm^{-1}), and to withstand laboratory and field operation without constant manual realignment. It was also learned that the calibration method, developed previously for the spaceborne radiometers (to expose the field of view of the instrument to blackbodies of different temperatures), works equally well for the interferometer. The Michelson interferometer also has disadvantages; the optical alignment is critical, a large dynamic range is required in the data channel, and a Fourier transformation is needed before a spectrum can be displayed in the conventional intensity-versus-wave-number plot. Thanks to the Cooley–Tukey (1965) algorithm which Forman (1966) applied to Fourier spectroscopy, the computing effort required to transform an interferogram of 2^{12} samples was reduced from almost 1 min to about 1 sec. Therefore, data reduction seemed to be a manageable task considering that plans called for one interferogram to be received every 16 sec in orbital operation. It also became clear that the calibration process and the ground-based computer program had to be treated and optimized together with the interferometer. Furthermore, it was recognized that careful thermostating of the instrument was required in order to achieve the desired accuracy. Thermostating in the midrange of the expected brightness temperatures of the target object (the earth's atmosphere) also helps the dynamic range problem. The Nimbus interferometer was then designed and constructed at Texas Instruments, Inc., in Dallas, Texas.

A. Nimbus Interferometers

1. *Principle of Operation*

The operating principle of the Michelson interferometer used as an IR spectrometer may be discussed with the help of Fig. 2.2. The essential part of the interferometer is the beamsplitter, which divides the incoming electromagnetic radiation into two beams of nearly equal intensity. The beams are reflected back to the beamsplitter by the fixed and the movable mirrors, respectively. The reflected beams recombine at the beamsplitter with a phase difference proportional to the difference in the optical path between both arms in the interferometer and a phase shift caused by the difference in phase changes for internal and external reflection at the beamsplitter (Born and Wolf, 1975).

Let us suppose that quasi-monochromatic radiation enters the interferometer and that the optical paths in both arms of the interferometer are equal. For a nonabsorbing (dielectric) beamsplitter the difference in the phase changes is 180°. Destructive interference takes place and none of the incoming radiation reaches the detector; the central fringe is dark. The interferometer as a whole acts like a mirror. The same condition repeats itself at positions of the movable mirror corresponding to path differences of full wavelength $n\lambda$, where n is a whole number. At positions $(n \pm \frac{1}{2})\lambda$, opposite conditions exist; we have constructive interference, and the interferometer transmits the incoming radiation to the detector. Since the interferometer is symmetrical, radiation emitted by the detector also passes through the instrument, but, of course, in the opposite direction.

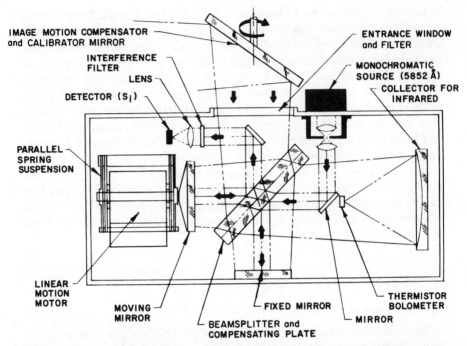

FIG. 2.2. Schematic cross section of the IRIS. The monochromatic source is a neon discharge bulb. The interference filter isolates the 5852-Å line (Hanel *et al.*, 1970).

If the Michelson mirror moves at a constant speed, the interferometer alternates periodically between being a reflector and a transmitter. The frequency f of this alternating state is proportional to the wave number v of the incident radiation and the mirror velocity v:

$$f = 2vv \qquad (2.1)$$

The factor 2 accounts for the doubling of the optical path as the Michelson mirror moves a certain distance. This process is precisely what takes place in the reference interferometer, which is the small interferometer operating in the center of the beamsplitter (Fig. 2.2). The neon discharge lamp generates a discrete line spectrum with a large number of widely spaced monochromatic lines. A narrow-band interference filter isolates the strong neon line at 0.58525 μm. The detector of the reference interferometer then records a sinusoidal signal with a frequency proportional to the mirror velocity. Only the alternating component of the signal is used in the Nimbus instrument. The amplitude of the reference signal is nearly constant over the displacement of interest, that is, over a few millimeters. Amplitude changes are caused by mirror tilt; their smallness is a measure of the quality of the drive motor alignment.

The same process also takes place in the main interferometer, but with two significant differences. First, the incoming radiation from a planet is not monochromatic but consists of radiation of different wave numbers. This does not matter if the detector and amplifiers are linear (and we have to make sure that this is the case). The signal at the detector is then simply the superposition of the modulation pattern of the individual spectral elements. Each spectral element generates its cosine signal of frequency $2vv$ and an amplitude proportional to its radiative net power at the detector. In a completely symmetrical instrument (one which is well compensated), the zero path difference is at the same mirror position for all wave numbers. If the detector and amplifiers do not introduce dispersion, all electrical frequencies are in phase with each other at the zero-path-difference point, as shown in Fig. 2.3. Second, thermal emission from the detector is not necessarily negligible and needs to be taken into account. The electrical signal at the detector is proportional to the difference of incoming and outgoing power at the detector surface. This net power in watts may be calculated from the specific intensity or radiance (W cm^{-2} sr^{-1}/cm^{-1}) knowing the dimensions (cm^2) of the detector, the solid angle over which the detector is illuminated by the interferometer (sr), and the wave-number range under consideration (cm^{-1}). Since the area-times-solid-angle product is invariant in optical systems, the specific intensity at the interferometer input may be used instead of the intensity at the detector. Parameters, such as the detector emissivity and the transmission characteristic of the interferometer, are combined into a responsivity factor r_v. If we define $i(\delta)$ as the alternating component of the signal, which is the only component that is amplified, and choose the arbitrary sign of the net power to obtain a positive

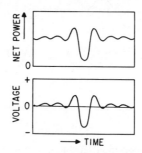

FIG. 2.3. The upper diagram shows the intensity as a function of mirror displacement. All frequencies are in phase at the zero-path-difference point. The lower diagram shows the electrical signal after suppression of the direct current level; this is the interferogram that is transmitted to the ground station.

central peak when the observed scenery is warmer than the instrument, then
the interferogram is

$$i(\delta) = \int r_v [I_v - B_v(T_i)] \cos 2\pi v\delta \, dv \qquad (2.2)$$

The interferogram amplitude $i(\delta)$, at the mirror position δ, is the integral of
the net intensity referred to the interferometer input $r_v[I_v - B(T_i)]$, modulated by frequencies proportional to the product $v\delta$. In other words with δ
changing linearly with time (v constant), each spectral interval is tagged by a
modulation frequency proportinal to v. $B_v(T_i)$ is the Planck function corresponding to the detector temperature T_i.

Recovery of the spectrum, or more precisely of the term $r_v(I_v - B_v) = C_v$,
is accomplished by sorting the amplitudes in the interferogram $i(\delta)$ according to frequency. This operation is carried out by a Fourier analysis in a
ground-based computer. Taking advantage of the symmetry properties of
the Fourier transform, one finds

$$r_v(I_v - B_v) = \int_{-\infty}^{+\infty} i(\delta)A(\delta) \cos 2\pi v\delta \, d\delta \qquad (2.3)$$

This equation is strictly true for $A(\delta) = 1$. In reality the interferogram can
be measured only up to a maximum path δ_0; A is then unity up to, and zero

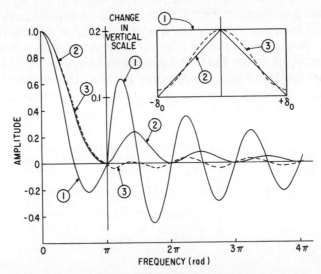

FIG. 2.4. Weighting and apodization functions. The rectangular or boxcar function (1)
produces the sharpest line shape but has large undesirable sidelobes. The triangular weighting
function (2) has a wider line shape (lower spectral resolution) but also lower sidelobes. The
"Hamming function" (3) has nearly the same line shape as (2) but still lower sidelobes with
alternating polarity.

beyond, δ_0. In effect, A is a weighting function that affects the shape of spectral features, called apodization (Jacquinot and Roizen-Dossier, 1964). In the above example A is a rectangular (boxcar) function, but other weighting functions are sometimes advantageous. In our data reduction we prefer the "Hamming" function, $[A(\delta) = 0.54 + 0.46 \cos \pi\delta/\delta_0]$. Figure 2.4 shows several weighting functions and the corresponding line shapes which they produce. Blackman and Tukey (1958) discuss additional apodization functions.

In order to extract the quantity of interest I_v from the spectral amplitude $C_v = r_v[I_v - B_v(T_i)]$, the responsivity and the instrument temperature must be obtained. This is the task of the calibration process. In case of the Nimbus measurements every fifteenth and sixteenth interferogram was taken while viewing deep space and a warm on-board blackbody, respectively. For our purpose deep space can be considered to be a perfect sink, $I_{space} = 0$. The temperature of the warm blackbody is carefully monitored and transmitted within each telemetry frame. The planetary measurement, the deep space, and warm blackbody calibrations yield, after Fourier transformation, three spectral amplitudes for each wave number:

$$C_{planet} = r(I_{planet} - B_{instr}) \tag{2.4a}$$

$$C_{space} = r(0 - B_{instr}) \tag{2.4b}$$

$$C_{warm} = r(B_{warm} - B_{instr}) \tag{2.4c}$$

These equations are then used to find

$$I_{planet} = [(C_{planet} - C_{space})/(C_{warm} - C_{space})]B_{warm} \tag{2.5a}$$

$$r = (C_{warm} - C_{space})/B_{warm} \tag{2.5b}$$

$$B_{instr} = [C_{space}/(C_{space} - C_{warm})]B_{warm} \tag{2.5c}$$

With the help of the calibration spectra, interspersed with the planetary measurements, it is possible not only to find the desired specific intensity in an absolute radiometric sense, but also to monitor the instrument performance, expressed in terms of the responsivity, and to derive an effective instrument temperature. All these quantities are obtained for each resolved wave-number interval. Furthermore, the repeatability of the response and the stability of the instrument can be evaluated from the standard deviation s, of the individual responsivities r_i, computed from pairs of individual hot (warm-blackbody) and cold (deep-space) measurements

$$S = \left\{ \left[\sum_{i=1}^{k} (r_i - \bar{r})^2 \right] /(k - 1) \right\}^{1/2} \tag{2.6}$$

where k is a large number of calibration pairs and $\bar{r}$ is the mean value of the responsivity. The noise-equivalent spectral radiance (NESR) may be calculated from

$$\text{NESR} = s(r)B_{\text{warm}}/r\sqrt{2} \qquad (2.7)$$

This definition of the NESR is the most realistic one; it is based on the repeatability of the spectral measurements and, therefore, includes all sources of noise, detector and quantization noise, the effects of temperature drift, and errors in the transmission link. This is the noise that is relevant to the interpretation of the data.

In deriving Eqs. (2.2) and (2.3) we have made several tacit assumptions which simplified the derivations but which in reality are not always justified. For example, real instruments are not perfectly compensated and, therefore, the zero-path position depends somewhat on wave number. The interferogram is not perfectly symmetrical. Either it needs to be symmetrized (Forman *et al.*, 1966) or a full-power transformation, including sine and cosine terms, has to be made. In the case of the Nimbus and Mariner instruments, we used the second approach; in the case of Voyager we used symmetrization.

2. *Nimbus 3*

The design of the Nimbus 3 interferometer, called IRIS for infrared interferometer spectrometer, was dictated by various performance requirements and the space environment. The desire to resolve 5 cm^{-1} (apodized) required a physical mirror displacement of 0.2 cm. The spectral band to be covered influenced the choice of the beamsplitter substrate, potassium bromide (KBr). The beamsplitter itself is a multilayer coating on the substrate. The required spectral resolution and the highest wave number of interest determined the 4° half-cone-angle field of view. The desire to operate the instrument at the midrange of expected brightness temperatures dictated an operating temperature of about 250 K. This was obtained in practice by thermally isolating the instrument from the spacecraft and letting it radiatively cool to space to an equilibrium temperature below 250 K. Small electrical heaters in a thermostat circuit brought the temperature up to 250 K and maintained it. The required precision of the measurement and the frequency response of the thermistor bolometer demanded an interferogram recording time of 10.9 sec, as well as a wide dynamic range of about 2000 to 1. The relatively long integration time and the high orbital velocity of Nimbus required image motion compensation. This was achieved by slowly rotating a 45° mirror in front of the instrument. The same mirror allows the field of view to see space and the warm blackbody in the calibration cycle.

The Michelson mirror is attached to one end of a shaft moving linearly in the direction of its axis of symmetry. The whole assembly is suspended by parallel springs, which ensure movement with minimum tilt and without bearing friction. Two coils in magnetic fields are attached to this shaft. The first coil drives the linear motor and the second coil measures the velocity. The signal from the velocity coil is amplified and controls the drive current in a feedback circuit. This analog servoloop controls the velocity fairly well, but more important, it suppresses the effect of the prime motor resonance. A second servoloop makes use of the reference interferometer signal. As mentioned before, the frequency in the reference signal is proportional to mirror velocity and may therefore also be used as a tachometer. A phase-sensitive detector compares the reference frequency to a stable clock frequency derived from the master clock in the spacecraft. In effect, this servoloop phase locks the mirror motion to the spacecraft clock. Another practical advantage results from this procedure. The signal from the reference interferometer also generates the sample command for the analog-to-digital converter ensuring sampling of the interferogram at the proper mirror positions. Therefore, the phase-locked operation of the Michelson mirror results in a constant bit rate which is synchronized with the spacecraft clock, greatly simplifying the data readout and timing process. A block diagram and further details of the Nimbus 3 interferometer are discussed by Hanel *et al.* (1970).

3. *Nimbus 4*

The Nimbus 4 instrument, which was launched in April 1970, was an improved version of the Nimbus 3 interferometer launched a year earlier. The improvements included an increase of the spectral resolution from 5 to 2.8 cm^{-1} and a reduction in the field of view from 4° to 2.5° half-cone angle. In addition, the NESR was slightly lowered to about 0.5×10^{-7} W cm^{-2} sr^{-1}/cm^{-1}.

Another improvement concerned incorporation of a wide-band phase detector in the phase-locked loop. The design permitted a phase-locked condition from the start of the Michelson mirror. The start position was also actively controlled by a vane on the motor shaft which interrupted the light beam emitted by a gallium arsenide source. The active control of the mirror start position resulted in a constancy of the interferogram peak position within 0.6 words or about 1 μm. This was helpful in the data reduction process.

The calibration procedure was also improved by taking into account the emissivity of the on-board "blackbody" surface and small temperature variations which occurred at certain orbital positions. These procedures, as well as many details of the data handling and calibration process, are discussed by Hanel et al. (1972a). A detailed instrument description, including the constancy of the responsivity of the instrument between the thermal vacuum test at spacecraft integration and in orbit, and values of the NESR are given by Hanel et al. (1971).

B. Mariner 9

The next interferometer in this series was to fly to Mars in 1971. The instrument was based on the successful Nimbus designs but with a number of changes so that it could adapt to a new spacecraft and respond to the objectives of the new investigation. One major design change was the extension of the spectral range down to 200 cm^{-1}. This was done to cover strong rotational lines of water vapor, which provided the best chance of seeing the minute amounts of water expected on Mars. The change required abandoning the KBr beamsplitter substrate and switching to Cesium Iodide (CsI). From an optical point of view, CsI is an almost ideal material. However, its mechanical properties nearly disqualify it as a substrate material for beamsplitters: it is soft, difficult to polish, high in thermal expansion coefficient; and very hygroscopic. The beamsplitter coatings were computer designed and consisted of layers of lead fluoride, KRS-5, and germanium. The reference interferometer used the central area of the same substrate but a different coating with zinc sulfide and thorium oxyfluoride. The substrate and the compensating plates were then bonded with silicone rubber into aluminum mounting rings.

The spectral resolution of the Mariner 9 interferometer was increased to a nominal 2.4 cm^{-1} (apodized) by using the weaker but longer wavelength 0.6929-μm neon line instead of the 0.58525-μm line. The shift to higher spectral resolution required a smaller field stop in the reference channel, which further reduced the available flux. Thus a more sensitive photomultiplier was needed to replace the silicon photodiode of the Nimbus design.

The Mariner 9 interferometer was mounted together with other instruments on a platform that could be actuated on command to point the field of view in desired directions. Therefore the interferometer had to operate properly under conditions of small acceleration and at higher ambient vibration levels than on Nimbus. Much effort was devoted to making the Mariner 9 interferometer insensitive to external disturbances. Further tightening of the servoloops was carried out, but the main improvement came from realizing that the group velocities (delays) in the data and reference channel had to be the same. That means first that the phase shift in the data channel has to be linear with frequency. Higher frequencies are then shifted proportionally more than lower frequencies, and the shape of the interferogram is independent of the mirror's velocity. Second, this phase shift corresponds to a time delay between the interferogram at the detector and the electrical signal at the point of digitization. If the reference signal has an identical delay, the sampling takes place at the proper interferogram position; otherwise the sampling process may be correct in the average but not at each sampling point. Therefore, the pulses derived from the reference interferometer were fed to an electronic delay line before being sent to the analog-to-digital converter.

Another interesting design feature of the Mariner 9 instrument is the digital filter. Instead of sampling every third neon fringe, as was done on Nimbus 4 and which would be adequate as far as the Nyquist criterion is concerned, the Mariner 9 interferometer samples once every neon fringe and then sums three adjacent digital words. The higher sampling rate is consistent with the wider bandwidths in the analog channel required for the phase linearity. The summing in blocks of three is equivalent to applying a numerical filter of the form of $\sin 2\pi\omega k/\sin 2\pi\omega$ where $k = 3$. The effect of the numerical filter is shown in Fig. 2.5. The Mariner 9 interferometer was very stable. The responsivities between the thermal-vacuum test about 4 months before launch, before orbit insertion, and in orbit around Mars were virtually identical (Hanel *et al.*, 1972b).

C. VOYAGER

The IR instrument on Voyager consists of a Michelson interferometer with a 4.3-cm^{-1} spectral resolution in the 180–2500-cm^{-1} range and a single-channel radiometer for the visible and near IR; both devices share a Cassegrain telescope. The design of the Voyager instrument is based on the Mariner 9 interferometer but with a number of substantial changes. First, the generally greater distance between the spacecraft and the object of interest on a fly-by trajectory as compared with distances experienced on the orbiters demanded a drastic reduction in the field of view. Therefore, the Voyager IRIS uses a telescope of 50-cm diam, which allowed a field reduction from ~4° to 0.25°. With this telescope, Jupiter filled the field of view approximately 4 weeks before Voyager's closest approach. Second, the low level of spectral radiance expected from cold objects in the outer region of the solar system required a substantial reduction in the NESR of the instrument. Careful optimization of the optical and electronic design, a slightly lower spectral resolution, and a longer interferogram time all contributed to the order-of-magntiude improvement in NESR demonstrated on Voyager over the Nimbus and Mariner orbiters. Third, dynamic range considerations called for an operating temperature well below the 250 K used on earlier instruments. As a compromise between the desire for a low

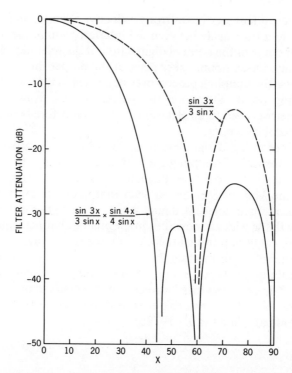

FIG. 2.5. Attenuation of numerical filters. The dashed line represents the filter of the Mariner interferometer and the solid line the attenuation of the Voyager filter. The data band is from $X = 0$ to about $X = 30$ and $X = 20$ for Mariner and Voyager, respectively (Hanel and Kunde, 1975).

operating temperature and the various material, power, weight, and schedule realities, an operating temperature of 200 K was chosen for the Voyager IRIS; as in earlier instruments, this was realized in practice by combining radiative coolers and thermostatically controlled electrical heaters. Fourth, in order to capitalize on information from the 1900–2300-cm⁻¹ atmospheric spectral windows on Jupiter, the so-called 5-μm hot spots, it was desirable to extend the spectral range of the interferometer toward the near IR. Good spectra of hot spots have been recorded on Jupiter; however, no useful information has been obtained with the interferometer above 2500 cm⁻¹. Fifth, for the purpose of estimating the energy balance of Jupiter and Saturn and the albedo and phase functions of their satellites and rings, a single-channel radiometer, sensitive to reflected solar radiation, was incorporated in the Voyager design. Sixth, a new in-flight calibration method was developed. The previous method, using a flat mirror in front of a large telescope to expose the whole instrument field of view to warm and cold calibration sources, was no longer practical. Instead, the in-flight calibration of the interferometer used deep space and a precisely known instrument temperature. In addition, a large diffuser plate mounted on the spacecraft structure was occasionally exposed to sunlight by turning the whole spacecraft. The IRIS, cameras, and other instruments mounted on the scan platform and bore-sighted to each other used the diffusely reflected sunlight for calibration purposes. Seventh, considerable effort was invested in radiation-hardening the instrument to ensure proper operation in the high-energy particle environment expected inside the Jovian magnetosphere.

The optical layout of the instrument is shown in Fig. 2.6. The Cassegrain telescope focuses an image of the scene at the field-limiting aperture. Radiation passing through the aperture is divided into two beams by a spherical dichroic mirror. Visible and near IR radiation (0.3–1.8 μm) is transmitted and focused onto the radiometer thermopile. Radiation with wavelengths longer than 2.5 μm is collimated into the main interferometer.

The telescope and interferometer mirrors, the housing, and the mechanical parts of the reference interferometer are all made of beryllium. As in previous IRIS designs the motor motion is phase locked to a spacecraft timing signal. The signal from the reference interferometer is used by the phase comparator and the digital sampling circuit to control the motor speed and to quantize the analog signal from the main IR detector. In the previous Nimbus and Mariner designs the reference interferometer was coaxial with the main interferometer and used the same substrate material, potassium bromide and cesium iodide, respectively. To avoid scintillation effects from disturbing the reference signal, the reference interferometer was relocated to the opposite side of the Michelson motor from the main interferometer (Fig. 2.7). The reference interferometer operated with a high-purity quartz beamsplitter substrate. Lenses and the narrow-band interference filter of the reference channel that isolates the 0.5852-μm neon line were fabricated from radiation-resistant glasses. The low-impedance Schwartz-type thermopile detector of the main interferometer has a noise-equivalent power (NEP) of $\sim 2 \times 10^{-10}$ W Hz$^{-1/2}$ and a thermal time constant of ~ 12 msec.

In the Nimbus and Mariner designs both sides of the interferogram have been used in computing the power spectrum. On Voyager only one side and a few hundred words of the other side of the peak are recorded. The area around the central peak is then used to establish the phase of the individual frequency components with respect to an arbitrary reference point, the central peak, for example. Each interferogram is then symmetrized and cosine-transformed to yield the coefficients C_ν.

The calibration concepts for the Voyager, Nimbus, and Mariner interferometers are, in principle, the same. In all cases the spectral amplitudes of the

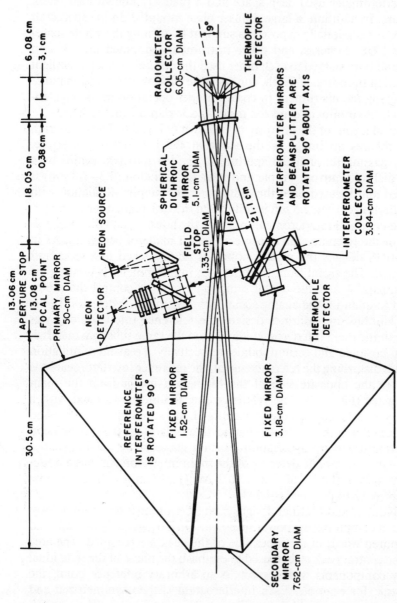

FIG. 2.6. Optical layout of Voyager IRIS. The primary and secondary telescope mirrors form an image of the scene at the field stop. The spherical dichroic mirror transmits shortwave radiation to the radiometer detector and reflects and collimates long-wave radiation to the IR interferometer. For clarity in the drawing both the IR and the reference interferometers are rotated 90° about the optical axis, defined by the dichroic mirror and the IR interferometer beamsplitter; also the reference interferometer is not to scale (Hanel et al., 1980).

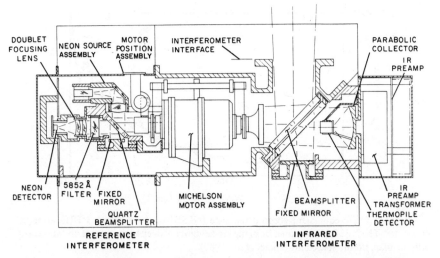

FIG. 2.7. Voyager IRIS main and reference interferometer configuration. The Michelson mirrors of both interferometers are mounted on opposite ends of a common motor shaft. The motor motion is phase locked to the spacecraft clock. The reference interferometer signal ensures data sampling at precise increments of mirror displacement. The motor scans in one direction and is returned to a predetermined start position at the beginning of each data frame (Hanel *et al.*, 1980).

planetary spectra are scaled, at each wave number, to the amplitudes of spectra recorded while viewing deep space and some other known source. On Nimbus and Mariner the other source was a real blackbody at a temperature somewhat above the instrument temperature. Spectra of the planet, deep space, and the warm blackbody were measured in sequence by rotating a 45° flat mirror in front of the interferometer. Owing to the size of the telescope, this method was impractical for Voyager. The warm calibration source was replaced by an imaginary blackbody at 200 K, precisely the same temperature as the instrument. If this blackbody were real, the interferometer detector would see only objects at a uniform temperature of 200 K. Motion of the Michelson mirror within this isothermal enclosure could not change the net flux to the detector, and the interferogram amplitude would therefore be zero. This calibration technique requires, however, that the interferometer and all elements within its field of view, such as the telescope mirrors, apertures, and baffles, be at precisely the same temperature. A very tight specification on the thermostatic controls of the interferometer and telescope was therefore necessary. It is also desirable that the interferometer detector be at the same temperature as the rest of the instrument. A detector without self-heating by bias current was therefore considered attractive; this was one of the reasons for selecting a thermopile.

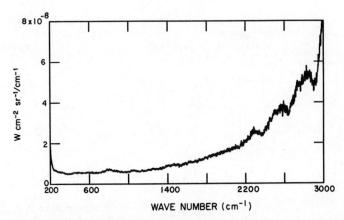

FIG. 2.8. Noise-equivalent spectral radiance (NESR) of the Voyager 1 IRIS at Jupiter encounter. The NESR is calculated from the repeatability of deep space spectra and spectra of a diffusor plate on the spacecraft (Hanel *et al.*, 1980).

The calibrated planetary radiance I is computed from

$$I = [(C_{\text{space}} - C_{\text{planet}})/C_{\text{space}}]B(T_i) \tag{2.8a}$$

The responsivity can be found from

$$r = C_{\text{space}}/B(T_i) \tag{2.8b}$$

and the NESR from the standard deviation of the responsivity:

$$\text{NESR} = [s(r)/r]B(T_i) \tag{2.9}$$

The NESR of the Voyager 1 IRIS measured at Jupiter is shown in Fig. 2.8. The increase in the NESR at high wave numbers is due to a small optical misalignment or lack of flatness in the CsI beamsplitter. More details of the Voyager instrument are given by Hanel *et al.* (1980).

2.3. Interpretation of Planetary Spectra

A. RADIATIVE TRANSFER

The interpretation of planetary IR spectra must be based on the theory of radiative transfer, which describes the interaction of electromagnetic radiation with matter. The classical text on radiative transfer is that by Chandrasekhar (1950), and a good insight into the physics is found in the book by Goody (1964); Kourganoff (1952) and Woolley and Stibbs (1953) also discuss the subject. In preparing this chapter we followed the first two authors primarily; however, the discussion is carried only to the point needed for the interpretation of the spectra.

1. Transfer Equation

The physical quantity that a spectrometer with a narrow field of view measures is the spectral radiance or the specific intensity I_v, as it is called in the astrophysical literature. To interpret a measurement, one needs a quantitative understanding of the physical processes which determine the spectral distribution of the measured radiation. As we see later, much of the interpretation process requires the calculation of the specific intensity with the help of computer models. Certain parameters are then adjusted in the model until calculated and measured spectra are in agreement within noise limits.

The specific intensity (Fig. 2.9) is defined as the radiant energy dE_v, which passes through the area element da, within the solid angle $d\omega$ inclined at angle θ to the surface normal, within the spectral interval dv, and within the time increment dt:

$$I_v = dE_v/\cos \theta \, da \, d\omega \, dv \, dt \qquad (2.10)$$

The units of the specific intensity are therefore erg cm^{-2} sr^{-1} (cm^{-1})$^{-1}$ sec^{-1} or W cm^{-2} sr^{-1}/cm^{-1}. For clarity we prefer to write the "per wave number" (/cm^{-1}) explicitly rather than the shorter form W cm^{-1} sr^{-1} which, of course, is equivalent. Within an atmosphere the intensity generally varies from location to location, and at each point it is different in different directions.

Let us now consider a small volume element $dV = da \times ds$ within the atmosphere, as shown in Fig. 2.10. Part of the intensity I that enters dV will penetrate the volume element and emerge unchanged on the other side. Another part of the original beam may interact with the matter inside dV and will not emerge on the other side within $d\omega$ but will be extinguished. The extinction may take two forms. Some of the extinguished radiation may reappear in directions other than the one given by the emerging beam, $I + dI$, and the incremental solid angle $d\omega$. There may be an energy change

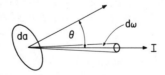

FIG. 2.9. The specific intensity I is defined as the radiative energy which passes through the area element da, within the solid angle $d\omega$ inclined at angle θ to the surface normal, within the spectral range dv, and within the time increment dt.

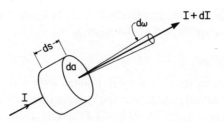

FIG. 2.10. The intensity I enters the volume element of cross section da and thickness ds. The emerging intensity differs by the increment dI.

involved at the same time. A quantum impinging on a molecule may cause a transition to an excited state. If the molecule reemits the quantum before colliding with another molecule, the process is called scattering. If the transition is in one step and without delay, the emitted quantum (wave packet) has the same wave number and the same phase as the incoming quantum, and we speak of coherent scattering. If the transition cascades in several steps or is delayed, the phase relationship is destroyed, and we speak of incoherent scattering. If the molecule redistributes the energy of the extinguished quantum by collisions with other molecules and reemission does not take place, we speak of absorption. The absorbed energy raises the temperature of the volume element and may eventually reapper in the form of thermal radiation or may take part in thermodynamic processes.

If we define a function $p(\theta,\zeta)(d\omega'/4\pi)$ as the fraction of extinguished radiation which is scattered into the solid angle $d\omega'$ and integrate over all directions, we obtain the ratio of energy scattered to the energy extinguished (absorbed plus scattered) from the beam:

$$\frac{1}{4\pi} \int_0^{2\pi} d\zeta \int_0^{\pi} d\theta \, p(\theta,\zeta) \sin \theta = \tilde{\omega}_0 \qquad (2.11)$$

The function p is called the phase function and $\tilde{\omega}_0$ the single scattering albedo of the element dV. This concept has been borrowed from the theory of the scattering of light on small particles, but it is applied here to a volume element which may contain many particles, as well as gas molecules. The fraction $(1 - \tilde{\omega}_0)$ of extinguished radiation is then truly absorbed within dV. The difference between the emerging beam, $I + dI$, and the incoming beam, I, can be expressed by

$$dI_{\nu(\text{extinction})} = - e_\nu \rho I_\nu \, ds \qquad (2.12)$$

where e_ν is the mass extinction coefficient, ρ the density, and ds the thickness of the volume element along the direction of I. The term extinction is always meant to include scattering as well as absorption processes.

The change in I may not be only due to extinction. The emerging beam may also include radiation which enters dV from other directions than the beam I, considered in the preceding discussion. Furthermore, true emission from molecular transitions within dV may take place. All these processes are expected to contribute to the emerging beam within the solid angle $d\omega$.

The incremental change due to emission (scattering from the outside as well as true emission) is

$$dI_{\nu(\text{emission})} = e_\nu \rho \mathcal{J}_\nu \, ds \qquad (2.13)$$

where $\mathcal{J}_\nu$ is called the source function and the other quantities have the same meaning as above. The source function is examined further subsequently, but first we add Eqs. (2.12) and (2.13) and define dI_ν as the incremental change in I_ν due to extinction and emission processes. Furthermore, we call $-e_\nu \rho \, ds$ the incremental optical path $d\tau_\nu$ in the direction of I, where τ_ν is a dimensionless quantity, and obtain the equation of radiative transfer

$$dI_\nu/d\tau_\nu = I_\nu - \mathcal{J}_\nu \qquad (2.14)$$

Before we discuss solutions to the radiative transfer equation, we need to examine the source function $\mathcal{J}_\nu$ more closely.

The element dV inside the atmosphere is imbedded in a radiation field which is characterized by a stream of intensities $I_\nu(\delta',\phi')$, striking from all directions, where δ' and ϕ' are polar and azimuth angles in spherical coordinates. Each one of these intensities contributes by scattering a small fraction to the emerging intensity within $d\omega$, according to the phase function of the volume element dV. In the case of perfect scattering the intensity within $d\omega$ due to all impinging intensities is the source function

$$\mathcal{J}_\nu(\delta,\phi)_{(\text{scattering})} = \frac{1}{4\pi} \int_0^{2\pi} d\phi' \int_0^\pi d\delta' p_\nu(\delta,\phi;\delta',\phi') I_\nu(\delta', \phi') \sin \delta'$$
$$(2.15)$$

Let us now consider the true emission case, that is, the case in which scattering processes are negligible. If the volume element is surrounded by an isothermal enclosure, all the intensities $I_\nu(\delta',\phi')$ are the same from all directions and, according to Kirchhoff's law, only a function of temperature and wave number. This function, describing the intensity of radiation within an isothermal cavity, is now known as the Planck function

$$\pi B_\nu(T) = (2\pi h\nu^3/c^2)[\exp(-h\nu/kT) - 1]^{-1} \qquad (2.16)$$

where h is the Planck constant, ν the wave number, k the Boltzmann constant, c the velocity of light, and T the temperature. It is convenient in radiative transfer calculations to call the emission from a "blackbody" into a steradian the Planck function $B_\nu(T)$, $(\pi B = \sigma T^4)$. Then B_ν has the same dimensions as the intensity; σ is the Stefan–Boltzmann constant. The same is advisable in the definition of radiative flux:

$$\pi F_v = \int_0^\pi d\delta \int_0^{2\pi} d\phi\, I_v(\delta,\phi)\, \sin\delta\, \cos\delta \tag{2.17}$$

In the case of a volume element at the same temperature as the surrounding isothermal cavity, the source function must be the Planck function

$$\mathcal{J}_{v\text{(thermodynamic equil)}} = B_v(T) \tag{2.18}$$

Although in a real atmosphere a particular volume element is not surrounded by an isothermal enclosure, Milne (1930) has shown that the source function is still the Planck function as long as molecular collisions are more frequent than the lifetime involved in the emissions of photons. If deactivation of molecules by collision dominates emission, a Gaussian velocity distribution exists within dV and a kinetic temperature can be specified. The volume element is said to be in "local thermodynamic equilibrium." In a volume element where scattering and true emission take place, as is the case in a real atmosphere, the source function is the sum of both effects, with the single scattering albedo characterizing the relative importance of the processes. In abbreviated notation

$$\mathcal{J}_v = \frac{\tilde{\omega}_0}{4\pi} \int_{\omega'} p_v I_v\, d\omega' + (1 - \tilde{\omega}_0) B_v(T) \tag{2.19}$$

where the phase function p is now normalized to unity.

2. Solution of the Transfer Equation

Before we proceed to solve the equation of transfer, we need to specify the overall geometry and define boundary conditions. It is convenient to consider a horizontally stratified atmosphere over a flat solid surface. In most cases of interest the field of view of the instrument covers only a small area of the planet, and the curvature of the surface can be ignored. Obviously this "plane-parallel" geometry does not apply to measurements at the limb or to spectra of the full planetary disk. For thermally emitted radiation the specific intensity at a certain location and in a certain direction within a plane-parallel atmosphere depends only on a parameter expressing the vertical position of dV and another parameter expressing the angle from the vertical, δ. If solar radiation is considered, then symmetry with respect to the surface normal does not necessarily exist, and an azimuthal angle is also required.

The vertical position of dV may be expressed by height above the surface or by atmospheric density; however, the nondimensional optical depth τ is

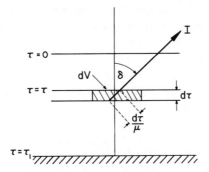

FIG. 2.11. Plane parallel atmosphere. The optical depth τ is zero at the top and τ_1 at the lower boundary. The increment in optical depth of the layer $d\tau$ in the direction of I is $d\tau/\mu$; μ is the cosine of the zenith angle δ.

more convenient. The optical depth is the optical path in the vertical and is defined to be zero at the "top" of the atmosphere and equal to τ_1 at the surface (Fig. 2.11). Unfortunately the same symbol τ is often used in the literature for the optical path in general [i.e., in the direction of I, as in Eq. (2.14)], as well as for the optical depth. To make things even more confusing, τ is sometimes used to describe the atmospheric transmittance. Unless otherwise noted, we use the symbol τ for the optical depth and the symbol $\tilde{\tau}$ for the transmittance in the vertical, $\tilde{\tau} = \exp(-\tau)$.

The boundary condition at $\tau = 0$ ($\tilde{\tau} = 1$) states that only a solar flux, πF_0, from the direction (μ_0, ϕ_0) penetrates the boundary in the downward direction. The intensity $I(0; \mu, \phi; \mu_0, \phi_0)$ is the quantity to be measured by the instrument on the spacecraft. The zenith angle δ is normally expressed by $\mu = \cos \delta$; the subscript zero refers to solar radiation. At the lower boundary $\tau = \tau_1$, the atmosphere is limited by a surface, which has its own optical properties and, in general, absorbs, emits, and scatters radiation as well.

Now we return to solving the radiative transfer equation. The transfer equation may be converted to an integral equation which expresses the specific intensity, the quantity of interest, as an integral of the source function. Multiplying both sides of the transfer equation by $\exp(-\tau/\mu)$ yields

$$\frac{d(Ie^{-(\tau/\mu)})}{d(\tau/\mu)} = -\mathcal{J}e^{-(\tau/\mu)} \tag{2.20}$$

Integrating from the top ($\tau = 0$) to the lower boundary ($\tau = \tau_1$) and rearranging terms yields

$$I(\tau = 0, \mu) = I(\tau = \tau_1, \mu) \exp\left(-\frac{\tau_1}{\mu}\right) + \frac{1}{\mu} \int_0^{\tau_1} \mathcal{J} \exp\left(-\frac{\tau}{\mu}\right) \, d\tau \tag{2.21}$$

The intensity at $\tau = 0$ in the direction μ consists of the intensity at the lower surface, $I(\tau = \tau_1, \mu) = I_G(\mu)$ attenuated by $\exp(-\tau_1/\mu)$, and the integral over the source function from the top to the lower boundary.

With these preparations one may now give a general solution of the transfer equation which satisfies both boundary conditions, includes solar flux πF_0, and expresses the source function by its individual components (numbered 1 through 5):

$$I(0; \mu,\phi; \mu_0,\phi_0)$$

(1)
$$= I_G(\tau_1; \mu,\phi; \mu_0,\phi_0) \exp\left(-\frac{\tau_1}{\mu}\right)$$

(2)
$$+ \frac{1}{\mu} \int_0^{\tau_1} [1 - \tilde{\omega}_0(\tau)] \exp\left(-\frac{\tau}{\mu}\right) B(\tau)\, d\tau$$

(3)
$$+ \frac{1}{4\pi\mu} \int_0^{\tau_1} d\tau \int_0^{2\pi} d\phi' \int_0^1 d\mu' \exp\left(-\frac{\tau_1}{\mu}\right) \exp\left[-\tau\left(\frac{1}{\mu} - \frac{1}{\mu'}\right)\right]$$

$$\times \tilde{\omega}_0(\tau) p(\tau; \mu,\phi; \mu',\phi') I_G(\tau_1; \mu',\phi'; \mu_0,\phi_0)$$

(4)
$$+ \frac{F_0}{4\mu} \int_0^{\tau_1} d\tau \exp\left[-\tau\left(\frac{1}{\mu} + \frac{1}{\mu_0}\right)\right] \tilde{\omega}_0(\tau) p(\tau; \mu,\phi; -\mu_0,\phi_0)$$

(5)
$$+ \frac{1}{4\pi\mu} \int_0^{\tau_1} d\tau \int_0^{2\pi} d\phi' \int_{-1}^{+1} d\mu' \exp\left(-\frac{\tau}{\mu}\right)$$

$$\times \tilde{\omega}_0(\tau) p(\tau; \mu,\phi; \mu',\phi') I(\tau; \mu',\phi'; \mu_0,\phi_0) \qquad (2.22)$$

The five terms in this expression for the specific intensity at the top of the atmosphere represent the following:

(1) intensity from the lower boundary I_G, attenuated by the overlying atmosphere;
(2) thermal emission from atmospheric layers;
(3) intensity from the lower boundary scattered into the field of the instrument by the atmosphere;
(4) solar flux backscattered by the atmosphere directly into the field of view; and
(5) the component of the diffuse intensity I, scattered into the field of the instrument.

It should be remembered that the equation is for monochromatic light only and all quantities, exclusive of the angular coordinates, are implicitly wavenumber dependent.

The intensity at the lower boundary may be expressed in terms of a scattering function S_G, defined such that if the incoming intensity field at τ_1 is given by

$$I(\tau_1; \mu,\phi; \mu_0,\phi_0) = \pi F_0 \delta(\mu_0 - \mu) \delta(\phi_0 - \phi) \qquad (2.23)$$

then the outgoing field due to ground reflection is given by

$$I(\tau_1; \mu,\phi; \mu_0,\phi_0) = (F_0/4\mu) S_G(\mu,\phi; \mu_0,\phi_0) \qquad (2.24)$$

The delta function in Eq. (2.23) indicates that the solar flux impinges only from within a small solid angle from the direction defined by μ_0 and ϕ_0 and is zero outside this angle. Upon including both emitted and reflected radiation, the monochromatic ground intensity becomes

$$I_G(\tau_1; \mu,\phi; \mu_0,\phi_0)$$

$$= B_G(\tau_1) \left[1 - \frac{1}{4\pi\mu} \int_0^{2\pi} d\phi' \int_0^1 d\mu' \, S_G(\mu,\phi; \mu',\phi') \right]$$

$$+ \frac{F_0}{4\mu} \exp\left(-\frac{\tau_1}{\mu_0}\right) S_G(\mu,\phi; \mu_0,\phi_0)$$

$$+ \frac{1}{4\pi\mu} \int_0^{2\pi} d\phi' \int_0^1 d\mu' \, S_G(\mu,\phi; \mu_0,\phi_0) I(\tau; -\mu',\phi'; \mu_0,\phi_0) \qquad (2.25)$$

The first term on the right describes thermal emission from the surface; the second term, reflected direct solar radiation; and the last term, diffuse atmospheric radiation reflected by the surface.

A general solution to the transfer equation is given here for the sake of completeness and to show what assumptions have been made in obtaining simplified forms of the solution to be discussed later. Even with the speed of modern computers, computations based on Eqs. (2.22) and (2.25) of the specific intensity are prohibitively time consuming. One must also remember that the intensity calculations must be carried out for a very fine mesh of wave numbers ($\Delta\nu \approx 0.01$ cm^{-1}) because the optical depth τ_ν changes rapidly with wave number in the presence of molecular lines (Kunde and Maguire, 1974). Therefore, the question is not whether the solution should be simplified but how it should be done.

First we restrict the case to the thermal IR, the subject of this chapter; then all terms that contain the solar flux may be neglected. As Fig. 2.1 shows, this is generally a valid assumption below about 2000 cm^{-1} for Earth and Mars, and lower for the giant planets. In the near IR (i.e., above 3000 cm^{-1}) terms which contain the Planck function can safely be ignored. Within the crossover region a careful analysis of individual cases must be made. Furthermore, in the thermal IR the azimuthal dependence of the intensity does not exist in a stratified atmosphere. Hence, from Eq. (2.22),

$$I(0,\mu) = I_G(\tau_1,\mu) \exp\left(-\frac{\tau_1}{\mu}\right)$$

$$+ \frac{1}{\mu} \int_0^{\tau_1} d\tau [1 - \tilde{\omega}_0(\tau)] \exp\left(-\frac{\tau}{\mu}\right) B(\tau)$$

$$+ \frac{1}{2\mu} \int_0^{\tau_1} d\tau \int_0^1 d\mu' \exp\left(-\frac{\tau_1}{\mu'}\right) \exp\left[-\tau\left(\frac{1}{\mu} - \frac{1}{\mu'}\right)\right]$$

$$\times \tilde{\omega}_0(\tau)p(\tau; \mu,\mu')I_G(\tau_1,\mu')$$

$$+ \frac{1}{2\mu} \int_0^{\tau_1} d\tau \int_{-1}^1 d\mu' \exp\left(-\frac{\tau}{\mu}\right) \tilde{\omega}_0(\tau)p(\tau;\mu,\mu')I(\tau,\mu') \quad (2.26)$$

But even in this simplified form the solution of the transfer equation is still to complex to be used routinely in the interpretation of data, and further simplifying assumptions have to be made. For example, the atmospheres of Jupiter and Saturn are so deep that the surfaces cannot be seen, and $\exp(-\tau_1/\mu)$ vanishes completely. Even in the atmospheres of Earth and Mars this assumption is valid in the centers of strong absorption bands.

Another important, often applied, assumption is that of an atmosphere in which scattering is negligible compared to absorption, and $\tilde{\omega}_0 \ll 1$. Inclusion of scattering is particularly demanding on computer time. With $\tilde{\omega}_0$ equal to zero, Eq. (2.26) reduces to

$$I(0,\mu) = \exp\left(-\frac{\tau_1}{\mu}\right) I_G(\tau_1,\mu) + \frac{1}{\mu} \int_0^{\tau_1} \exp\left(-\frac{\tau}{\mu}\right) B(\tau)\, d\tau \quad (2.27)$$

If we substitute the slant path transmittance $\tilde{\tau}(\mu) = \exp(-\tau/\mu)$ for the optical path and remember that $\tilde{\tau} = 1$ for $\tau = 0$, the solution is

$$I(1,\mu) = \tilde{\tau}_1(\mu)I_G(\tilde{\tau}_1,\mu) - \int_1^{\tilde{\tau}_1} B(\tilde{\tau})\, d\tilde{\tau} \quad (2.28)$$

This form has been used most commonly in the interpretation of data.

In many applications Eq. (2.25) also may be drastically simplified further. The surface emissivity $\varepsilon(\mu,\phi)$ can be introduced through the relation

$$\varepsilon(\mu,\phi) = 1 - \frac{1}{4\pi\mu} \int_0^{2\pi} d\phi' \int_0^1 d\mu'\, S_G(\mu,\phi; \mu',\phi') \quad (2.29)$$

For most naturally found surfaces the emissivity in the thermal IR is close to unity and the angular dependence small, although deviations from unity have been seen in certain spectral regions and in certain places on Earth, for example.

Furthermore, in most cases of real surfaces $S_G(\mu,\phi; \mu',\phi')$ does not strongly depend on μ' and ϕ', although exceptions exist again, for example, in smooth ice surfaces and when under certain conditions stratified minerals are exposed. In general, however, S_G may be taken outside the integral in the last right-hand term of Eq. (2.25) and the remaining part integrated:

$$\int_0^{2\pi} d\phi' \int_0^1 d\mu' \, I(\tau_1; -\mu',\phi') = \bar{I}(\tau_1) \qquad (2.30)$$

where $\bar{I}(\tau_1)$ is the mean intensity in the downward direction at the surface. Since S_G must also be independent of μ and ϕ in this case, Eq. (2.25) reduces to

$$I_G(\tau_1) = \varepsilon B_G(\tau_1) + (1 - \varepsilon)\bar{I}(\tau_1) \qquad (2.31)$$

and, furthermore, if $\varepsilon_v \approx 1$,

$$I_G(\tau_1) = B_G(T_G) \qquad (2.32)$$

where T_G is the surface temperature.

It is important to realize that the degree to which the general solution of the transfer equation may be simplified depends on a number of considerations. First, different planets and different planetary satellites have their specific properties, such as deep atmospheres versus shallow or no atmospheres, which allow certain simplifications. Clear-versus-cloudy atmospheric cases fall into the same category. Second, lack of information on some parameters, for example, on the phase function and vertical distributions of scatterers, make it often necessary to use rather crude assumptions as far as clouds are concerned. Clouds may in first approximation be assumed to be absorbing only, and their effect may then be included in the definition of optical depth:

$$\tau(z) = \int_z^{\infty} \left[\sum_i k_i(z',T)\rho_i(z',T) + \sum_j N_j(z')\chi_j(z') \right] dz' \qquad (2.33)$$

where z and z' are altitudes above a reference surface. The first term in the brackets accounts for absorption by gases and the second term for absorption by particulates. The mass absorption coefficient and density of the ith gas are k_i and ρ_i, respectively. The number density and absorption cross section of the jth particulate are N_j and χ_j, respectively; usually j refers to size rather than composition, which is assumed to be unique at a certain pressure–temperature level. Including the absorption characteristic of particles in the definition of τ permits first-order consideration of cloud effects in spite of the assumption of $\tilde{\omega}_0 = 0$, that is, in spite of neglecting their scattering properties. Third, the theoretical treatment has to be commensurate with the quality of the measured data. In the discussion of the individual objects we will return to some of these questions.

B. Temperature and Minor Constituents

The extraction of the atmospheric temperature profile plays a central role in the interpretation of most planetary emission spectra. The atmospheric temperature field provides information on the general circulation (specifically, it permits calculation of the wind shear) and gives other facts of interest, such as the levels of condensation of gaseous constituents. In addition, the vertical temperature distribution, either directly or indirectly, must be known to obtain information on atmospheric constituents.

First the derivation of the temperature profile from the spectrum and then methods to extract composition information are discussed. The solution of the radiative transfer equation [Eq. (2.28)] may be expressed in the form

$$I(v,\mu) = B(v,T_G)\tilde{\tau}_G(v,\mu) - \int_{x(1)}^{x(\tau_G)} B(v,T(x))\frac{\partial \tilde{\tau}(v,x,\mu)}{\partial x} dx \quad (2.34)$$

where $\tilde{\tau}(v,x,\mu)$ is the slant path transmittance, and $\exp(-\tau/\mu)$, is a function of a parameter x, which characterizes the vertical position in a plane-parallel atmosphere. Often it is convenient to use $x = -\log p/p_s$ where p and p_s are atmospheric pressure at a particular level and at the surface, respectively. The problem on hand is to derive $T(x)$, which appears inside the Planck function under the integral in Eq. (2.34) from a measurement of $I(v,\mu)$, assuming that $\tilde{\tau}(v,x,\mu)$ is a known function.

Before $T(x)$ can be derived, the surface term, the first term on the right side of Eq. (2.34), has to be discussed. For Jupiter and Saturn $\tilde{\tau}_G$ is vanishingly small; therefore the surface term is zero. But in general the surface term does not disappear, certainly not in the case of Earth or Mars. The procedure is then to find a spectral interval where the atmosphere is nearly transparent, that is, an interval where $\tilde{\tau}_G$ is nearly 1. At that wave number the integral representing the atmospheric contribution in Eq. (2.34) is then negligible (or may be approximated by a small correction), and the measured intensity is the Planck function corresponding to the surface temperature. This is strictly true for a surface emissivity of unity, which is often approximately true. The surface temperature T_G may then be determined. Complications arise when the surface is not "black" or when aerosols in the form of clouds or dust prevent finding a transparent spectral region. Such cases are discussed later in the treatment of the individual planets, but for the time being let us assume that a transparent spectral interval has been found and the surface temperature can be evaluated. The surface term in Eq. (2.34) is then known.

The next step in the task of deriving the vertical temperature profile is to find a spectral region where uniformly mixed gases of known abundance are the only significant absorbers. In practice, one tries to find a region where preferably only one gas has a strong absorption band which is completely opaque in the center and more and more transparent as one moves away from the center toward the wings of the band. Fortunately, such regions can be found in many cases, but, as we shall see, not in all. On Earth the strong CO_2 band at 667 cm^{-1} fulfills the above requirement, and the CO_2 abundance is well known from *in situ* measurements; the conditions for deriving the atmospheric temperatures from remote measurements of the specific intensity are therefore favorable (Kaplan, 1959).

It should be mentioned also that a temperature profile may be derived from measurements of the intensity by varying μ but holding the spectral interval constant. This procedure, for example, is used in deriving temperatures on the sun from limb curves. For Earth this method was proposed by King (1958). Since μ does not change substantially until the emission angle becomes large, it is difficult to observe a small and well-defined area on Earth under conditions suitable for this method. Therefore, mainly the Kaplan method has been used so far.

Let us return now to the problem of deriving the atmospheric temperature profile after the surface term has been established and a spectral region has been found where only one uniformly mixed constituent of known concentration is the absorber. In that case the atmospheric transmittance $\tilde{\tau}(v, x, \mu)$ is then a known function. We tacitly assume that laboratory measurements have been carried out over a sufficient range of temperature and pressure conditions to specify molecular parameters sufficiently well to allow computation of the transmittance.

The integral in Eq. (2.34) (a Fredholm integral of the second kind; see, e.g., Courant and Hilbert, 1931) has either no solution or an infinite number. Suppose we know the true vertical temperature profile $T(x)$, which yields the correct value of the specific intensity. Consider then a temperature profile which has a temperature structure that oscillates rapidly with altitude superimposed on the solution $T(x)$. After integration over x the oscillations will be smoothed out, and the same intensity $I(v, \mu)$, is obtained with and without oscillations. Therefore, given a set of intensity measurements, the solution for $T(x)$ can not be unique. Other physical insights must be invoked to restrict the solution to physically meaningful terms. For example, spurious oscillations in the computations may be suppressed by a damping function. Early inversion methods, particularly, were very sensitive to noise, which is unavoidable in experimental data (Wark and Fleming, 1966). The propagation of random errors in the nonlinear computational processes is sometimes difficult to see, but must be studied before applying a particular inversion method.

There now exist a large number of computational techniques which permit inversion of Eq. (2.34) and which derive $T(x)$. For meteorological forecasting purposes in the earth's atmosphere, *a priori* information can be used in the form of correlation functions which can be derived from a large number of conventional radiosonde data (e.g., Smith, 1968). For planetary exploration purposes this is not possible, for rather obvious reasons. Only nonstatistical techniques are useful in such case. Some of the nonstatistical technqiues linearize the Planck function by development into a Taylor series:

$$B(v, T(x)) = B(v, T_{(x)}^{(0)}) + \frac{\partial B(v, T_{(x)}^{(0)})}{\partial T} [T(x) - T_{(x)}^{(0)}] + \cdots \quad (2.35)$$

where $T_{(x)}^{(0)}$ is an estimate (first guess) of the temperature profile. Introducing Eq. (2.35) into Eq. (2.34) yields

$$\Delta I(v) = \int_{x=1}^{x=\tilde{\tau}_G} \frac{\partial \tilde{\tau}(v, x)}{\partial x} \frac{\partial B(v, T_{(x)}^{(0)})}{\partial T} \Delta T(x) \, dx \quad (2.36)$$

where ΔI is the difference between the measured $I(v)$ and the intensity computed from the guess $I_{(v)}^{(0)}$, and $\Delta T(x)$ is the analogous difference between the true and estimated temperatures, $T(x)$ and $T_{(x)}^{(0)}$, respectively. An iterative process may then be used until $\Delta I(v)$ becomes vanishingly small. The final estimate then represents the solution. Others (Chahine, 1968; Smith, 1970) prefer to iterate without linearization. The paper by Conrath and Revah (1972) provides a good summary of the merits of different techniques.

The function $(\partial \tilde{\tau}/\partial x)(dB/dT)$ which appears in Eq. (2.36) is called the weighting function and is shown for the case of the Nimbus 4 measurements in Fig. 2.12. In a physical sense the weighting function gives the relative contribution of atmospheric layers to the measurement at a particular wave number. At 2.8-cm^{-1} resolution, the 667.5-cm^{-1} channel (number 1) receives its main contribution from layers at 20 mbar, but small contributions exist from layers as high as 100 and as low as 0.5 mbar. For more transparent spectral intervals the weighting functions shift to lower atmospheric levels.

At the spectral resolutions obtained by the interferometers, that is, resolutions of a few wave numbers, several spectral lines are often within a resolved spectral element. The weighting function associated with such an element is the average of the several weighting functions associated with these lines. In effect, the functions to be used with the data are therefore somewhat wider than one would expect them to be for the monochromatic case. Conversely, some narrowing of the weighting functions would occur if the spectrum were recorded at a higher spectral resolution.

From an inspection of Fig. 2.12 it may appear that the use of many spectral intervals assures the best vertical resolution in the retrieved temperature profile. However, one must also consider that adjacent weighting

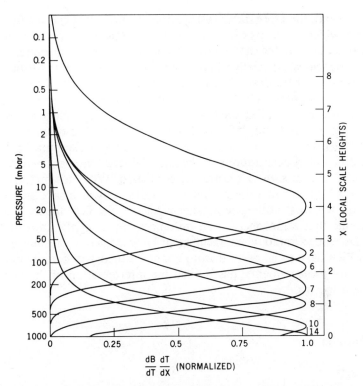

FIG. 2.12. Normalized weighting functions indicate the relative contribution of atmospheric layers to the outgoing intensity. Each number corresponds to a particular spectral interval of the Nimbus 4 interferometer (Conrath, 1977).

functions overlap significantly and are therefore highly correlated. Genuine information on the vertical structure is contained only in the noncorrelated part of the weighting function. Measurements corresponding to highly overlapping weighting functions are largely redundant and need to be made very precisely to be of use. There results a trade-off between vertical resolution and temperature error. This trade-off was analyzed by Conrath (1972) using Nimbus 4 interferometer data. Under favorable conditions a vertical resolution of about $\frac{1}{2}$ atmospheric scale height is obtained. Under less favorable conditions, such as in the stratosphere near the upper limit of the temperature retrieval range, a resolving limit of only about 2 scale heights is possible.

Having obtained the vertical temperature structure, we are ready to derive the concentration and, possibly, the vertical distribution of other gaseous constituents which have sufficiently strong signatures in the recorded spectrum. Equation (2.34) is employed again, but this time with the assumption that $T(x)$ and, therefore, $B(v,T(x))$ are known and that $\tilde{\tau}(x)$ is the unknown quantity which needs to be determined. In some cases a direct inversion can be carried out, as in the case of water vapor in the earth's atmosphere, but in many other cases, especially where more than one absorber contributes to a spectral range or the desired concentration has to be inferred from a weak signature, it is often preferable to use Eq. (2.34) to compute $I(v,\mu)$ over a spectral interval including the desired range where a particular constituent has an absorption band. It is good practice to carry the calculation sufficiently far from the band to gain confidence in the background spectrum. Then different concentrations of the gas of interest are assumed, and the calculated and measured spectra are compared. With this method it has been possible to obtain information on constituents which have only a small effect on the total atmospheric transmittance. Needless to say it is very important that atmospheric transmittances are precisely known. Many cases have been found where insufficient knowledge of molecular parameters, which have to be derived from quantum theory in conjunction with laboratory measurements, has limited the interpretation of the planetary emission spectra.

2.4. Results

A. Earth

The Nimbus 3 interferometer observed the earth for about 3.5 months until the IR detector malfunctioned. The Nimbus 4 interferometer outlived the spacecraft, but after nearly continuous operation for almost a year data were read out only occasionally. By that time more than a million spectra had been logged. In the following discussion we refer to both Nimbus 3 and Nimbus 4, but spectra from the latter represent the preferred set because of the higher spectral and spatial resolution and the greater seasonal coverage. An image of the earth recorded by Apollo 10 is shown in Fig. 2.13.

1. *Spectra*

The 667-cm^{-1} carbon dioxide (CO_2) and the 1042-cm^{-1} ozone (O_3) band dominate the Nimbus 3 spectrum of the Gulf of Mexico (Fig. 2.14) (Conrath *et al.*, 1970). Most of the other spectral features are due to water vapor (H_2O), with minor contributions from methane (CH_4) and nitrous oxide (N_2O) noticeable near 1300 cm^{-1}. The higher spectral resolution of the Nimbus 4 instrument is apparent in the spectra of North Africa (Fig. 2.15) (Hanel *et al.*, 1972c). Curves of constant brightness temperature (Planck function) are superimposed in the form of dashed lines. In the lower

FIG. 2.13. View of Earth recorded by the astronauts on Apollo 10 in May 1969 (NASA, Project Apollo).

spectrum of Fig. 2.15 the intensity maxima within the atmospheric window (800 – 1250 cm^{-1}) tend to follow the Planck function for 320 K reasonably well, which indicates that the surface emissivity is constant with wave number. Most natural surfaces, such as grassland, woods, fields, and water have emissivities close to unity. In that case the measured brightness temperature must be close to, but still slightly lower than, the actual surface temperature because the surface emissivity is not exactly unity; even be-

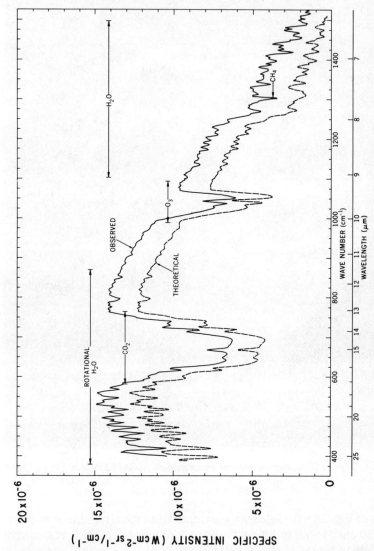

FIG. 2.14. Observed Nimbus 3 spectrum of the Gulf of Mexico and calculated spectrum using radiative transfer formulation and nearby radiosonde and sea surface data. The theoretical spectrum has been shifted downward by 0.2×10^{-5} W cm^{-2} sr^{-1}/cm^{-1} (Conrath et al., 1970).

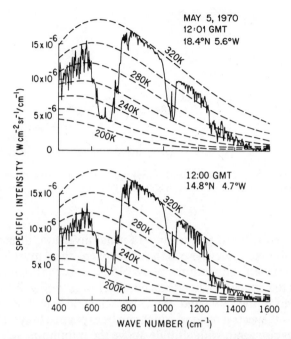

FIG. 2.15. Nimbus 4 spectra recorded over North Africa. The upper spectrum shows a surface emissivity of less than unity between 1100 and 1250 cm⁻¹ owing to coarse quartz sand of the Sahara. The lower spectrum does not show this "reststrahlen" effect. The dashed lines are Planck functions corresponding to the indicated temperatures (Hanel *et al.*, 1972a).

tween the water vapor lines it is a weak absorption continuum due to the contributions from far wings of numerous strong lines. The air temperature (meteorological shelter temperature) at the time of measurement, local noon, is expected to be somewhat lower than the surface temperature.

Just a few degrees in latitude further north, in the upper spectrum of Fig. 2.15, the intensities in the $1100-1250$-cm⁻¹ part of the atmospheric window are distinctly different. The lower brightness temperatures are due either to an atmospheric absorber or a surface emissivity substantially less than unity. The second hypothesis turns out to be correct. The shape of the emissivity curve is similar to that of coarse quartz sand. Crystalline substances often have broad reflection regions which, before the turn of the century, were used to isolate spectral regions by preferential reflections from crystals. Therefore, they are called *reststrahlen* or residual rays. The detection of the reststrahlen effect in the quartz sand of the Sahara provides a diagnostic characteristic of desert areas. Prabhakara and Dalu (1976) have mapped the global distribution of deserts using this phenomenon.

Let us return to spectral regions where atmospheric gases are srong

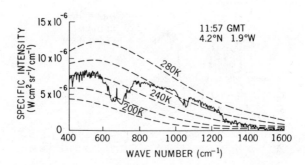

FIG. 2.16. Nimbus 4 spectrum recorded over a cloud-covered area at low latitudes. The change in brightness temperature between 800 and 1000 cm⁻¹ is characteristic of dense cloud cover (Hanel *et al.*, 1972a).

absorbers. Even without performing a formal inversion, inspection of the spectra reveals that, somewhere in the atmosphere, there must be a temperature minimum with temperatures below 215 K, since the brightness temperature within the strong CO_2 band reaches that low level (Fig. 2.15). The most absorbing part of the CO_2 band, the Q-branch at 667 cm⁻¹, is warmer than the neighboring spectral regions, which can be explained only if atmospheric temperatures rise again with altitude above the minimum.

Other low-latitude spectra, such as the spectra of Fig. 2.16 (Hanel *et al.*, 1972a), behave quite differently than the spectra from clear areas discussed so far. Even in the atmospheric window the maximum brightness temperature is below 270 K, and the effective emissivity changes with wave number between 800 and 1000 cm⁻¹. This was found to be characteristic of clouds.

The Antarctic spectra (Fig. 2.17) are different again (Hanel *et al.*, 1972a). The appearance of the whole 667-cm⁻¹ CO_2 band in emission indicates a cold surface at nearly 200 K overlaid by a slightly warmer atmosphere. Although the atmosphere must be very dry, many strong H_2O lines appear in emission between 400 and 600 cm⁻¹. The O_3 band, also in emission, is weak not because there is little O_3 in the Antarctic, but because the stratospheric O_3 layer is at nearly the same temperature as the surface. This result demonstrates the necessity of a temperature contrast if compositional information is to be extracted from a thermal emission spectrum.

Although much insight may be gained from a visual inspection of the spectra, quantitative interpretation requires more elaborate procedures. The first step in preparing for the interpretation of the spectra is a comparison between a measured spectrum and one which has been synthesized using independently obtained temperature and composition information. If the independent information, the computational procedures, and the atmospheric transmittances used in the computations are correct, the measured spectrum should be reproduced within limits set by instrumental noise. Such calculations were carried out for several test areas, for example, for the Gulf of Mexico, by Conrath *et al.* (1970). A cloud-free area over the ocean near Brownsville, Texas, was chosen because the values for the pressure, temperature, and emissivity at the lower boundary were uniform within the field of view and known; air temperature and humidity were available from nearby radiosonde data taken within half an hour of the satellite measurements. As shown in Fig. 2.14, the overall agreement between the measured and the computed spectrum is good. However, closer inspection shows differences, for example, near 1300 cm^{-1}, which result from (at that time) inadequately known CH_4 and N_2O transmittances.

A similar comparison of Nimbus 4 spectra with calculated spectra based on oceanographic measurements and on radio and rocketsonde data was carried out over the Atlantic Ocean, just off the coast of Wallops Island and over Guam (Kunde *et al.,* 1974). The Guam comparison (Fig. 2.18) shows good overall agreement, except for a small systematic temperature difference, possibly resulting from a calibration error or a bias in the radiosonde and sea surface data. The Wallops comparison also shows good agreement between IRIS and SIRS data except in two or three CO_2 channels where differences exceeding the error bars exist; it was found that the standard deviations in the more local radiosonde and rocketsonde data generally exceeded errors in the satellite measurements, which represent average conditions over a large area. The comparison studies demonstrated that the spectral measurements from Nimbus, as well as the radiative transfer formulation and atmospheric transmittance functions, were of adequate quality and sufficiently well understood to proceed with the derivation of temperature, relative humidity, and ozone information from the spectra.

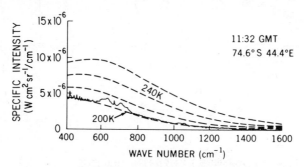

FIG. 2.17. Antarctic spectrum recorded by Nimbus 4. Spectral features appear in emission indicating a cold surface below a slightly warmer atmosphere (Hanel *et al.,* 1972a).

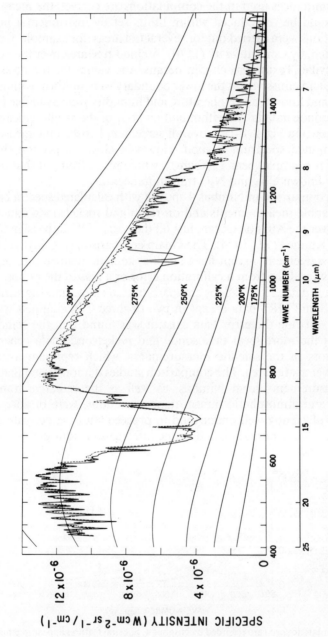

FIG. 2.18. Comparison of measured (—) and calculated (—) spectra. The measured spectrum was recorded by Nimbus 4 off the coast of Guam, 27 April 1970. The calculated spectrum is based on nearby radiosonde and sea surface data (Kunde et al., 1974).

2. *Temperatures, Humidity, and Ozone*

Spectra for which nearby radiosonde data were available for comparison purposes were then subjected to different inversion algorithms. In the case of the earth's atmosphere, where large sets of conventional radiosonde data are available, it was possible to use the statistical method of temperature retrieval (Smith, 1970). Since the effect of water vapor absorption on the spectral intervals used for the temperature inversion is weak but not negligible (at least not in the tropical cases), the water vapor distribution was retrieved simultaneously with the temperature profile in an iterative process. The statistical method even allows retrieval of sharp temperature minima, as shown over Brownsville in Fig. 2.19.

Of special interest are the cases in which part of the field of view is covered by clouds. A simple technique, suggested by Smith (1969), assumes that an opaque cloud at pressure P_c occupies the fraction N of the field of view. Using an estimate of the surface temperature (either from nearby measurements of cloud-free areas or from climatology) and the measurement in the more opaque spectral intervals, which are not much influenced by clouds (668 and 695 cm^{-1}), a first-order estimate of the temperature profile is obtained. From this profile and the measured data at 735 and 900 cm^{-1},

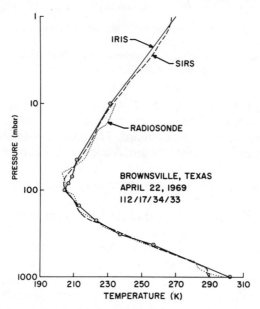

FIG. 2.19. Comparison of temperature profiles derived from the interferometer, IRIS, and the grating instrument, SIRS, on Nimbus 3 with nearby radiosonde data (NASA, Project Nimbus).

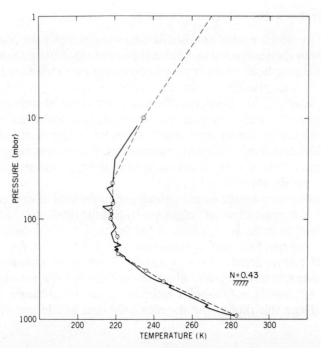

FIG. 2.20. Comparison of a temperature profile derived under partly cloudy conditions with radiosonde data: April 27, 1969; Dodge City, Kansas; (—) radiosonde, 1800 GMT; (---) IRIS, 1800 GMT. The cloud deck was determined to be at 420 mbar and to cover 43% of the instrument's field of view (Conrath *et al.,* 1970).

estimates of P_c and N are derived. With P_c and N available, the effect of the clouds can be removed from the spectrum; a "clear" spectrum and a new temperature profile are then calculated. The process is iterated until P_c and N change less than a specified amount. A temperature profile derived from a case in which 43% of the field of view was covered by a cloud at 420 mbar compares favorably with a nearby radiosonde (Fig. 2.20) (Conrath *et al.,* 1970).

After the validity of the method of retrieval of the temperature profile is established, the data can be processed on a larger scale. From numerous individual temperature profiles zonal cross sections have been constructed as shown for the month of October 1970 (Fig. 2.21) (Prabhakara *et al.,* 1976). In addition to the monthly mean temperatures, the standard deviation is plotted indicating the pressure level and latitude at which most of the atmospheric activity takes place at this time. The temperature data have also been displayed in latitude versus longitude for a certain pressure level, as shown in Fig. 2.22. Similar diagrams for other months and other levels, as

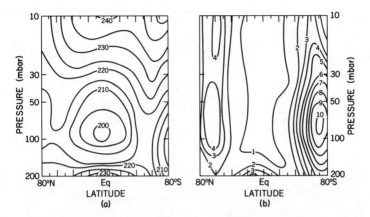

FIG. 2.21. Meridional cross section of (a) zonal mean temperatures and (b) standard deviation about the zonal mean for October 1970 (Prabhakara *et al.*, 1976).

well as a discussion of the meteorological significance, are found in Prabhakara *et al.* (1976) and Prabhakara and Rodgers (1976).

Although the O_3 band at 1042 cm^{-1} is a prominent feature of the IRIS spectra, our ability to determine the abundance and vertical distribution of this constituent is limited because of the nature of the weighting functions

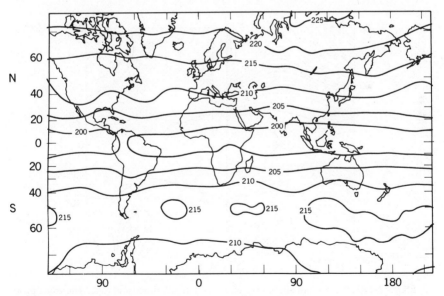

FIG. 2.22. Global distribution of temperatures (K) at 100 mbar for April 1970 (Prabhakara *et al.*, 1976).

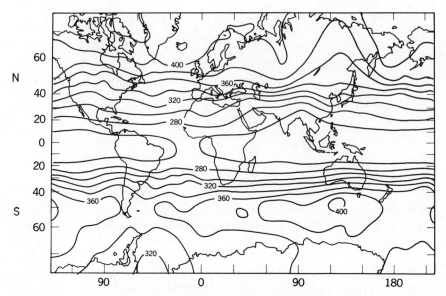

FIG. 2.23. Global ozone distribution (Dobson units) for July 1970, derived from Nimbus 4 spectra. A Dobson unit is 10^{-3} cm atm of O_3 at STP (Prabhakara *et al.*, 1976).

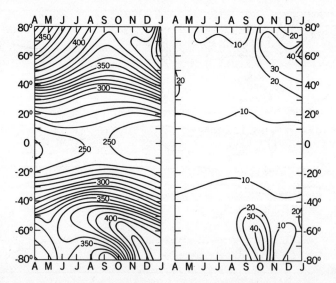

FIG. 2.24. Ozone column abundance as a function of latitude and time. The zonal mean ozone abundance in Dobson units is shown on the left and the standard deviation about the zonal mean is shown on the right (Prabhakara *et al.*, 1976).

and the fact that O_3 is distributed primarily in a stratospheric layer. A study of the "characteristic patterns" (empirical orthogonal functions) of the O_3 band suggest that only one significant parameter, such as the total O_3 amount, may be derived (Prabhakara et al., 1970). Samples of the global total O_3 amount for the month of July 1970 and a latitudinal distribution of O_3, including the standard deviation, are shown in Figs. 2.23 and 2.24, respectively. More information on the O_3 measurements and their meteorological and climatological interpretations, as well as comparison to Dobson and other data, is discussed by Conrath et al. (1971) and Prabhakara et al. (1970, 1972, 1976, 1980).

The IRIS on Nimbus measured for the first time the thermal emission spectrum of the earth on a global scale and over a full seasonal cycle. Although over a decade old, the Nimbus spectra are still the best thermal emission spectra of the earth available.

B. MARS

Mars orbits the sun at 1.52 astronomical units (AU) and has a diameter slightly larger than one-half that of Earth. A Mariner 9 mosaic image of Mars is shown in Fig. 2.25. Before planetary spacecraft arrived at Mars, the red planet was thought to have a nitrogen (N_2) atmosphere with a surface pressure of 80 ± 4 mbar, small amounts of CO_2, white and yellow clouds, blue variable hazes, and greenish areas which change colors with season (Kuiper, 1952; de Vaucouleurs, 1954). Needless to say this picture changed drastically after the Mariner missions. The atmosphere was found to be predominantly CO_2 with a surface pressure of only 5–8 mbar (Fjeldbo and Eshleman, 1968); clouds were hardly visible in the limited sample of pictures obtained by Mariner 4, 6, and 7; and the surface more nearly resembled that of the moon than one where vegetation, no matter how primitive, would be likely. The Mariner 9 orbiter was the first spacecraft capable of investigating Mars in a systematic way. After almost 24 weeks of space travel, Mariner 9 entered orbit around Mars on 14 November 1971 and operated until the gas supply for the attitude control system was depleted in August 1972. The cameras mapped nearly the whole surface, the infrared (IRIS) and ultraviolet (UVS) spectrometers recorded numerous spectra, and the infrared radiometer (IRR) obtained a large number of broadband measurements.

1. Spectra

At the time of arrival a major dust storm engulfed the whole planet and obscured most of the surface. Early spectra (Fig. 2.26) showed the already familiar CO_2 band, but with the Q-branch at 667 cm^{-1} not inverted as in the

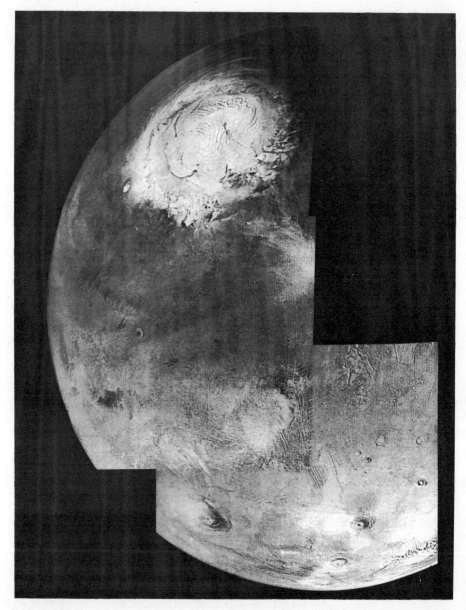

FIG. 2.25. Composite of three Mariner 9 images of Mars, recorded in August 1972, shows the northern hemisphere from the polar cap to a few degrees south of the equator. At that time the north polar cap was shrinking (late spring) and shows complex sedimentary systems. In the bottom picture are the huge Martian volcanoes and the west end of the great equatorial canyon; Olympus Mons appears at the lower left (NASA, JPL, Project Mariner 9).

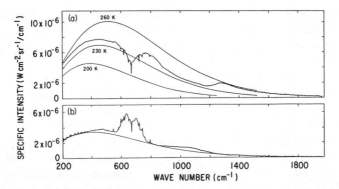

FIG. 2.26. Early Mariner 9 spectrum of Mars recorded during the dust storm of 1971. The upper spectrum (a) is from mid-latitudes and the lower spectrum (b) is from the south polar region. The solid line in (b) is the superposition of two Planck functions; see text (Hanel *et al.*, 1972c; copyright © 1972 by the American Association for the Advancement of Science).

earth spectra, an indication that Mars does not have an atmospheric temperature minimum over the pressure range sampled (Hanel *et al.*, 1972c). A striking and unexpected feature was a broad absorption regime which affected nearly the whole spectral range. In Fig. 2.26a, the brightness temperatures below 260 K could not be surface emissivity effects; otherwise the south polar region, which includes an entirely different surface, would not show complimentary emission features in its spectrum (Fig. 2.26b). However, mid-latitude and polar spectra could be explained qualitatively with the assumption of solid particles (dust) suspended in the atmosphere, quite consistent with the surface obscuration in the visible. While the dust was considered a nuisance by the geologists who wanted to map the surface, the IRIS team had the opportunity to study the composition of the dust, as well

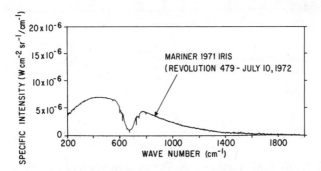

FIG. 2.27. Mariner 9 spectrum recorded in July 1972 after clearing of dust storm. Dust features are absent, as well as surface emissivity effects. Except for the strong CO_2 band and weak water vapor lines, the spectrum follows a Planck function.

as its effect on the atmospheric and surface temperatures and indirectly on the atmospheric circulation. Later in the mission the dust settled and the atmosphere was nearly clear, as shown in the mid-latitude spectrum recorded in July 1972 (Fig. 2.27).

During the first days after orbit insertion the south polar spectrum was puzzling. The CO_2 band, the dust features, and the weak water vapor lines (200–400 cm^{-1}) all appeared in emission, indicating, as in the Antarctic spectrum of the earth (Fig. 2.17), a warmer atmosphere over a colder surface, but the surface emission did not at all resemble a Planck function. A surface emissivity effect would not yield a reasonable solution either. Contrast-enhanced pictures from the Mariner 9 cameras of the south polar area showed the polar cap already in the process of breaking up, with dark and bright areas interlocked in a complex pattern. It was late spring in the south at that time. Presumably the bright areas in the pictures are ice or snow and the dark areas solid ground. The temperature of the snow is regulated by the phase change of the evaporating substance and that of the darker ground by

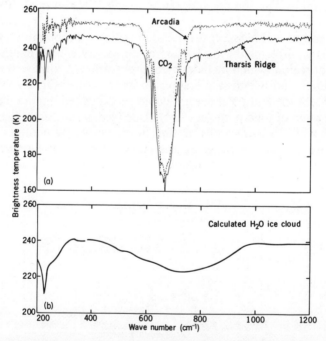

FIG. 2.28. Upper panel: spectrum of the Tharsis Ridge which contains white clouds in its field of view and spectrum of Arcadia, an adjacent nearly cloud-free area. Lower panel: calculated spectrum of a cloud of small particles of water ice (Curran *et al.*, 1973; copyright © 1973 by the American Association for the Advancement of Science).

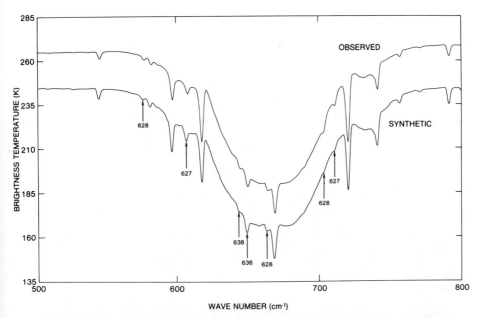

FIG. 2.29. Observed and calculated CO_2 spectra. The observed spectrum is the average of a large number of mid-latitude IRIS spectra. The synthetic spectrum is displaced by 25 K. Only after many weak bands, including bands with isotopic carbon and oxygen atoms, were included in the calculations could a reasonable agreement between measured and calculated spectrum be obtained. Isotopes are indicated by a 3-digit code; for example, 638 means $^{16}O^{13}C^{18}O$. Features from the main isotopes $^{16}O^{12}C^{16}O$ are not marked (Maguire, 1977).

radiative equilibrium. Accordingly, a two-temperature surface model was introduced and fitted to the measured intensities at 295, 840, and 1330 cm^{-1}. The resulting superposition of two Planck functions yielded a solution for 0.65 ± 0.05 of the field of view covered by a surface at 140 ± 10 K and the rest at 235 ± 10 K. The ratio of $0.65/0.35$ between snow-covered and clear areas was in good agreement with the pictures. The temperature of ~ 140 K is consistent with CO_2 ice at the expected surface pressure, which is strong evidence that the polar cap was frozen CO_2. With the complete evaporation of CO_2 from the soil the temperature rises rapidly to the radiative equilibrium value. The temperature change also liberates small amounts of H_2O which have been trapped in and below the CO_2 cap. About 10–20 precipitable μm of H_2O were detected in the atmosphere at that time (Hanel et al., 1972c,d).

With the south polar spectra understood, the spectral features of the dust emission could be studied, together with the signatures of the mid-latitude dust absorption. Silicon-dioxide- (SiO_2) bearing minerals have broad ab-

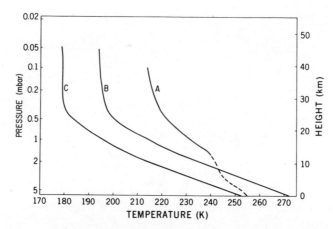

FIG. 2.30. Mariner 9 IRIS atmospheric temperature profiles. Temperature profile from revolution 20 (A) was taken when much dust was in the atmosphere. Later, at revolution 92 (B) much of the atmospheric dust had settled, and by revolution 174 (C) the atmosphere was nearly clear (Hanel *et al.*, 1972d).

sorption features near 1000 and 500 cm⁻¹ (Lyon, 1964; Hovis and Callahan, 1966; Aronson *et al.*, 1967; Conel, 1969; Salisbury *et al.*, 1970). Although a large scatter exists in the laboratory data, there is a general dependence of the spectral position of the absorption peak on the SiO_2 content. The observed peak position corresponds roughly to a SiO_2 content of 60 ± 10%, indicating that Mars is differentiated in a geochemical sense.

In addition to the mineral dust, water ice clouds could be identified in the atmosphere using spectra of the Tharsis ridge, as shown in Fig. 2.28 (Curran *et al.*, 1973). As suspected for a long time, the white clouds seen by ground-based observers where shown to be water ice.

Inspection of the detailed structure of the CO_2 band revealed the necessity to include many more weak bands due to carbon and oxygen isotopes in the computer model before agreement with the measured spectra was satisfactory (Fig. 2.29) (Maguire, 1977). With the CO_2 absorption coefficients well in hand temperature profiles could be retrieved.

2. *Temperatures, Winds, and Other Information*

Individual temperature profiles showed a strong cooling trend with the dissipation of the dust, as illustrated in Fig. 2.30. The same trend may be observed in the planetary maps (Figs. 2.31–2.33), on which isotherms for 0.3 mbar (∼ 30 km) and 2 mbar (∼ 10 km) are displayed as functions of latitude and local time. Data plotted in Fig. 2.31 were recorded between orbits 1 and 85 when a large amount of dust was suspended in the atmo-

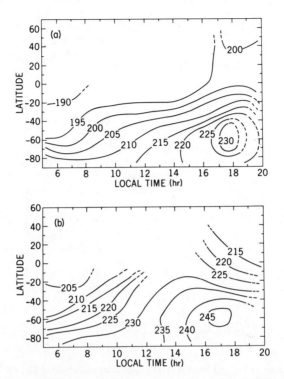

FIG. 2.31. Mariner 9 IRIS atmospheric temperatures (revolutions 1–85) in degrees Kelvin as a function of latitude and local time for (a) the 0.3-mbar level and (b) the 2-mbar level. At both levels the maximum temperature occurred at low latitudes and late in the afternoon, consistent with a high thermal inertia due to large amounts of particulates (dust) in the atmosphere (Hanel *et al.*, 1972d).

sphere. Temperature maxima are seen at both levels near latitude −60° late in the afternoon. Between orbits 85 and 120, atmospheric clearing was evident, and the temperature maxima decreased in magnitude and shifted toward the equator and earlier local time (Fig. 2.32). By orbits 161–186 (Fig. 2.33) further clearing had occurred, and the maximum at the 2-mbar level had shifted to approximately the subsolar latitude (−7°) and 1400 hours local time. This behavior can be explained by a large thermal inertia for the dust-laden atmosphere. It was rather fortunate that Mariner 9 was able to observe the decay of the storm. The dust storm on Mars may be considered a large-scale laboratory experiment in which it is possible to study the effects of particulate matter on a planetary atmosphere on a global scale.

With the global temperature field available from the IRIS data (with some

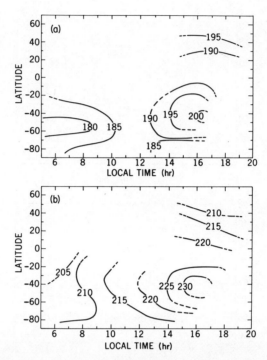

FIG. 2.32. Same as Fig. 2.31 but several weeks later (revolutions 85–120). By that time some of the dust had settled out of the atmosphere. The temperature maxima had shifted toward lower latitudes and earlier in the afternoon (Hanel *et al.*, 1972d).

extrapolations into sparsely covered areas), the wind velocities may be calculated using the assumption of hydrostatic equilibrium and the linearized momentum equations. A linear damping term was used to represent frictional forces. The wind field for the dust-laden conditions at an altitude of 1 scale height is shown in Fig. 2.34. The lower boundary was a geopotential surface on which a constant pressure was assumed.

With atmospheric and surface temperatures known, a search for the signatures and upper limits of minor constituents was made. An average of a large number of mid-latitude spectra (Fig. 2.35) revealed no unknown gaseous components; in addition, upper limits for a large number of possible constituents were derived (Maguire, 1977).

The wings of the 667-cm^{-1} CO_2 band may also be used to derive the total abundance of CO_2 in a vertical column, which may then be converted to a measure of topographic height. As an example, the topography of the Hellas depression is illustrated in Fig. 2.36 (Hanel *et al.*, 1972d). Other examples and a semiglobal topographic map of Mars are discussed by Conrath *et al.* (1973). The Martian topography was shown to have a significant effect on the global temperature and wind field (Conrath, 1976, 1981).

Since the Mariner 9 mission, the Viking landers have measured the atmospheric composition and other parameters. The reader is referred to the special issue of the *Journal of Geophysical Research* (Volume 82, Number 28, Sept. 30, 1977), which is devoted entirely to the outstanding results from the Viking mission. Another *Journal of Geophysical Research* issue (Vol. 84, Number B6, June 10, 1979) is devoted to the volatiles on Mars. Some of the instrumentation on the landers was designed for the detection of life; a negative result was obtained. The Viking orbiter pictures were more numerous and provided higher spatial resolution than those from Mariner 9. The Viking water vapor detector mapped the water vapor distribution on a seasonal scale (Farmer *et al.*, 1977). The IR radiometer obtained surface temperature maps and limited atmospheric temperatures (one broad chan-

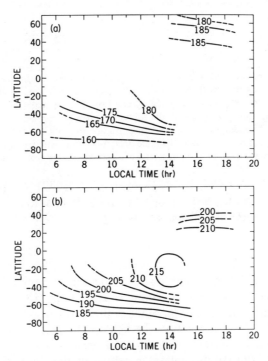

FIG. 2.33. Same as Figs. 2.31 and 2.32 but still later when the atmosphere had cleared (revolutions 161–186). The temperature maximum is near the subsolar latitude and at 1400 hours local time, as expected for a dust-free atmosphere (Hanel *et al.*, 1972d).

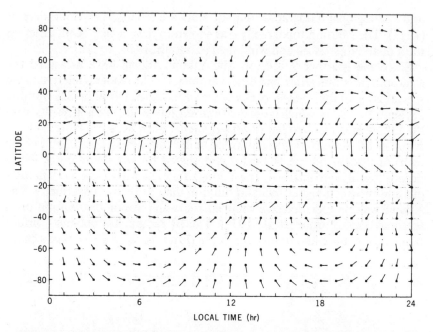

FIG. 2.34. Wind field from linear equations at one scale height generated from the temperature field measured by IRIS during the early part of the mission, revolutions 1–85. The wind velocities were calculated using the assumption of hydrostatic equilibrium and the linearized momentum equations, with the frictional forces represented by a linear damping term. The lower boundary was a geopotential surface on which a constant pressure was assumed. The wind direction is away from the dots. A vector of length equal to the horizontal and vertical separation of the dots represents a wind speed of 50 m sec^{-1} (Hanel et al., 1972d).

nel in the 667-cm^{-1} CO$_2$ band) (Kieffer et al., 1977). In spite of all this progress, the Mariner 9 IRIS spectra are still unsurpassed for spectral resolution and spectral and spatial coverage.

C. JUPITER

Jupiter (Fig. 2.37), the largest planet of the solar system, orbits the Sun at 5.2 AU. It has over 11 times the diameter and nearly 318 times the mass of Earth. The enormous mass, combined with a low exospheric temperature, has prevented the escape of even the lightest element, hydrogen, over the lifetime of the solar system. Therefore, the present composition of Jupiter reflects that of the primordial solar nebula at the time and location of Jupiter's formation. If the composition of the nebula was homogenous and Jupiter grew from a gravitational instability, it should have the same composition as the sun had at an early stage, that is, before nuclear synthesis commenced. On the other hand, if the nebula was not homogenous or if the temperature at Jupiter's distance was low enough so that a core of heavier compounds and ices (H_2O, CH_4, and ammonia (NH_3)) formed first and noncondensible gases such as hydrogen (H_2), helium (He), and the noble gases collapsed onto the core subsequently, an enrichment of heavier elements over solar abundances is possible. Therefore a precise determination of the Jovian composition is very important for theories of solar system formation. Unfortunately, a measurement of the composition of the accessible outer layers is not necessarily representative of the planet as a whole; Jupiter may not be homogenous with depth but may have differentiated during its history. Nevertheless, precise abundance information pertaining to the outer layers is an indispensible first step in the construction of models of the Jovian interior and, by inference, of the primordial solar nebula.

A summary of the state of knowledge of Jupiter as of 1976 (after Pioneer but before Voyager) is found in the book "Jupiter" edited by T. Gehrels (1976). The overviews in Part 1 by Smoluchowski (1976) and Hunten (1976), the Pioneer results by Ingersoll *et al.* (1976) and Orton and Ingersoll (1976), as well as the papers by Prinn and Owen (1976) and Ridgway *et al.* (1976), are all pertinent to this discussion. Temperature profiles and composition information were known in a general sense, but large numerical uncertainties remained.

Voyager 1 and 2 were launched on 5 September and 20 August 1977,

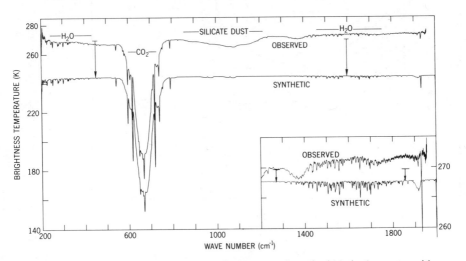

FIG. 2.35. Comparison of an average of a large number of mid-latitude spectra with a synthetic spectrum calculated for nominal Martian conditions. The synthetic spectrum is displaced for clarity. The insert shows the same spectra expanded in the vertical (Maguire, 1977).

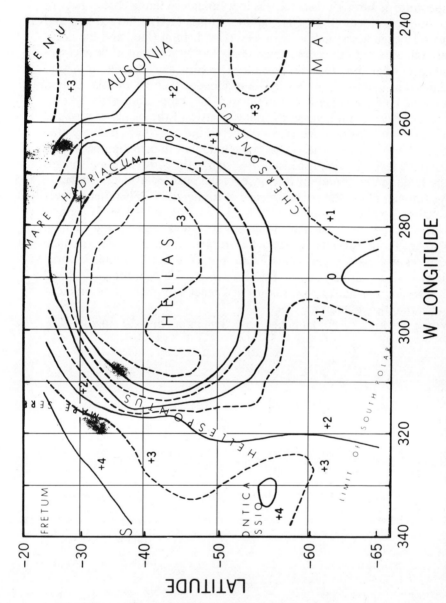

FIG. 2.36. Topography of the Hellas depression. The altitude contours in kilometers are referenced to the triple point of water vapor (6.11 mbar). The altitudes are derived from the column abundance of CO_2 measured in the wings of the 667-cm^{-1} band (Hanel *et al.*, 1977d).

FIG. 2.37. This Voyager 2 image shows the region of Jupiter extending from the equator to high southern latitudes in the neighborhood of the Great Red Spot (NASA, JPL, Project Voyager).

respectively, shortly after publication of the Jupiter book. Flying a slightly faster trajectory, Voyager 1 arrived on 5 March, and Voyager 2 four months later on 9 July 1979. In order to continue toward Saturn, both spacecraft were constrained to pass Jupiter near the equatorial plane. The Voyager 1 trajectory was timed to allow a very close approach to Io and to observe one hemisphere of both Ganymede and Callisto reasonably well. The Voyager 2 trajectory was designed to be complimentary, with close approaches to Europa and the other hemispheres of Ganymede and Callisto. But even weeks before the actual encounter dates, the Voyager instruments, including IRIS, were fully active in gathering data.

1. *Spectra*

Emission spectra of Jupiter between 180 and 1400 cm^{-1} are displayed in Fig. 2.38 for the North Equatorial Belt, at low and high emission angles, and for the south polar region. The spectra agree reasonably well with a computed spectrum based on a representative temperature profile and composition information derived from ground-based data (Hanel *et al.*, 1979a). Voyager 2 spectra, taken 4 months later showed similar characteristics (Hanel *et al.*, 1979b). The reasonable agreement between measured and computed spectra suggest that the assumed temperatures, estimated abundances, and absorption coefficients are correct in first approximation.

The spectral features evident in Fig. 2.38 include the high *J* rotational lines of NH$_3$ near 200 cm^{-1}, the broad pressure-induced translation–rotation $S(0)$ and $S(1)$ lines of H$_2$ between 300 and 700 cm^{-1}, the acetylene

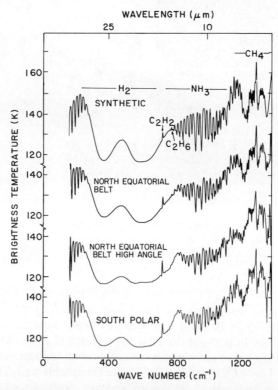

FIG. 2.38. Jovian emission spectra of the North Equatorial Belt at high and low emission angles and a south polar spectrum. A calculated spectrum is shown for comparison purposes. (Hanel *et al.*, 1979a; copyright © 1979 by the American Association for the Advancement of Science.)

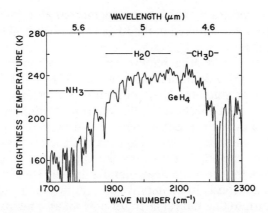

FIG. 2.39. Spectrum of a Jovian "hot spot" displayed between 1700 and 2300 cm⁻¹. (Hanel *et al.*, 1979a; copyright © 1979 by the American Association for the Advancement of Science.)

(C_2H_2) feature at 729 cm⁻¹, the broad emission band of ethane (C_2H_6) centered at 822 cm⁻¹, the NH_3 band between 800 and 1100 cm⁻¹, a Q-branch of phosphine (PH_3) at 1118 cm⁻¹ and of monodeuterated methane (CH_3D) at 1156 cm⁻¹, and the strong CH_4 band at 1304 cm⁻¹. The C_2H_6 band can be identified best in the high-emission-angle spectra. The C_2H_2, C_2H_6, and the central portions of the CH_4 band appear in emission, indicating their formation in a warm stratosphere. All other features appear in absorption, testifying to their tropospheric origin.

In the spectrum of "hot spots," that is, of regions of strong emission at 2000 cm⁻¹ (Fig. 2.39), the brightness temperatures reach a maximum of 260 K. This spectral region is transparent to the dominant gaseous absorbers H_2, CH_4, NH_3, and PH_3 and, in the absence of dense clouds, allows IR radiation to emerge from atmospheric layers as deep as 2–5 bars. In first order these spectra are also understood, and the task of quantitative interpretation may commence.

2. Temperatures and Winds

The atmosphere of Jupiter is so deep that the surface term in Eq. (2.28) is completely negligible. The first task in the temperature analysis is then to find a spectral region where one gas of known abundance is the only absorber. This is more difficult for Jupiter than for Earth and Mars where the 667-cm⁻¹ CO_2 band served so well. On Jupiter the best spectral region for deriving the tropospheric temperatures is between 280 and 620 cm⁻¹ where pressure-induced absorption by H_2 provides a wave-number-dependent opacity. The hydrogen molecule has a center of symmetry and, consequently, no intrinsic IR spectrum. However, there exists a weak collision-induced dipole spectrum, which causes significant absorption for the very long path lengths encountered in the Jovian atmosphere, about 40 km atm above the 1-bar level.

The temperature derivation requires knowledge of the abundance of H_2. Clearly H_2 must be the dominant constituent, but He, if in solar abundance, may account for as much as a quarter of Jupiter's mass. Helium has another even more important effect on the IR spectrum. Hydrogen–helium collisions result in a different pressure-induced hydrogen absorption spectrum than do H_2–H_2 collisions. As often happens in planetary investigations, this difficulty can be exploited; it provides the opportunity to deduce the He abundance from the spectrum; temperatures and the He abundance can be retrieved simultaneously by an iterative procedure (Gautier and Grossman, 1972). We return to this subject later; for now we assume that atmospheric transmittances can be calculated for all wave numbers of interest, 280–620 cm^{-1}.

The absorption caused by pressure-induced transitions is proportional to the square of the pressure, which in effect limits the useful pressure range of the H_2 lines for temperature retrievel. Above the altitude corresponding to about 150 mbar, that is, in the stratosphere, the H_2 lines are nearly transparent. Deeper than about the 700-mbar level, the atmosphere becomes too opaque in the accessible spectral range. In the stratosphere the 1304-cm^{-1} CH_4 band may be used for temperature determination, and the CH_4 con-

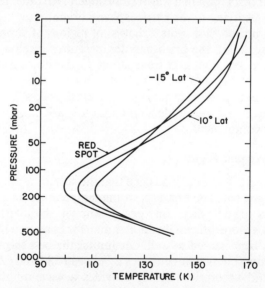

FIG. 2.40. Vertical temperature profiles for different locations on Jupiter. (Hanel *et al.*, 1979a; copyright © 1979 by the American Association for the Advancement of Science.)

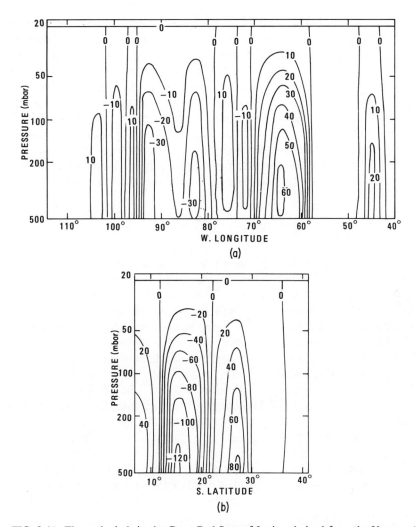

FIG. 2.41. Thermal winds in the Great Red Spot of Jupiter derived from the Voyager 1 temperature field: (a) east–west section; (b) north–south cross section. Wind speed is given in meters per second; positive numbers refer to winds into the plane and negative numbers to winds out of the plane of the paper (Flasar *et al.*, 1981b).

centration may be derived by requiring that the temperatures obtained from H_2 and CH_4 be identical in a small overlap region centered at 100–200 mbar. With this method temperatures can be obtained between roughly 1 and 700 mbar. Profiles (Fig. 2.40) and latitudinal cross sections of the temperature field have been constructed (Hanel *et al.*, 1979a).

Of special interest are the thermal structure and wind field in and around the Great Red Spot (Flasar *et al.*, 1981a). Lower temperatures just above the spot, compared to temperatures in the surrounding regions, and high-brightness temperatures at 2000 cm^{-1} in the surrounding areas suggest an upward motion within the spot and a region of subsidence around it. Thermal winds up to 120 m sec^{-1}, gradually reducing with altitude (Fig. 2.41), have been derived from the horizontal temperature gradients. This interpretation is consistent with the Great Red Spot's being a gigantic anticyclonic disturbance with a warm core below the observable levels. Another case study on the thermal structure and dynamics of various features by Conrath *et al.* (1981) shows a similar behavior over white ovals and an opposite structure over "hot spots" and the dark-brown oval areas called "barges."

3. *Composition*

As mentioned in the preceding, the interpretation of the shape of the pressure-induced H$_2$ lines yields the He abundance as well as temperatures. From the IR spectra Gautier *et al.* (1981) found a helium mass fraction of 0.19 ± 0.05. By combining the IRIS spectra with the ratio of temperature to molecular weight derived by the Radio Science Investigation (Eshleman *et al.*, 1979), Gautier *et al.* (1981) derived a helium mass fraction of 0.21 ± 0.06. Comparison of the Jovian helium abundances with that of the sun and of galactic and extragalactic sources may be an indicator of helium differentiation within Jupiter (Smolouchowski, 1967; Salpeter, 1973; Stevenson and Salpeter, 1977; Hubbard, 1977). Such differentiation could conceivably contribute to the excess energy which Jupiter radiates in the IR above the level expected if Jupiter were in equilibrium with absorbed solar radiation. The helium mass fraction of ~0.2 found by IRIS is consistent with estimates of the solar, galactic, and extragalactic abundances, considering the presently large uncertainties in all of these measurements. However, a modest depletion of helium in the outer layers of Jupiter, say of 0.05, cannot be excluded.

With the thermal structure and major atmospheric constituents H$_2$ and He known, the abundances of minor constituents may be derived from the spectra. By comparing the measured spectra to model spectra calculated with several assumed CH$_4$ concentrations, Gautier *et al.* (1982) derived a Jovian CH$_4$/H$_2$ volume ratio of 1.95 ± 0.22 × 10^{-3}. Because most of the carbon is expected to be in the form of CH$_4$, this yields the Jovian C/H ratio of 2.07 ± 0.24 times the solar C/H ratio given by Lambert (1978). This enrichment of C in Jupiter over the solar concentration seems to favor imhomogenous accretion models of Jupiter's formation. Analysis of the v_4 band of CH$_4$ by Courtin *et al.* (1983a) yielded an enrichment of the C^{12}/C^{13} ratio of 1.8 ± $^{0.4}_{0.6}$ over the terrestrial value.

The tropospheric abundance of NH_3, PH_3, CH_3D, H_2O, and germane (GeH_4) of Jupiter's North Equatorial Belt, a cloud-free area, was investigated by Kunde *et al.* (1982). An example of a comparison of a measured spectrum with a spectrum computed under the assumption of the atmosphere is being saturated with NH_3 and a spectrum with an inferred NH_3 distribution is shown in Fig. 2.42. The profiles for NH_3 and PH_3 were found to be depleted in the upper troposphere by condensation and photochemistry but in agreement with their corresponding solar abundances below the 1-bar level. The mole fraction of H_2O is $\sim 1 \times 10^{-6}$ at 2.5 bars, increasing to $\sim 3 \times 10^{-5}$ at 4 bars, where it is still a factor of 30 below the value expected from solar abundance of oxygen. The cloud-free areas are expected to be areas of subsidence and may therefore not be representative of the concentration of condensibles on Jupiter as a whole.

The mole fraction of CH_3D is $3.5 \pm ^{1.0}_{1.3} \times 10^{-7}$. Using IRIS values for CH_3D and CH_4, a D/H ratio of $3.6 \pm ^{1.0}_{1.4} \times 10^{-5}$ is derived by Kunde *et al.* (1982). Assuming that this value is representative of the protosolar nebula and correcting for galactic chemical evolution yield a value of 5.5 to 9.0×10^{-5} for the primordial D/H ratio. The mole fraction of GeH_4 is $7 \pm 2 \times 10^{-10}$ at the 2–5-bar level, about a factor of 10 lower than the

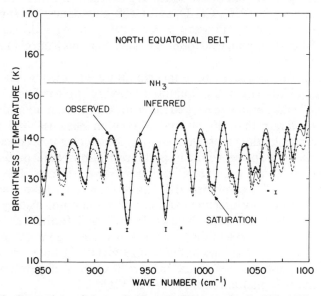

FIG. 2.42. Comparison of observed and synthetic spectra for the 850–1100-cm⁻¹ region. The observed spectrum from Voyager IRIS is compared to two synthesized spectra. One of the computed spectra assumes saturation of NH_3, whereas the inferred spectrum assumes a vertical distribution of NH_3 somewhat below saturation. (Reprinted courtesy of Kunde *et al.*, 1982, and *The Astrophysical Journal,* published by the University of Chicago Press. Copyright © 1982, The American Astronomical Society.)

TABLE 2.1

Trace Constituents in Jupiter's Atmosphere from Voyager IRIS—
North Equatorial Belt

Gas	Mole fraction	Reference
Methane, CH_4	1.75×10^{-3}	Gautier et al., 1982
Acetylene, C_2H_2	2×10^{-8}	Maguire[c]
Ethylene, C_2H_4	7×10^{-7}	Kim et al., 1982
Ethane, C_2H_6	5×10^{-6}	Maguire[c]
Methylacetylene, C_3H_4[a]	3.5×10^{-9}	Kim et al., 1982
Benzene, C_6H_6[a]	2×10^{-9}	Kim et al., 1982
Deuterated methane, CH_3D	3.5×10^{-7}	Kunde et al., 1982
Ammonia, NH_3	1.8×10^{-4}[b]	Kunde et al., 1982
Phosphene, PH_3	6×10^{-7}[b]	Kunde et al., 1982
Water vapor	$0.1-3 \times 10^{-5}$[b]	Kunde et al., 1982
Germane, GeH_4	7×10^{-10}	Kunde et al., 1982

[a] Tentative identification.

[b] Value at 1–4 bars; decreases with altitude.

[c] Private communication, 1982.

corresponding solar value but much higher than chemical equilibrium models predict. The PH_3, CH_3D, and GeH_4 abundances on Jupiter have also been analyzed by Drossart et al. (1982), using IRIS data in the $2100-2250$-cm^{-1} region, who found similar deviations from chemical equilibrium.

The properties of Jovian ammonia clouds were studied by Marten et al. (1981) using IRIS data of the equatorial region of Jupiter. The clouds have only a small effect on the measured intensities. They seem to be dominated by particles larger than 30 μm and of column densities 1–2 orders of magnitude smaller than those derived from thermochemical considerations alone, implying the presence and importance of atmospheric motion. Below the ammonia clouds a deeper cloud layer was confirmed. The study by Bézard et al. (1983) combined IRIS spectra and data from the imaging system of Voyager to infer the existence of ammonium hydrogen sulfide (NH_4SH) clouds at an intermediate level ($\sim$ 1.9 bars); further below, a dense H_2O cloud could be present too, consistent with the theoretical predictions of Lewis (1969) and Weidenschilling and Lewis (1973), but it should not be responsible for the observed spread in 5-μm brightness temperatures. Minor constituents of Jupiter are summarized in Table 2.1.

4. Energy Balance

Jupiter is so massive and the processes of transporting energy by convection from the interior and radiating it at low temperatures so inefficient that some of the gravitational energy, which was converted to heat in the collapse and contraction phases of Jupiter's evolution, is still emerging. These internal heat sources may even be augmented by gravitational energy released by a separation of hydrogen and helium in the interior (Smolu-chowski, 1967; Salpeter, 1973; Stevenson, 1980). To study these processes, it is crucial to obtain a precise measurement of the excess energy that Jupiter now radiates in the IR over the level that would be expected if it were in equilibrium with absorbed solar radiation. To obtain this excess radiation, two quantities need to be established: First, the thermal emission must be measured; second, the Bond albedo (the ratio of absorbed solar power to total available solar power) must be established. The internal energy source is then the difference between emitted IR and absorbed solar energy. It has become customary to call the ratio of emitted to absorbed energy the "energy balance," although energy imbalance would be a more appropriate term. Pre-Voyager measurements of the Jovian energy balance from ground-based, airborne, and Pioneer measurements ranged from as low as 1.6 to as high as 2.5, with very large uncertainties (see Hanel *et al.,* 1981a).

The Voyager IRIS was specifically designed to address this important question. The Michelson interferometer measures a large fraction of the thermal emission directly and, with temperature and composition also available, allows a reliable extrapolation of the emitted intensity in spectral regions not directly covered by the interferometer. The radiometer of IRIS measures a large fraction of the reflected solar radiation, which in turn allows a determination of the energy absorbed by Jupiter. Full disk measurements by the IRIS radiometer indicate a geometric albedo of 0.274 ± 0.013. Combining this measurement with the Pioneer-derived phase integral (Tomasko *et al.,* 1978) yields a Bond albedo of 0.343 ± 0.032. Infrared spectra

TABLE 2.2

COMPARISON OF ENERGY BALANCE PARAMETERS OF JUPITER AND SATURN

Quantity	Jupiter	Saturn
Geometric albedo	0.274 ± 0.013	0.242 ± 0.012
Phase integral	1.25 ± 0.1	1.42 ± 0.1
Bond albedo	0.343 ± 0.032	0.342 ± 0.030
Total absorbed power (10^{17} W)	5.014 ± 0.248	1.114 ± 0.050
Total emitted power (10^{17} W)	8.365 ± 0.084	1.977 ± 0.032
Effective temperature (K)	124.4 ± 0.3	95.0 ± 0.4
Energy balance	1.67 ± 0.09	1.78 ± 0.09
Internal energy source (10^{17} W)	3.35 ± 0.26	0.863 ± 0.060
Internal energy flux (10^{-4} W cm^{-2})	5.44 ± 0.43	2.01 ± 0.14
Internal power/mass, (10^{-13} W g^{-1})	1.76 ± 0.14	1.52 ± 0.11
Luminosity: log (L/L_{Sun})	-9.062 ± 0.034	-9.651 ± 0.030

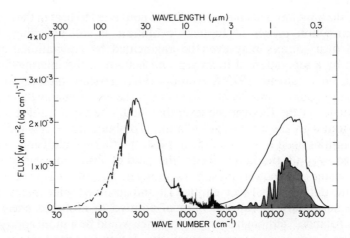

FIG. 2.43. The low-wave-number spectrum represents the thermal emission of Jupiter. Between 200 and 2300 cm⁻¹ it is based on measured IRIS spectra and below 200 cm⁻¹ on calculations using the measured temperature profile and atmospheric transmittances. The upper curve at high wave numbers represents solar radiation available at the distance of Jupiter; the crosshatched area is the reflected spectrum, computed from the derived Bond albedo and ground-based spectral information. The ratio of the areas under the left curve (thermal emission) and between both curves on the right (absorbed solar radiation) is the energy balance of Jupiter (Hanel *et al.*, 1981a).

recorded by the Michelson interferometer yield a thermal emission equivalent to that of a blackbody of 124.4 ± 0.3 K. From these measurements the internal heat flux of Jupiter was estimated to be $5.44 \pm 0.43 \times 10^{-4}$ W cm⁻², and the energy balance to be 1.67 ± 0.09 (Hanel *et al.*, 1981a) (see Table 2.2).

Comparison of these values with results from models of the Jovian interior (e.g., Grossman *et al.*, 1980; see also Stevenson, 1982) shows that the measured energy balance can be accounted for by gravitational contraction alone and that energy release by separation of helium and hydrogen is not required. This result is in agreement with the helium concentration measured by IRIS (Gautier *et al.*, 1981). The IRIS data yielded the important conclusion that significant helium separation has not started on Jupiter. The spectral information used in determining the energy balance of Jupiter is illustrated in Fig. 2.43.

5. *Satellites*

The four largest satellites of Jupiter, first observed by Galileo in 1610, appear small in comparison to the planet but are sizable objects in their own right. Europa (diameter, 3130 km) is only slightly smaller than our Moon

(3476 km), but Io (3640 km), Ganymede (5280 km), and Callisto (4840 km) are larger; Ganymede is even larger than the planet Mercury (4834 km). The densities of the Galilean satellites decrease with the distance from Jupiter: 3.53 gm cm^{-3} for Io, 3.03 gm cm^{-3} for Europa, 1.93 gm cm^{-3} for Ganymede and 1.79 gm cm^{-3} for Callisto, indicating a higher fractional content of light material (ices) in objects formed successively from Jupiter. The fraction of ices was governed by the temperatures during their stage of formation (Cameron and Pollack, 1976). The Voyager cameras have recorded data from all these satellites, showing a great number of diverse land forms (Smith *et al.*, 1979a,b).

IRIS has also observed the Galilean satellites and has measured the temperatures and in some cases the thermal inertia of their surfaces (Hanel *et al.*, 1979a,b). However, the most fascinating object was clearly Io (Fig. 2.44). Pre-Voyager knowledge of Io (and of the other Galilean satellites) is summarized by Morrison and Burns (1976) and Brown and Yung (1976). In a memorable paper published only a few days before the arrival of Voyager 1, Peale *et al.* (1979) reported on calculations of the energy dissipated by Io owing to gravitational stresses induced by tidal interaction with the gravitational fields of Jupiter, Europa, and Ganymede. Peal and his colleagues predicted a molten interior and possibly volcanic activity. The Voyager team expected a surface heavily cratered by impact and possibly a few formations caused by volcanism. To find a large number of *active* volcanos and *no* impact craters was certainly a surprise (Morabito *et al.*, 1979; Smith *et al.*, 1979a). IRIS detected a number of "hot spots," that is, areas with surface temperatures higher than what is expected from a surface element in radiative balance with the sun (Hanel *et al.*, 1979a). By the very nature of volcanic eruptions the source is relatively small, in all cases much smaller than the IRIS field of view. A reasonable match to the measured spectra was obtained by assuming that the field contains several areas of distinctly different temperatures. The method applied in the analysis is similar in concept to the two-temperature model of the south polar spectrum of Mars. An example of a three-temperature model for the volcanic area around Pele (Fig. 2.45) shows about 89.9% of the field of view at 114 K, 10% at 175 K, and only 0.0577% at 654 K (Pearl and Sinton, 1982). The high temperature of Pele is somewhat uncertain, possibly by as much as 50 K. The actual area of this high-temperature source is about 6 km^2. It is likely that this represents the central area, the caldera. Pele was the smallest but hottest region among nine hot spots seen by IRIS.

The hot spot and plume at Loki (Hanel *et al.*, 1979a; Smith *et al.*, 1979a) turned out to be of special significance. The signatures of sulfur dioxide (SO_2) gas and possibly also of SO_2 frost particles have been identified in the

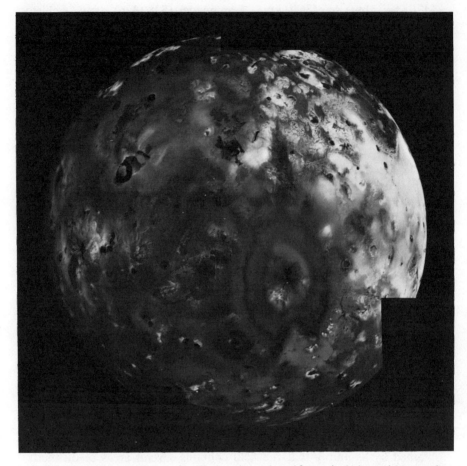

FIG. 2.44. Composite image of Io. The large heart-shaped feature in the lower right center is
Pele. The horseshoe-shaped dark area in the upper left quadrant is near the source of the Loki
plume (NASA, JPL, Project Voyager).

IRIS spectrum (Fig. 2.46) (Pearl *et al.,* 1979). About 0.2 cm atm of gaseous
SO_2 are needed to produce the measured spectrum. Of equal interest are
upper limits, derived from the same spectrum, for the gases carbonyl sulfide
(COS), carbon disulfide (CS_2), hydrogen sulfide (H_2S), CO_2, N_2O, and NH_3.
The upper limits of all these gases are well below the abundances expected if
their ices were present on the surrounding surface (~ 130 K). It seems that
the lighter elements H, C, and N have been reduced considerably in
comparison to S in the recycling process to which the surface of Io is
subjected. The constant recycling has also obliterated all evidence of the
impact craters which must have existed at an early epoch.

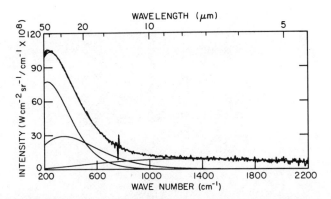

FIG. 2.45. Voyager spectrum of region of Io containing Pele. The ringing in the spectrum near 760 cm⁻¹ is caused by interference. The smooth curves through the data represent a least-squares fit using three weighted blackbody spectra. The lower curves are the three components; from left to right, their temperatures (and fractional areas) are 114 K (0.899), 175 K (0.100), and 654 K (5.77 10⁻⁴). (By permission, Pearl and Stinton, 1982. Copyright © 1982, University of Arizona Press.)

D. SATURN

Saturn (Fig. 2.47), only second in size among the planets (equatorial diameter 9 times and mass 95 times that of Earth), orbits at a heliocentric distance of 9.55 AU, about twice as far from the sun as Jupiter. The pre-Voyager and pre-Pioneer state of knowledge is summarized in a work-shop report "The Saturn System" [National Aeronautics and Space Admin-

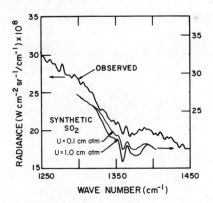

FIG. 2.46. Voyager spectrum of region of Io containing Loki. The observed spectrum is compared to two computed spectra containing 0.1 and 1.0 cm atm of SO_2 gas. (Pearl *et al.*, 1979. Reprinted by permission from *Nature*, Vol. 280, pp. 755–758. Copyright © 1979— Macmillan Journals Limited.)

FIG. 2.47. Voyager 1 image of Saturn taken three and one-half weeks before closest approach (NASA, JPL, Project Voyager).

istration (NASA), 1978]. Ground-based measurements had already established the presence of an atmospheric temperature inversion; the constituents H_2, CH_4, NH_3, PH_3, CH_3D, and C_2H_6 had been detected; helium was expected on cosmological grounds. But, as in the case of Jupiter, large numerical uncertainties existed.

Pioneer data improved our knowledge of the temperature profile but contributed little to the compositional information, except for the He abundance. Orton and Ingersoll (1980) derived an He mole fraction of 0.10 ± 0.03 from a comparison of the IR broadband radiometer data and radio occultation measurements. Neglecting the small effect of heavy elements, this mole fraction corresponds to an He mass fraction, $Y = 0.18 \pm 0.05$, very close to the He mass fractions of 0.19 ± 0.05 and 0.21 ± 0.06 found by IRIS for Jupiter. The probable error of the Pioneer measurement is actually larger, since the quoted error is only due to uncertainties in the radiometer data and does not include uncertainties in the radio occultation data. This leads to the conclusion that the He abundance is nearly the same on both planets; however, Orton and Ingersoll (1980) estimated the Saturnian energy balance to be 2.8 ± 0.9, which would indicate a very strong internal heat source for Saturn and, implicitly, the occurrence of helium differentiation. This dilemma remained unresolved until the Voyager–Saturn encounters.

What has been said about the significance of composition measurements for Jupiter applies equally to Saturn. Saturn provides another sample of the primordial nebula, about twice as far from the sun as Jupiter; therefore similarities as well as differences in composition between both planets are important.

1. *Spectra*

Figure 2.48 compares thermal emission spectra of Saturn measured by Voyager IRIS with a calculated spectrum and a spectrum of Jupiter. As expected, the brightness temperatures on Saturn are about 30–40 K lower than on Jupiter. In both planets the pressure-induced lines of molecular hydrogen appear at 360 and 600 cm^{-1}. However, the line shapes differ, partly because of different vertical temperature profiles and emission angles, and partly because of different He and NH_3 concentrations. In the south polar spectrum of Saturn the extremely high emission angles shift the weighting functions of the hydrogen lines to near and above the temperature minimum and cause the line centers to appear in emission.

The spectral features of tropospheric NH_3, so prominent in the Jovian spectrum, are weak on Saturn, where NH_3 is strongly depleted in the upper troposphere by condensation. With the reduced NH_3 concentration the

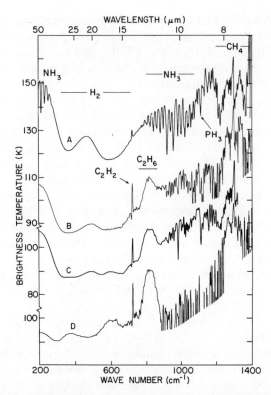

FIG. 2.48. Saturn spectra and comparison spectra: A, Jovian Belt spectrum; B, large average of Saturn spectra taken in two bands between 15° and 50° northern and southern latitudes; C, synthesized Saturn spectrum, and D, south polar spectrum of Saturn recorded at an emission angle of 76°. (Hanel *et al.*, 1981b; copyright © 1981 by the American Association for the Advancement of Science.)

1000-cm^{-1} region of Saturn is dominated by spectral features of PH_3, rather than of NH_3, as was the case on Jupiter. On both planets emissions by stratospheric CH_4 and its photochemical derivatives C_2H_2 and C_2H_6 are apparent. The high emission angle of the south polar spectrum (Fig. 2.48) emphasizes spectral features of stratospheric origin. In addition to the well-known features of C_2H_2 and C_2H_6, marked in Fig. 2.48, emissions due to methylacetylene (C_3H_4) and propane (C_3H_8) have tentatively been identified by IRIS (Hanel *et al.*, 1981b). The same gases are clearly observed in the Titan spectrum shown for comparison in Fig. 2.49.

2. *Temperatures*

As in the Jovian temperature analysis the 200–600-cm^{-1} region provides information on the thermal structure between approximately 70 and

700 mbar, while data from the Q-branch of the 1304-cm^{-1} CH$_4$ band are sensitive to the temperature within a broad atmospheric layer centered near 1 mbar. Two Saturnian profiles are compared with a Jovian profile in Fig. 2.50. Understandably, the Saturnian profile is colder, but both planets have a temperature minimum at about 100 mbar. This is also understandable because both planets have a similar gross composition (H$_2$, He, CH$_4$) and both have an internal energy source. In the deep interior the energy flux is, to a large extent, carried by convection, resulting in a lapse rate only slightly higher than adiabatic. In cloud layers, where phase changes occur, the lapse rate may be closer to the wet adiabatic. In the upper troposphere the hydrogen opacity diminishes with the lower pressure, and more and more of the flux is carried by radiation. The convective equilibrium of the deep layers yields to radiative equilibrium. The demarcation between the two regimes, at several hundred millibars, is characterized by a change in lapse rate. Higher up a warm stratosphere exists, because absorption of solar radiation takes place by CH$_4$ and other constituents which absorb well in the near IR but emit poorly in the far IR. This simplified picture is perturbed by dynamic effects.

The temperature cross section of Saturn (Fig. 2.51) indicates a large-scale

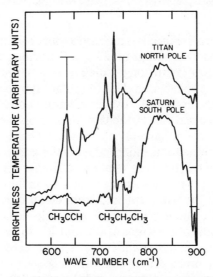

FIG. 2.49. Tentative identification of C$_3$H$_4$ and C$_3$H$_8$ features on Saturn and on Titan. The upper spectrum is an average of 72 spectra of the north polar region of Titan, while the lower spectrum is an average of 62 spectra from the south polar region of Saturn. Only relative brightness temperatures are shown, since both data sets contain spectra not fully on the disk. (Hanel *et al.*, 1981b; copyright © 1981 by the American Association for the Advancement of Science.)

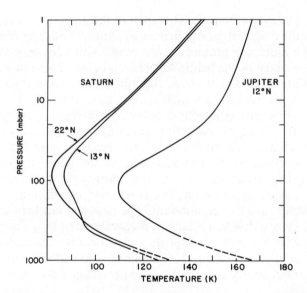

FIG. 2.50. Vertical temperature profiles for Saturn and Jupiter, as derived by inversion of Voyager IRIS spectra. The dashed portions of the curves represent extrapolations along adiabats. (Hanel *et al.*, 1981b; copyright © 1981 by the American Association for the Advancement of Science.)

seasonal effect. Saturn's spin axis is inclined about 26.7° to the orbital plane, more so than the Earth's obliquity (23.5°). Therefore, Saturn may show strong seasonal effects. With long radiative time constants the seasonal amplitudes near the 150-mbar level lag the polar tilt by nearly 90° and were near maximum at the arrival of Voyager (Conrath and Pirraglia, 1982). In addition to these seasonal effects, the latitudinal cross section shows small-scale features which are remarkably correlated between both hemispheres. Only a deep-seated circulation, independent of the seasonally changing solar input, can be the source of this correlation. A similar conclusion is derived from a comparison of the wind shear calculated from the horizontal temperature gradients with the winds inferred from cloud motion. The IRIS-derived wind shear of about 10 m sec^{-1} per scale height results in little reduction with altitude of the winds of 400 and 500 m sec^{-1} obtained by the imaging observations (Smith *et al.*, 1981). The observed jet streams must indeed be very deep, much deeper than the range over which absorption of solar radiation is significant (Conrath and Pirraglia, 1983).

3. Composition

As in the case of Jupiter, the spectral region of the H_2 lines permits an estimate of the helium abundance. Preliminary results (Hanel *et al.*, 1981b)

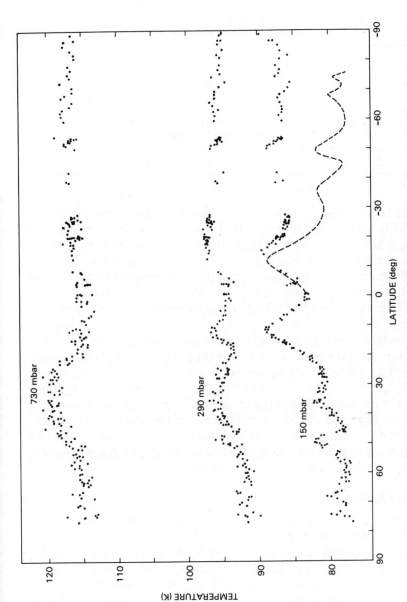

FIG. 2.51. Temperatures retrieved by inversion of Voyager IR spectral measurements. The values shown represent mean values for atmospheric layers approximately $\frac{1}{2}$ scale height thick. The broken curve is a fit to the northern hemisphere 150-mbar temperature cross section which has been folded over at the equator to permit a comparison with southern hemisphere results (Conrath and Pirraglia, 1982).

TABLE 2.3

TRACE CONSTITUENTS IN SATURN'S ATMOSPHERE FROM
VOYAGER IRIS—DISK AVERAGE

Gas	Mole fraction	References
Methane, CH_4	1.76×10^{-3}	Courtin, 1983a
Acetylene, C_2H_2	1.1×10^{-7}	Courtin, 1983a
Ethane, C_2H_6	4.8×10^{-6}	Courtin, 1983a
Methylacetylene, C_3H_4[a]	No estimate available	Hanel et al., 1981b
Propane, C_3H_4[a]	No estimate available	Hand et al., 1981
Deuterated methane, CH_3D	2.3×10^{-7}	Courtin, 1983a
Phosphine, PH_3	2×10^{-6}	Courtin, 1983a

[a] Tentative identification.

yielded a helium mass fraction $Y = 0.11$. A more recent estimate (Conrath et al., 1983) determined Y to be 0.13; the investigation is still incomplete and error bars have not yet been established. In either case the helium abundance of Saturn is lower than the results obtained by similar methods on Jupiter (Gautier et al., 1981). Although the (conservative) error bars will probably overlap somewhat, it appears that Saturn's observable atmospheric layers are depleted in helium in comparison with the same layers on Jupiter.

Preliminary information on the minor constituents of the Saturnian atmosphere are given by Hanel et al. (1981b) and more recently by Courtin et al. (1983b). Table 2.3 summarizes these results. Interestingly, the enrichment of carbon is about a factor of 2 over the solar value on Jupiter and Saturn. For phosphorus, possibly a small enrichment was found for Jupiter, but a much larger factor, about 4, was discovered for Saturn (Courtin et al., 1982b). With the Saturn spectra in hand for less than two years, as of this writing, many analyses are incomplete and further results, especially comparisons with Jupiter and the sun, may be expected in the years to come.

4. Energy Balance

Voyager IRIS also investigated the energy balance of Saturn (Hanel et al., 1983). The energy balance measurement of Saturn is more complex than that of Jupiter because the rings of Saturn have a significant effect on the solar and thermal radiative fluxes. The ring effect varies also with season owing to the high obliquity of Saturn. The geometric albedo, derived from the IRIS radiometer measurement, is 0.242 ± 0.012, considerably lower than the values obtained by previous investigations. Combining this geometric albedo with the Pioneer-derived phase integral (M. G. Tomasko, private communication, 1982) yields a Bond albedo of 0.343 ± 0.032, nearly the same as for Jupiter. Measurements of the thermal emission spectrum by the Voyager interferometer and an extrapolation of the spectrum to spectral regions not covered by the instrument but derived with the help of the IRIS temperature profiles yield an effective temperature of Saturn of 95.0 ± 0.4 K. From these measurements the internal heat flux of Saturn is 2.01 ± 0.14 10^{-4} W cm^{-2} and the energy balance, defined as the ratio of total emitted to total absorbed energy, is 1.78 ± 0.09. The energy balance parameters of Saturn are compared with those of Jupiter in Table 2.2, and a summary of the pertinent spectral information is given in Fig. 2.52 (Hanel *et al.*, 1983).

The energy balance of Saturn, 1.78 ± .09, is only slightly larger than that of Jupiter, 1.67 ± 0.09. Since Saturn is less massive than Jupiter, it has much less primordial heat stored in its interior and must, therefore, augment its thermal emission with energy from another source. This energy source may very well be the differentiation of helium, as Smoluchowski (1967) originally suggested.

5. *Titan*

With a diameter of 5150 km, Titan (Fig. 2.53) is the second largest satellite in the solar system. Since Kuiper (1944) discovered CH_4 absorption bands in its reflection spectrum, Titan has been known to have an atmosphere. Somewhat earlier, Comas Solá (1908) had already reached a similar conclusion from limb-darkening observations. Despite substantial progress in ground-based observation techniques (Gillett *et al.*, 1973; Gillett, 1975;

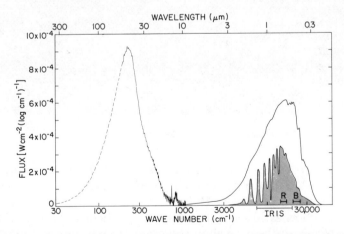

FIG. 2.52. Energy balance of Saturn. This figure is similar to Fig. 2.43. Also shown are the nominal spectral ranges of the IRIS radiometer and the red (R) and blue (B) channels of the Pioneer photometer (Hanel *et al.*, 1983).

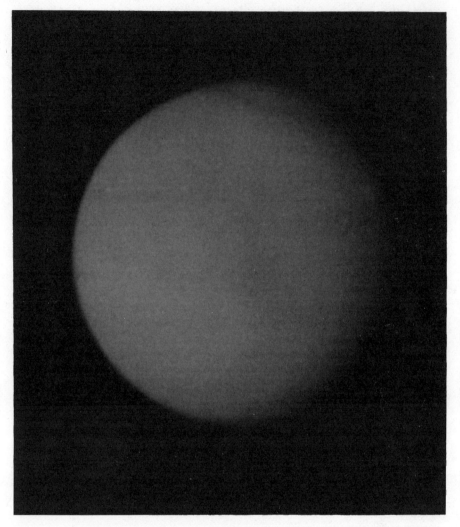

FIG. 2.53. Voyager 1 image of Titan (NASA, JPL, Project Voyager).

McCarthy *et al.*, 1980; Tokunaga, 1980), it was not possible to discriminate among several widely differing atmospheric models. The most extreme models include one in which CH_4 is the most abundant gas and the surface pressure is as low as 20 mbar (Danielson *et al.*, 1973; Caldwell, 1978) and one in which N_2 is the most abundant gas (CH_4 only a minor constituent) and the surface pressure is possibly as high as 21 bars (Hunten, 1978). A discussion of these models and a summary of our knowledge of Titan before

Voyager appear in "The Saturn System" (NASA, 1978). In either model the presence of CH_4 and of solar UV radiation should lead to a complex hydrogen photochemistry (Strobel, 1974; Chang *et al.*, 1978; Raulin *et al.*, 1979). The hydrocarbons C_2H_2, C_2H_6, and possibly ethylene (C_2H_4) had already been detected (Tokunaga, 1980; Gillett *et al.*, 1969). Therefore, Titan promised to be an interesting object. The Voyager 1 trajectory was chosen to pass very close to Titan, with the sacrifice of a possible Uranus encounter. Voyager 2 was given the task of investigating Uranus. The Voyager 1 trajectory also permitted the spacecraft to fly behind Titan as seen from Earth, allowing Titan to occult the Voyager radio signals, which offered the best observational technique for finding the surface pressure and the radius of the solid body. This strategy worked well; the Radio Science Investigation derived a surface pressure of 1.5 bars and a radius of the solid body of Titan of 2575 km (Lindal *et al.*, 1983). Moreover, Tyler and his colleagues (1981) found an atmospheric scale height in the lower atmosphere of 16.4 km, which corresponds to a ratio of temperature to atomic mass units of 2.55 K/amu.

At the same time IRIS obtained spectra from the center of the disk, the morning and evening limbs, the southern hemisphere and the north polar

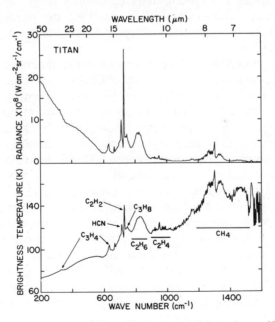

FIG. 2.54. Voyager 1 spectrum of Titan. The upper panel shows the specific intensity, and the lower panel the same spectrum in terms of brightness temperature (Hanel *et al.*, 1981b; copyright © 1981 by the American Association for the Advancement of Science).

region (Hanel et al., 1981b). The Titan spectrum, displayed in radiance and brightness temperatures in Fig. 2.54, shows a broad continuum with a number of strong emission features superimposed. Before we pursue the analysis of atmospheric composition, a temperature profile must be established. The CH_4 band at 1304 cm⁻⁴ is clearly present in emission and should yield temperatures in the warm stratosphere, but the precise CH_4 abundance is not known. Inspection of the spectrum (Fig. 2.54) reveals no spectral interval in which a known constituent is the dominant absorber and which would permit retrieval of tropospheric temperatures. It is not even clear at what wave number, if any, the emission originates from the surface. Fortunately, several other pieces of information can be used to solve the puzzle.

First, the minimum brightness temperature of ⁓ 73 K at 200 cm⁻¹ and the stratospheric temperatures derived from the 1304 CH_4 band (although with some uncertainties in the corresponding pressures) constrain the temperature-per-molecular-weight (T/M) profile obtained by the Radio Science Investigation and yield not only a temperature profile (Fig. 2.55), but also a mean molecular weight of approximately 28 amu. An atmosphere with N_2 or possibly carbon monoxide (CO) as the dominant gas is therefore established, ruling out models with CH_4 (16 amu) as the dominant constituent. Since the Voyager UV spectrometer (Broadfoot et al., 1981) identified nitrogen emission features and IRIS identified the nitrogen-containing compound HCN, N_2 is generally accepted as the dominant constituent in Titan's atmosphere.

The second important evidence that helps in the understanding of conditions on Titan came from a comparison of IRIS spectra from the equatorial limb and the center of the disk. Between 200- and 520-cm⁻¹ limb darkening was observed, indicating that emission in this spectral range originates predominantly in the troposphere, below the temperature minimum. Above 600 cm⁻¹ limb brightening was observed, indicating emission from the warm stratosphere. However, between 520 and about 600 cm⁻¹ neither brightening nor darkening exists (Hanel et al., 1981a; Samuelson et al., 1981). At these wave numbers Titan's atmosphere must be fairly transparent ($\tau < 0.1$), and the emission must originate primarily from the surface. The inferred surface temperature is about 95 K. The tropospheric opacity, tentatively identified as due to pressure-induced absorption of N_2–N_2 and N_2–CH_4 collisions and to absorption in CH_4 haze or clouds, increases toward the 200-cm⁻¹ lower limit of the IRIS spectral range. At 200 cm⁻¹ the atmospheric weighting function is centered near the temperature minimum. At 1304 cm⁻¹ the weighting function is high in the stratosphere, at about 1 mb.

Using IRIS data from the surface (⁓ 530 cm⁻¹), the temperature minimum (⁓ 200 cm⁻¹), and the stratosphere (1304 cm⁻¹), Flasar et al. (1981b)

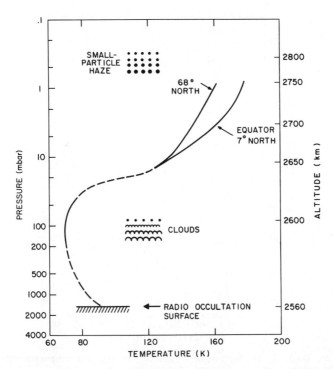

FIG. 2.55. Temperature profile of Titan. The solid curves are from IRIS data, and the dashed parts from the profile of the ratio of temperature to molecular weight obtained by the Voyager radio science investigation. Haze and condensation zones are indicated schematically. (Hanel *et al.*, 1981b; copyright © 1981 by the American Association for the Advancement of Science.)

investigated the latitudinal temperature distribution and dynamic effects. Diurnal temperature variations appear to be absent. At the surface the polar regions are only 3-K cooler than the equator (Fig. 2.56). The 200-cm^{-1} temperatures show little meridional variations beyond a 1-K difference between northern and southern hemispheres. Stratospheric temperatures are about 20 K lower in the north polar region than at the equator. This behavior is understandable in terms of the radiative relaxation time; near the surface this is much longer than a season. Furthermore, the absence of detectable diurnal and longitudinal structure suggests the absence of baroclinic waves and eddies. Near the surface the weather must be remarkably constant throughout all seasons, not even changing in the polar regions. There only exists a zonally symmetric flow, which provides some latitudinal heat transport. Meridional velocities of this large-scale circulation are ~0.04 cm sec^{-1} near the surface.

In the upper stratosphere the radiative time constant is short in compari-

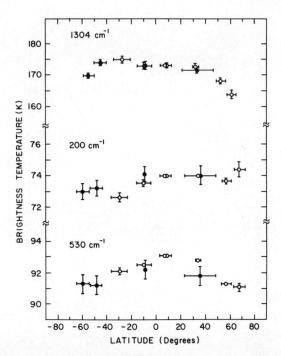

FIG. 2.56. Brightness temperature of Titan versus latitude. The temperature at 530 cm⁻¹ corresponds closely to that of the surface, at 200 cm⁻¹ to the temperature minimum, and at 1304 cm⁻¹ to that of the stratosphere. (Flasar *et al.*, 1981a. Reprinted by permission from *Nature*, Vol. 292, pp. 693–698. Copyright © 1981—Macmillan Journals Limited.)

son with a season, but still long compared to the diurnal time scale (assumed equal to Titan's revolution around Saturn). The large temperature drop near the north pole reflects a stratospheric response to the polar winter. In contrast to the gentle meridional circulation, a strong zonal wind (∼ 100 m sec⁻¹) is required in the stratosphere to produce a balance between pressure gradients and centrifugal forces (cyclostrophic flow). In this respect Titan and Venus show similarities in their global circulations. Unlike Venus, however, Titan, with a large obliquity (∼ 27°) and short radiative time constants in the stratosphere, should have a seasonally varying cyclostrophic flow.

Combining IRIS data with preliminary T/M profiles from the Radio Science Investigation (Tyler *et al.*, 1981), Samuelson *et al.* (1981) obtained a refined mean molecular mass between 28.2 and 29.3 amu. If this preliminary result is confirmed, the atmosphere must contain, in addition to N_2 and CH_4, a heavier gas than N_2 (28 amu). Argon 36 is the most likely candidate. Samuelson and his colleagues also found evidence of a small opacity due to stratospheric haze and a mole fraction of H_2 of 0.002 ± 0.001 from the presence of the pressure-induced H_2 line near 360 cm^{-1} superimposed on the tropospheric absorption continuum.

However the most remarkable composition information came from the analysis of the sharp emission features which are most prominent in the spectra from the north polar area. In addition to the hydrocarbons already known to be present (CH_4, C_2H_2, C_2H_6, and C_2H_4), IRIS discovered hydrogen cyanide (HCN) (Hanel *et al.*, 1981a); C_3H_8 and C_3H_4 (Maguire *et al.*, 1981); diacetylene (C_4H_2), cyanoacetylene (HC_3N), and cyanogen (C_2N_2) (Kunde *et al.*, 1981); and, even more surprising, CO_2 (Samuelson *et al.*, 1983). The identification of these constituents is made by comparison of Titan and laboratory spectra; examples are shown for C_4H_2 in Fig. 2.57 and for HC_3N and C_2N_2 in Fig. 2.58. The estimated abundances shown in Table 2.3 are derived from radiative transfer calculations, assuming a uniform stratospheric distribution down to a condensation level (~ 20–50 mbar). In the case of CO_2 a photochemical model was used to derive the vertical distribution. CO_2 is in a steady state, constantly being formed and destroyed. The abundance is primarily regulated by removal owing to condensation at the ~ 73-K cold trap near the tropopause and by the rate at which water-bearing meteoritic material (the source of the oxygen) enters the top of the atmosphere. Although not directly observed by IRIS, the presence of CO_2

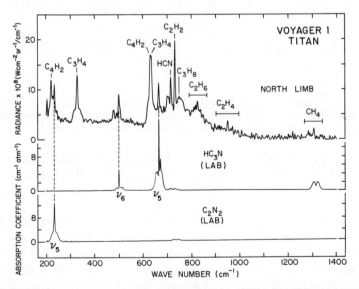

FIG. 2.57. Voyager 1 spectrum of the north polar limb of Titan, and laboratory spectra of cyanoacetylene (HC_3N) and cyanogen (C_2N_2) Kunde *et al.*, 1981. Reprinted by permission from *Nature*, Vol. 292, pp. 686–688. Copyright © 1981 — Macmillan Journals Limited.

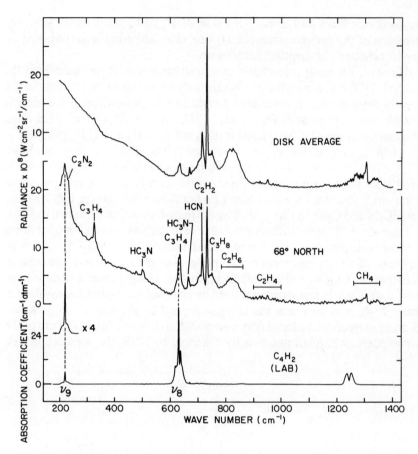

FIG. 2.58. Voyager 1 spectrum of the Titan disk, of the north polar region, and a laboratory spectrum of diacetylene (C_4H_2) (Kunde *et al.*, 1981. Reprinted by permission from *Nature*, Vol. 292, pp. 686–688. Copyright © 1981—Macmillan Journals Limited.)

also requires a small amount of CO to be present. Interestingly, many of the compounds found by IRIS have been observed by radio spectroscopy in large interstellar clouds (Thaddeus, 1981) and in laboratory attempts to simulate conditions on Titan (Gupta *et al.*, 1981).

Most of the hydrocarbons and nitriles are at a stratospheric abundance higher than one would expect from vapor pressure curves at the temperature minimum (Fig. 2.59), which implies photochemical production in the upper and removal by condensation in the lower stratosphere. The condensation products form smoglike layers of aerosols which eventually coagulate and precipitate. The temperatures at the surface are not high enough to permit recycling of the components or decomposition to form CH_4 again. Over times comparable to the age of the solar system, a layer, perhaps as large as several hundred meters, may have formed at the surface.

It is interesting to speculate whether this accumulation of organic matter at the surface of Titan could have lead to more complex organic compounds, such as amino acids and other precursors of life forms, had the temperatures not been prohibitively low. This strange layer at the surface may be unique in the solar system. Alternatively, the surface of Titan may be covered by an ocean of ethane with methane, nitrogen, and argon dissolved in it. We can only speculate at this time. Clearly, the most challenging task for future spacecraft is to explore Titan's surface. Minor constituents of Titan are summarized in Table 2.4.

2.5. Future Directions

As shown in this chapter, spectroscopy in the thermal IR has so far played a major role in planetary exploration from space (Fig. 2.60). The degree to which this will continue depends on the answers to several questions. First, do scientific questions remain which can best be resolved by spectroscopic techniques? Second, will spaceborne platforms be available? Third, if so, what advances in instrumentation and observational techniques can be expected?

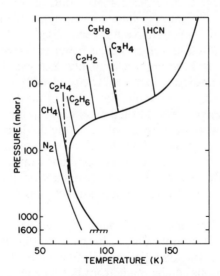

FIG. 2.59. Vertical temperature profile of Titan and the condensation curves of N_2 and several hydrocarbons with mole fractions listed in Table 2.3 (Maguire *et al.*, 1981. Reprinted by permission from *Nature,* Vol. 292, pp. 683–686. Copyright © 1981—Macmillan Journals Limited.)

TABLE 2.4

TRACE CONSTITUENTS IN TITAN'S ATMOSPHERE FROM VOYAGER IRIS

Gas	Mole fraction	References
Hydrogen, H_2	2×10^{-3}	Samuelson et al., 1981
Acetylene, C_2H_2	3×10^{-6}	Hanel et al., 1981b
Ethylene, C_2H_4	4×10^{-7}	Kunde et al., 1981
Ethane, C_2H_6	2×10^{-5}	Hanel et al., 1981b
Methylacetylene, C_3H_4	3×10^{-8}	Maguire et al., 1981
Propane, C_3H_8	$1-5 \times 10^{-6}$	Kunde et al., 1981
Diacetylene C_4H_2	$0.1-1 \times 10^{-7}$	Kunde et al., 1981
Carbon dioxide, CO_2	$1-5 \times 10^{-9}$	Samuelson et al., 1983
Cyanogen, C_2N_2	$0.1-1 \times 10^{-7}$	Kunde et al., 1981
Hydrogen cyanide, HCN	2×10^{-7}	Hanel et al., 1981b
Cyanoacetylene, HC_3N	$0.1-1 \times 10^{-7}$	Kunde et al., 1981

Certainly, much further progress can be expected in planetary astronomy by application of remote spectroscopic sensing. As of 1982, not even half the planets have been investigated by spaceborne IR spectrometers; Mercury, Venus, Uranus, Neptune, and Pluto remain to be explored. Admittedly Mercury, without a substantial atmosphere, would not require high-resolution spectroscopy, but the other planets would. Even among the planets which have been investigated by spacecraft equipped with IR spectrometers, large segments of the spectra have not been observed; furthermore, higher spectral and spatial resolution, as well as better coverage in latitude, longitude, phase angle, and season, are all highly desirable. Beyond this, many specific scientific questions which could be resolved by spectroscopic means are still unanswered. For example, the colors of the Jovian and Saturnian clouds and the presence of additional organic compounds in Titan's stratosphere, together with their seasonal variation in latitude, are potential subjects of future spectroscopic exploration. Despite the rapid increase in our knowledge, the present list of atmospheric constituents of the giant planets is certainly incomplete, and error bars on the abundances and vertical and horizontal distributions of known constituents are frequently large.

The question of the future availability of spaceborne platforms is more difficult to answer. Certainly Earth observing platforms will be available. The International Ultraviolet Explorer (IUE) has already demonstrated that planetary observations can be made from Earth orbit. Later in this decade, the Space Telescope (ST) and the cryogenically cooled Shuttle Infrared Telescope Facility (SIRTF), and, eventually, telescopes on a permanent space station will be promising observing tools. With appropriate spectrom-

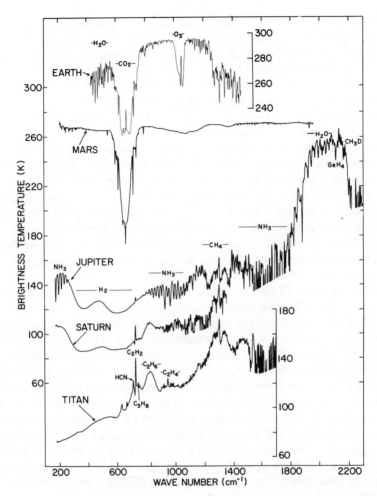

FIG. 2.60. Brightness temperatures of typical spectra of Earth, Mars, Jupiter, Saturn, and Titan. Earth and Titan temperature scales are to the right of their corresponding spectra (Hanel, 1981).

eters at the focal plane, high spectral resolution data of many planetary objects could be recorded. Unfortunately, the limited aperture (2.7 m for the ST and ~1 m for the SIRTF) will not allow good spatial resolution in the middle and far IR. For example, as seen from Earth orbit, Titan is less than 1 in. in diameter, which is the theoretical diffraction limit of SIRTF at 4 μm, and of the ST at about 10 μm. Infrared observations of the high latitudes of Titan, where most of the organic compounds discovered by IRIS are concentrated, will not be possible.

Planetary orbiters, with their advantages of close proximity and large phase-angle coverage, but more limited in weight and power (and in complexity of instruments), will therefore be complementary to Earth-orbiting platforms; both techniques are needed in a vigorous exploration program.

Some future composition and thermal structure measurements will undoubtedly be made by mass spectrometers and temperature sensors on atmospheric probes, such as presently planned by Project Galileo for Jupiter. Probes provide precise point measurements, which are especially valuable below dense clouds where remote spectroscopic measurements are often ineffective. However, the limitations of such highly localized observations can be appreciated by considering how unrepresentative of the earth's atmosphere, weather, and climate the data from a single radiosonde flight would be. Furthermore, probes are presently incapable of significant measurements in the stratosphere of Titan, where the interesting photochemical products are located. Probes and remote spectroscopic measurements turn out to be complementary, and both should be part of an energetic, well-balanced planetary exploration plan.

What will future IR spectrometers be like? Over the next 25 years I suspect that they will still be primarily Michelson interferometers; possibly with postdispersion systems. Very-high-spectral-resolution devices, such as heterodyne spectrometers, will also be used. On future planetary spacecraft the Michelson interferometers, probably augmented with high-spatial-resolution IR imaging systems, will be different than the Mariner and Voyager instruments, but with many similarities. I expect them to have two input beams for differential measurements; they will operate at lower temperatures and will have small Sterling cycle coolers for their cryogenic detectors. Spectral resolutions will be one or two orders of magnitude better than on Voyager, which will allow individual spectral lines to be resolved. These instruments will have several spectral ranges and much more complex on-board data systems than previous interferometers, which will allow, for example, an operational choice of spectral range and resolution.

Finally, one may still ask the old question "Why explore the planets at all with so many unresolved problems on Earth?" Of course, a great variety of material benefits may be enumerated; all material goods which we enjoy today were at one time "unnecessary" objects of research by scientists, engineers, and inventors. But I like best the answer which appears in one of Kepler's letters to his patrons (An Freiherrn von Herberstein und die Stände von Steiermark, Graz, 15 May, 1596). In free translation: "One tolerates painters because they please the eye, musicians because they please the ear . . . although they bring us no other material benefit. . . . Why should we not engage in science and explore the universe just to please the mind?" (see the excellent and touching book "Kepler, Life and Letters" by Carola

Baumgardt, 1951 and, in particular, the able and expanded translation of this book into German by Minkowski).

ACKNOWLEDGMENTS

I thank L. Watson and D. Vanous and the engineers at Texas Instruments, Inc., in Dallas, Texas, for building fine instruments. Without the help and dedication of my colleagues at the Goddard Space Flight Center, B. Conrath, M. Flasar, V. Kunde, W. Maguire, J. Pearl, J. Pirraglia, and R. Samuelson, this work could not have been accomplished. B. Conrath, V. Kunde, R. Samuelson, and especially J. Pearl helped me by reading this manuscript and by making valuable suggestions.

REFERENCES

Aronson, J. R., Emslie, A. G., Allen, R. V., and McLinden, H. G. (1967). *J. Geophys. Res.* **72**, 687–703.
Baumgardt, C. (1951). "Johannes Kepler. Life and Letters." Philosophical Library, Inc., New York (translation by H. Minkowski, Limes Verlag, Wiesbaden, 1953).
Bézard, B., Baluteau, J. P., and Marten, A. (1983). *Icarus* **54**, 434–455.
Blackman, R. B., and Tukey, J. W. (1958). "The Measurement of Power Spectra." Dover, New York.
Born, M., and Wolf, E. (1975). "Principles of Optics," 5th ed., pp. 300–304. Pergamon, Oxford.
Broadfoot, A. L., *et al.* (1981). *Science* **212**, 206–211.
Brown, R. A., and Yung, Y. L. (1976). *In* "Jupiter" (T. Gehrels, ed.), pp. 1102–1145. Univ. of Arizona Press, Tucson.
Caldwell, J. (1978). *NASA Conf. Publ.* **NASA CP-2068**, 113–126.
Cameron, A. G. W., and Pollack, J. B. (1976). *In* "Jupiter" (T. Gehrels, ed.), pp. 61–84. Univ. of Arizona Press, Tucson.
Chahine, M. T. (1968). *J. Opt. Soc. Am.* **58**, 1634–1637.
Chandrasekhar, S. (1950). "Radiative Transfer." Oxford Univ. Press, London and New York (reprinted by Dover, New York, 1960).
Chaney, L. W., Drayson, S. R., and Young, C. (1967). *Appl. Opt.* **6**, 347–349.
Chang, S., Scattergood, T., Arnowitz, S., and Flores, J. (1978). *NASA Conf. Publ.* **NASA CP-2068**, 161–184.
Comas Solá, J. (1908). *Astron. Nachr.* **179**, No. 4290, 289–290.
Conel, J. E. (1969). *J. Geophys. Res.* **74**, 1614–1634.
Connes, J. (1961). *Rev. Opt.* **40**, 45–79, 116–140, 171–190, 231–269.
Connes, J., and Connes, P. (1966). *J. Opt. Soc. Am.* **56**, 896–910.
Conrath, B. J. (1972). *J. Atmos. Sci.* **29**, 1262–1271.
Conrath, B. J. (1976). *J. Atmos. Sci.* **33**, 2430–2439.
Conrath, B. J. (1977). *In* "Inversion Methods in Atmospheric Remote Sensing." Academic Press, New York.
Conrath, B. J. (1981). *Icarus* **48**, 246–255.
Conrath, B. J., and Pirraglia, J. (1983). *Icarus* **53**, 286–292.

Conrath, B. J., and Revah, I. (1972). *NASA Tech. Memo.* **NASA TM-X-62150,** 1–36.

Conrath, B. J., Hanel, R. A., Kunde, V. G., and Prabhakara, C. (1970). *J. Geophys. Res.* **75,** 5831–5857.

Conrath, B. J., Hanel, R. A., Prabhakara, C., Kunde, V. G., Revah, I., and Salomonson, V. V. (1971). *Proc. Int. Astronaut. Congr.* **21,** 1009–1018.

Conrath, B., Curran, R., Hanel, R., Kunde, V., Maguire, W., Pearl, J., Pirraglia, J., and Welker, J. (1973). *J. Geophys. Res.* **78,** 4267–4278.

Conrath, B. J., Flasar, F. M., Pirraglia, J. A., Gierasch, P. J., and Hunt, G. E. (1981). *JGR, J. Geophys. Res.* **86,** 8759–8767.

Conrath, B. J., Gautier, D., Hanel, R., and Hornstein, J. (1983). Submitted for publication to *Astrophys. J.*

Cooley, S. W., and Tukey, J. W. (1965). *Math. Comput.* **19,** 297–301.

Courant, R., and Hilbert, D. (1931). "Methoden der Mathematischen Physik," 2nd ed. Springer-Verlag, Berlin and New York.

Courtin, R., Gautier, D., Marten, A., and Kunde, V. (1983a). *Icarus* **53,** 121–132.

Courtin, R., Baluteau, J. P., Gautier, D., Martin, A., and Maguire, W. (1983b). *Icarus* (submitted for publication).

Curran, R. J., Conrath, B. J., Hanel, R. A., Kunde, V. G., and Pearl, J. C. (1973). *Science* **182,** 318–383.

Danielson, R. E., Caldwell, J., and Larach, D. R. (1973). *Icarus* **20,** 437–443.

de Vaucouleurs, G. (1954). "Physics of the Planet Mars." Faber & Faber, London.

Dreyfus, M. G. (1962). *Appl. Opt.* **1,** 615–618.

Drossart, P., Encrenaz, T., Kunde, V., and Hanel, R. (1982). *Icarus* **49,** 416–426.

Eshleman, V. R., Tyler, G. L., Wood, G. E., Lindal, G. F., Anderson, J. D., Levy, G. S., and Croft, T. A. (1979). *Science* **204,** 976–978.

Farmer, C. B., Davis, D. W., Holland, A. L., LaPorte, D. D., and Doms, P. E. (1977). *J. Geophys. Res.* **82,** 4225–4248.

Fellgett, P. (1951). Ph.D. Thesis, University of Cambridge.

Fellgett, P. (1958). *J. Phys. Radium* **19,** 187–191.

Fjeldbo, G., and Eshleman, V. R. (1968). *Planet Space Sci.* **16,** 1035–1059.

Flasar, F. M., Samuelson, R. E., and Conrath, B. J. (1981a). *Nature (London)* **292,** 693–698.

Flasar, F. M., Conrath, B. J., Pirraglia, J. A., Clark, P. C., French, R. G., and Gierasch, P. J. (1981b). *J. Geophys. Res.* **86,** 8759–8767.

Forman, M. L. (1966). *J. Opt. Soc. Am.* **56,** 978–979.

Forman, M. L., Steel, W. H., and Vanasse, G. A. (1966). *J. Opt. Soc. Am.* **56,** 59–63.

Gautier, D., and Grossman, K. J. (1972). *J. Atmos. Sci.* **29,** 788–792.

Gautier, D., Conrath, B., Flasar, M., Hanel, R., Kunde, V., Chédin, A., and Scott, N. (1981). *J. Geophys. Res.* **86,** 8713–8720.

Gautier, D., Bezard, B., Marten, A., Baluteua, J. P., Scott, N. Chédin, A., Kunde, V., and Hanel, R. (1982). *Astrophys. J.* **257,** 901–912.

Gehrels, T., ed. (1976). "Jupiter." Univ. of Arizona Press, Tucson.

Gillett, F. C. (1975). *Astrophys. J.* **201,** L41–L43.

Gillett, F. C., Forrest, W. J., and Merrill, K. M. (1973). *Astrophys. J.* **184,** L93–L95.

Goody, R. M. (1964). "Atmospheric Radiation. I. Theoretical Basis." Oxford Univ. Press (Clarendon), London and New York.

Grossman, A. S., Pollack, J. B., Reynolds, R. T., and Summers, A. L. (1980). *Icarus* **42,** 358–379.

Gupta, S., Ochiai, E., and Ponnamperuma, C. (1981). *Nature (London)* **293,** 725–727.

Hanel, R. A. (1981). *Proc. SPIE* **289,** 331–344.

Hanel, R. A., and Chaney, L. W. (1966). *Proc. Int. Astronaut. Congr.* **17,** Vol. 2, 247–252.

Hanel, R. A., and Kunde, V. G. (1975). *Space Sci. Rev.* **18**, 201–256.

Hanel, R. A., Schlachman, B., Clark, F. D., Prokesh, C. H., Taylor, J. B., Willson, W. M., and Chaney, L. (1970). *Appl. Opt.* **9**, 1767–1774.

Hanel, R. A., Schlachman, B., Rodgers, D., and Vanous, D. (1971). *Appl. Opt.* **10**, 1376–1381.

Hanel, R. A., Conrath, B. J., Kunde, V. G., Prabhakara, C., Revah, I., Salomonson, V. V., and Wulford, G. (1972a). *J. Geophys. Res.* **77**, 2629–2641.

Hanel, R., Schlachman, B., Breihan, E., Bywaters, R., Chapman, F., Rhodes, M., Rodgers, D., and Vanous, D. (1972b). *Appl. Opt.* **11**, 2625–2634.

Hanel, R. A., Conrath, B. J., Hovis, W. A., Kunde, V. G., Lowman, P. D., Pearl, J. C., Prabhakara, C., Schlachman, B., and Levin, G. (1972c). *Science* **175**, 305–308.

Hanel, R., Conrath, B., Hovis, W., Kunde, V., Lowman, P., Maguire, W., Pearl, J., Pirraglia, J., Prabhakara, C., and Schlachman, B. (1972d). *Icarus* **17**, 423–442.

Hanel, R., Conrath, B., Flasar, M., Kunde, V., Lowman, P., Maguire, W., Pearl, J., Pirraglia, J., Samuelson, R., Gautier, D., Gierasch, P., Kumar, S., and Ponnamperuma, C. (1979a). *Science* **204**, 972–976.

Hanel, R., Conrath, B., Flasar, M., Herath, L., Kunde, V., Lowman, P., Maguire, W., Pearl, J., Pirraglia, J., Samuelson, R., Gautier, D., Gierasch, P., Horn, L., Kumar, S., and Ponnamperuma, C. (1979b). *Science* **206**, 952–956.

Hanel, R., Crosby, D., Herath, L., Vanous, D., Collins, D., Creswick, H., Harris, C., and Rhodes, M. (1980). *Appl. Opt.* **19**, 1391–1400.

Hanel, R. A., Conrath, B. J., Herath, L. W., Kunde, V. G., and Pirraglia, J. A. (1981a). *J. Geophys. Res.* **86**, 8705–8712.

Hanel, R., Conrath, B., Flasar, F. M., Kunde, V., Maguire, W., Pearl, J., Pirraglia, J., Samuelson, R., Herath, L., Allison, M., Cruikshank, D., Gautier, D., Gierasch, P., Horn, L., Koppany, R., and Ponnamperuma, C. (1981b). *Science* **212**, 192–200.

Hanel, R. A., Conrath, B. J., Kunde, V. G., Pearl, J. C., and Pirraglia, J. A. (1983). *Icarus* **53**, 262–285.

Hovis, W. A., and Callahan, W. R. (1966). *J. Opt. Soc. Am.* **56**, 639–643.

Hubbard. W. B. (1977). *Icarus* **30**, 305–310.

Hunten, D. M. (1976). *In* "Jupiter" (T. Gehrels, ed.), pp. 22–31. Univ. of Arizona Press, Tucson.

Hunten, D. M. (1978). *NASA Conf. Publ.* **NASA CP-2068**, 127–140.

Ingersoll, A. P., Munch, G., Neugebauer, G., and Orton, G. S. (1976). *In* "Jupiter" (T. Gehrels, ed.), pp. 197–205. Univ. of Arizona Press, Tucson.

Jacquinot, P., and Dufour, J. C. (1948). *J. Rech. C.N.R.S.* **6**, 91.

Jacquinot, P., and Roizen-Dossier, B. (1964). *Prog. Opt.* **3**, 29–186.

Kaplan, L. D. (1959). *J. Opt. Soc. Am.* **49**, 1004–1007.

Kieffer, H. H., Martin, T. Z., Peterfreud, A. R., Jakosky, B. M., Miner, E. D., and Palluconi, F. D. (1977). *J. Geophys. Res.* **82**, 4249–4291.

Kim, S. J., Caldwell, J., and Rivolo, A. (1982). *Bull. Am. Astron. Soc.* **14**, 732.

King, J. I. F. (1958). *In* "Scientific Uses of Earth Satellites" (J. A. Van Allen, ed.), pp. 133–136. Univ. of Michigan Press, Ann Arbor.

Kourganoff, V. (1952). "Basic Methods in Transfer Problems." Oxford Univ. Press, London and New York (reprinted by Dover, New York, 1963).

Kuiper, G. (1944). *Astrophys. J.* **100**, 378–383.

Kuiper, G. (1952). "The Atmospheres of the Earth and Planets," rev. ed. Univ. of Chicago Press, Chicago, Illinois.

Kunde, V. G., and Maguire, W. C. (1974). *J. Quant. Spectrosc. Radiat. Transfer* **14**, 803–817.

Kunde, V. G., Conrath, B. J., Hanel, R. A., Maguire, W. C., Prabhakara, C., and Salomonson, V. V. (1974). *J. Geophys. Res.* **79**, 777–784.

Kunde, V. G., Aikin, A. C., Hanel, R. A., Jennings, D. E., Maguire, W. C., and Samuelson, R. E. (1981). *Nature (London)* **292**, 686–688.

Kunde, V. G., Hanel, R., Maguire, W., Gautier, D., Baluteau, J. P., Marten, A., Chédin, A., Husson, N., and Scott, N. (1982). *Astrophys. J.* **263**, 443–467.

Lambert, D. L. (1978). *Mon. Not. R. Astron. Soc.* **182**, 249–272.

Lewis, J. S. (1969). *Icarus* **10**, 365–378.

Lindal, G. E., Wood, G. E., Hotz, H. B., Sweetnam, D. N., Eshleman, V. R., and Tyler, G. L. (1983). *Icarus* **53**, 348–363.

Loewenstein, E. V. (1966). *Appl. Opt.* **5**, 845–853.

Lyon, R. J. P. (1964). *NASA [Contract. Rep.] CR* **NASA-CR-100.**

McCarthy, J. F., Pollack, J. B., Houck, J. R., and Forrest, W. J. (1980). *Astrophys. J.* **263**, 201–205.

Maguire, W. C. (1977). *Icarus* **32**, 85–97.

Maguire, W. C., Hanel, R. A., Jennings, D. E., Kunde, V. G., and Samuelson, R. E. (1981). *Nature (London)* **292**, 683–686.

Marten, A., Rouan, D., Baluteau, J. P., Gautier, D., Conrath, B. J., Hanel, R. A., Kunde, V., Samuelson, R., Chédin, A., and Scott, N. (1981). *Icarus* **46**, 233–248.

Mertz, L. (1965). "Transformations in Optics." Wiley, New York.

Michelson, A. A., and Stratton, S. W. (1898). *Am. J. Sci.* **5**, 1–13.

Milne, E. A. (1930). *In* "Handbuch der Astrophysik," Vol. 3, Part 1, pp. 65–255. Springer-Verlag, Berlin and New York.

Morabito, L. A., Synnott, S. P., Kupferman, P. N., and Collins, S. A., (1979). *Science* **204**, 972.

Morrison, D., and Burns, J. A. (1976). *In* "Jupiter" (T. Gehrels, ed.), pp. 991–1034. Univ. of Arizona Press, Tucson.

National Aeronautics and Space Administration (NASA) (1978). *NASA Conf. Publ.* **2068.**

Orton, G. S., and Ingersoll, A. P. (1976). *In* "Jupiter" (T. Gehrels, ed.), pp. 206–215. Univ. of Arizona Press, Tucson.

Orton, G. S., and Ingersoll, A. P. (1980). *J. Geophys. Res.* **85**, 5871–5881.

Peale, S. J., Cassen, P., and Reynolds, R. T. (1979). *Science* **203**, 892–896.

Pearl, J., and Sinton, W. (1982). Hotspots of Io. *In* "Satellites of Jupiter" (D. Morrison, ed.), pp. 724–755. Univ. of Arizona Press, Tucson.

Pearl, J., Hanel, R., Kunde, V., Maguire, W., Fox, K., Gupta, S., Ponnamperuma, C., and Raulin, F. (1979). *Nature (London)* **280**, 755–758.

Prabhakara, C., and Dalu, G. (1976). *J. Geophys. Res.* **81**, 3719–1724.

Prabhakara, C., and Rodgers, E. B. (1976). *NASA Tech. Note* **NASA TN D-8134.**

Prabhakara, C., Conrath, B. J., Hanel, R. A., and Williamson, E. J. (1970). *J. Atmos. Sci.* **27**, 689–697.

Prabhakara, C., Conrath, B. J., Hanel, R. H., and Kunde, V. G. (1972). *Conf. Atmos. Radiat. [Prepr.], 1st, 1972* pp. 169–172.

Prabhakara, C., Rodgers, E. B., Conrath, B. J., Hanel, R. A., and Kunde, V. G. (1976). *J. Geophys. Res.* **81**, 6391–6399.

Prabhakara, C., Chandra, S., and Modali, S. B. (1980). *J. Geophys. Res.* **85**, 1618–1620.

Prinn, R. G., and Owen, T. (1976). *In* "Jupiter" (T. Gehrels, ed.), pp. 319–371. Univ. of Arizona Press, Tucson.

Raulin, F., Bossard, A., Toupance, G., and Ponnamperuma, C. (1979). *Icarus* **38**, 358–366.

Ridgway, S. T., Larsen, H. P., and Fink, U. (1976). *In* "Jupiter" (T. Gehrels, ed.), pp. 384–417. Univ. of Arizona Press, Tucson.

Salisbury, J. W., Vincent, R. K., Logan, L. M., and Hunt, G. R. (1970). *J. Geophys. Res.* **75**, 2671–2682.

Salpeter, E. E. (1973). *Astrophys. J.* **181**, L89–L92.

Samuelson, R. E., Hanel, R. A., Kunde, V. G., and Maguire, W. C. (1981). *Nature (London)* **292**, 688–693.

Samuelson, R. E., Maguire, W. C., Hanel, R. A., Kunde, V. G., Jennings, D. E., Yung, Y. L., and Aiken, A. C. (1982). *J. Geophys. Res.* (submitted for publication).

Smith, B. A., Soderblom, L. A., Johnson, T. V., Ingersoll, A. P., Collins, S. A., Shoemaker, E. M., Hunt, G. E., Masursky, H., Carr, M. H., Davies, M. E., Cook, II A. F., Boyce, J., Danielson, G. E., Owen, T., Sagan, C., Beebe, R. F., Veverka, J., Strom, R. G., McCauley, J. F., Morrison, D., Briggs, G. A., and Suomi, V. E. (1979a). *Science* **204**, 945–971.

Smith, B. A., Soderblom, L. A., Beebe, R., Boyce, J., Briggs, G., Carr, M., Collins, S. A., Cook II, A. F., Danielson, G. E., Davies, M. E., Hunt, G. E., Ingersoll, A., Johnson, T. V., Masursky, H., McCauley, J., Morrison, D., Owen, T., Sagan, C., Shoemaker, E. M., Strom, R., Suomi, V., and Veverka, J. (1979b). *Science* **206**, 927–950.

Smith, B. A., Soderblom, L., Beebe, R., Boyce, J. Briggs, G., Bunker, A., Collins, S. A., Hansen, C. J., Johnson, T. V., Mitchell, J. L., Terrile, R. J., Carr, M., Cook II, A. F., Cuzzi, J., Pollack, J. B., Danielson, G. E., Ingersoll, A., Davies, M. E., Hunt, G. E., Masursky, H., Shoemaker, E., Morrison, D., Owen, T., Sagan, C., Veverka, J., Strom, R., and Suomi, V. (1981). *Science* **212**, 163–191.

Smith, W. L. (1968). *Mon. Weather Rev.* **96**, 387–396.

Smith, W. L. (1969). *ESSA Tech. Rep.* **NESC 48**.

Smith, W. L. (1970). *Appl. Opt.* **9**, 1993–1999.

Smoluchowski, R. (1967). *Nature (London)* **215**, 691–695.

Smoluchowski, R. (1976). *In* "Jupiter" (T. Gehrels, ed.), pp. 3–21. Univ. of Arizona Press, Tucson.

Stevenson, D. J. (1980). *Science* **208**, 746–747.

Stevenson, D. J. (1982). *Annu. Rev. Earth Planet. Sci.* **10**, 257–295.

Stevenson, D. J., and Salpeter, E. E. (1977). *Astrophys. J., Suppl. Ser.* **35**, 221–237, 239–261.

Strobel, D. F. (1974). *Icarus* **21**, 466–470.

Thaddeus, P. (1981). *Philos. Trans. R. Soc. London Ser. A* **303**, 469–486.

Tokunaga, A. (1980). *Bull. Am. Astron. Soc.* **12**, 669.

Tomasko, M. G., West, R. A., and Castillo, N. D. (1978). *Icarus* **33**, 558–592.

Tyler, G. L., Eshleman, V. R., Anderson, J. D., Levy, G. S., Lindal, G. F., Wood, G. E., and Croft, T. A. (1981). *Science* **212**, 201–206.

Vanasse, G. A., and Sakai, H. (1967). *Prog. Opt.* **6**, 261–330.

Vanasse, G. A., Stair, A. T., and Baker, D. J., eds. (1970). *Proc. Aspen Int. Conf. Fourier Spectrosc., 1970* AFCRL-71-0019 (1971).

Wark, D. Q. (1970). *Appl. Opt.* **9**, 1761–1766.

Wark, D. Q., and Fleming, H. E. (1966). *Mon. Weather Rev.* **94**, 351–362.

Wark, D. Q., and Hilleary, D. T. (1969). *Science* **165**, 1256–1258.

Weidenschilling, S. J., and Lewis, J. S. (1973). *Icarus* **20**, 465–476.

Woolley, R. van der R., and Stibbs, D. W. N. (1953). "The Outer Layers of Star." Oxford Univ. Press (Clarendon), London and New York.

Chapter **3**

Pressure Modulator Radiometry

F. W. TAYLOR

DEPARTMENT OF ATMOSPHERIC PHYSICS
OXFORD UNIVERSITY
OXFORD, ENGLAND

3.1. Introduction

The pressure modulator radiometer (PMR) and its precursor, the selective chopper radiometer (SCR), are particular kinds of infrared (IR) gas

137

Copyright © 1983 by Academic Press, Inc.
All rights of reproduction in any form reserved.
ISBN 0–12–710403–8

correlation spectroradiometers which have been developed for remote sensing measurements of atmospheric parameters. The first applications of the PMR were to obtain vertical temperature profiles of the atmosphere from balloons and earth satellites. More recently, the technique has been used to measure the vertical distributions of minor constituents, such as water vapor and nitrogen oxides, on a global scale. The latest pressure modulator instruments also have the potential for measuring atmospheric pressure and wind fields. At the time of writing, three experimental PMR-based instruments have flown in space and several more are contemplated. A series of operational PMRs, the Stratospheric Sounding Units, have also operated successfully on the Tiros-N series of weather satellites.

The basis of the technique is the use inside the instrument of a path of the atmospheric gas to be monitored. The path is contained inside a gas cell, which is attached to a mechanical pressure modulator running at a frequency typically in the range from 10 to 50 Hz. (Fig. 3.1). The modulation of the pressure in the gas cell results in a corresponding modulation of the opacity of the absorption lines in the gas. This produces fluctuations in the incoming radiation at the detector only inside the spectral lines of the species in the cell — the so-called selective chopping effect. The part, usually small, of the signal at the detector which has been modulated in this way can then be selected by frequency- and phase-sensitive electronics using the pressure modulator drive frequency as a reference.

The apparatus that accomplishes this is extremely simple in concept, and even with the various refinements which are necessary in practice (as we shall see later), the PMR as an instrument compares very favorably to other optical space instruments in terms of performance versus complexity. The use of a sample of gas as the spectrally selective element means that the frequency calibration is absolutely reliable. It also means that an effective spectral resolution of the same order as the width of the lines in the cell (i.e., down to the Doppler width, or typically of the order of 0.001 cm^{-1}) is readily available. At the same time, contributions from all of the spectral lines in an IR vibration–rotation band can be obtained simultaneously, not as separate measurements, of course, but as a means of multiplying the energy on the detector to obtain a good signal-to-noise (SNR) ratio. Because of this effect, uncooled thermal detectors frequently are good enough to make useful measurements, a great advantage for spaceborne applications.

Disadvantages of the PMR approach are its limitation to preselected species and the need to understand the spectral properties of the bands of each species very fully in order to interpret the data correctly. Also, of course, some gases are too reactive to be contained in a modulator for long periods of time. These include some critical atmospheric species, particularly ozone. The simplicity and low cost of early instruments has to some

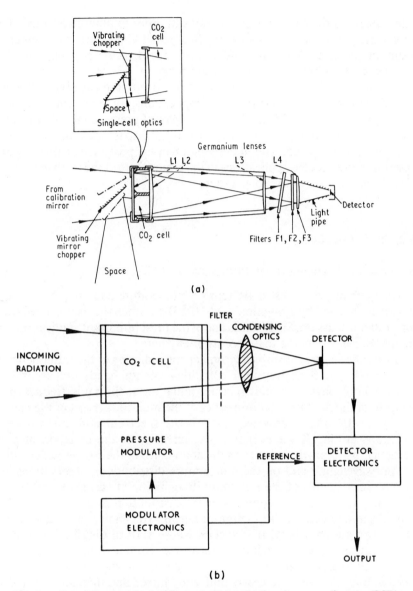

FIG. 3.1. Illustrating the principal features of (a) a selective chopper radiometer (SCR) and (b) a pressure modulator radiometer (PMR). In the SCR, the radiation from the atmosphere is directed alternately through a cell containing gas and an empty cell. The PMR uses a single optical path in which only the number of molecules of gas changes. [From Abel *et al.*, 1970 (a) and Taylor *et al.*, 1972 (b).]

extent been sacrificed in current versions in order to obtain coverage of a wide variety of trace species and very high sensitivity. These requirements result in the need for many modulators, for detector cooling, and for sophisticated calibration techniques and make for a large, complex instrument. Nevertheless, the PMR seems likely to outperform other remote-sounding instruments, for certain key applications, for some time to come.

This chapter deals with the basic principles of pressure modulator radiometry for the remote measurement of atmospheric temperature, pressure, composition, and wind. The underlying theory is presented, together with descriptions of specific applications to the atmosphere of the earth and some of the other planets of the solar system.

3.2. Basic Principles

A. REMOTE TEMPERATURE SOUNDING

The general principles of IR remote temperature sounding have been described in detail by Houghton *et al.* (1983), to which the reader is referred for a fuller discussion. Since this is one of the most important applications of the PMR, we review the main points briefly here.

Atmospheric gases absorb electromagnetic radiation at those frequencies corresponding to their molecular vibration–rotation bands and, according to Kirchhoff's law, also emit thermal radiation at the same frequencies. Because of the fundamental properties of the molecules, most of the bands are in the IR and microwave parts of the spectrum and the strongest emissions are at IR wavelengths. The intensity of the emission at any particular wavelength depends on the abundance of the species which emit at that wavelength and on the temperature distribution. Observations by satellite instruments of the upwelling IR radiation at various wavelengths therefore contain information about the distribution of emitters and the value of temperature as a function of height. The choice of a wavelength region containing a band of a species whose vertical distribution is well known means that the radiances measured contain information about vertical temperature profile only. Bands of carbon dioxide or molecular oxygen, both of which are nearly uniformly mixed and therefore make the retrieval of temperature profiles relatively easy, are normally employed.

In order to resolve different height levels in the atmosphere, measurements are made in several regions of an absorption band where the absorption coefficient of the molecule is different. In regions where the atmosphere is nearly transparent, photons emitted from deep in the atmosphere or from the surface of the earth reach the satellite without being reabsorbed. In a

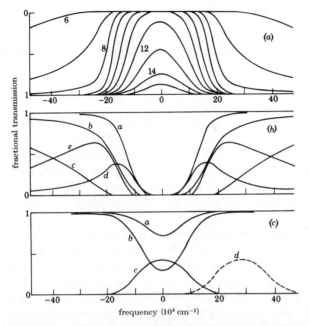

FIG. 3.2. The technique of pressure modulation is best understood by considering a single spectral line, in this case a line of intensity 2 cm^{-1} (atm cm)$^{-1}$ in the v_2 band of CO$_2$ at 667 cm^{-1}. The top set of curves, (a), shows how the profile of this line varies in the vertical atmospheric path above pressure p (the numbers on the curves are $-\log_e p$ atmospheres). The bottom two sets, (b) and (c), show the throughput of a 1-cm-long PMR in this line for various mean cell pressures coded as follows: in (b), $a = 2$ mbar, $b = 5$ mbar, $c = 14$ mbar, $d = a - b$, and $e = b - c$; in (c), $a = 0.25$ mbar, $b = 1$ mbar, $c = a - b$, and d is the same as c, except for the inclusion of a Doppler shift equal to that produced by viewing 10° from the nadir.

strongly absorbing region, only emission from high levels does so. Thus a set of measurements that includes intermediate opacities can be used to build up a profile of emission intensities, hence temperatures, over a complete vertical range. An important advantage of the PMR for making this kind of observation is that it can select different parts of the spectral lines (Fig. 3.2), and thus obtain a considerably wider range of absorption coefficients, than can a conventional IR spectrometer or filter radiometer, which must average over many spectral lines and the gaps in between. (Exceptions to this must be made for certain very sophisticated spectrometers which have sufficient resolution to resolve parts of an individual spectral line, but it is likely to be a long time before these are usable on satellites.) In particular, the PMR can measure up to higher altitudes than can a comparable non-PMR temperature sounder. This makes accessible regions of the atmosphere that are of great scientific and, increasingly, practical interest.

B. Weighting Functions

It can be shown (Houghton and Taylor, 1973) that the vertical distribution of the radiance I, measured at a particular frequency v is given by

$$I_v = \int_0^\infty B_v(T) \frac{d\tau_v}{dy} \, dy \qquad (3.1)$$

where B is the Planck function of temperature T, and τ_v is the transmission of the atmosphere at frequency v between space and the level where the pressure is $\exp(-y)$ atm. (Defining pressure this way introduces the convenient variable y, which is approximately proportional to height.) By examining Eq. (3.1) it can be seen that the function $K(y) = d\tau/dy$, called the *weighting function*, determines the contribution to I of each level in the atmosphere.

The actual performance of a real instrument is determined by the shape of the weighting functions and by the SNR associated with each. The latter determines the error in an individual temperature measurement and the former its vertical spread, hence the vertical resolution.

The accurate computation of weighting functions requires numerical integration over each of the lines in the spectral interval of observation. For a conventional spectrometer observing in a frequency interval Δv,

$$K_{\Delta v}(y) = \int_{\Delta v} f(v) \frac{d\tau_v}{dy} \, dv \qquad (3.2)$$

where f is the instrumental response function. If the same instrument were converted to a PMR by incorporation of a modulated gas cell in place of the mechanical chopper, then Eq. (3.2) would become

$$K_{\Delta v}(y) = \int_{\Delta v} f(v)[\bar{\tau}_v(p'_c) - \bar{\tau}_v(p''_c)] \frac{d}{dy} \, dv \qquad (3.3)$$

where $\bar{\tau}$ represents the transmission of the modulator cell at cell pressure p_c, and p'_c and p''_c are the pressures at the extremes of the modulation. Equations (3.2) and (3.3) can be evaluated using standard methods for the monochromatic transmission of the gases in cell and atmosphere and then integrating numerically over frequency. This tedious but straightforward and accurate approach has been used to calculate most of the weighting functions which appear in this chapter. Some useful approximations have been developed, however.

For example, Taylor *et al.* (1972) show that

$$K(y) = p^{*2}/(1 + p^{*2})^{3/2} \qquad (3.4)$$

where

$$p^* = [a/2(1 + \beta)l]^{1/2}(p/p_c) \qquad (3.5)$$

and a is the total amount of CO_2 in the atmosphere, l the cell length, and β the self-broadening coefficient for CO_2. A plot of $k(y)$ for two values of p_c shows (Fig. 3.3) that the weighting functions are sharply peaked with a full width at half maximum of about 17 km. By differentiating Eq. (3.4) we find that the peak is at a pressure p_{peak} given by

$$p_{peak} = \{[4(1 + \beta)l]/a\}^{1/2}p_c \qquad (3.6)$$

This places the peaks at roughy 50- and 65-km altitude for nadir viewing with $p_c = 3$ and 0.33 mbar, respectively, in a 6-cm cell. This is the type of coverage that was desired for the first spaceborne PMR on Nimbus 6, which was launched on 12 June 1976.

In fact, after more detailed calculations, the actual cell parameters selected for Nimbus 6 were as shown in Table 3.1. A range of pressures was available for each modulator, selectable by ground command, through the

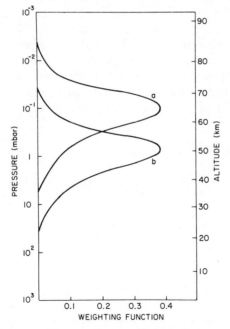

FIG. 3.3. Weighting functions for a two-channel nadir-viewing satellite radiometer, calculated from a simple analytical expression (see text). The cell length is 6 cm in each case and the pressures are 0.3 mbar (curve a) and 3 mbar (curve b). [From Taylor et al., 1972.]

TABLE 3.1

NIMBUS 6 PMR PARAMETERS

Channel No.	Cell length (cm)	Cell pressure (mb)	Height range sounded (km)
1	1	0.5–3	60–90
2	6	1–4	40–60

use of molecular sieves (Section 3.3.B). The effect of changing the cell pressure on the weighting function for channel 1 is illustrated in Fig. 3.4.

Figure 3.4 also illustrates another effect which is present in realistic weighting functions: a tendency toward the formation of double peaks. This is due to the fact that the atmospheric lines make a gradual transition from Lorentz to Doppler shape with increasing altitude, so that in the region sounded by the PMR the lines have mixed shape. The upper peak of the weighting function is attributable to the Doppler core of the lines, and the lower peak to the Lorentz wings. The effect is particularly pronounced for the atmosphere of Venus where, because of the nearly pure CO_2 composition, the pressure range that can be sounded is wider than for the earth. The weighting functions for the Pioneer Venus PMR, showing this effect, appear in Fig. 3.5. The splitting of the weighting function is a problem for the temperature retrieval process because it degrades the inherent vertical resolution of the measurements. Generally, one seeks to separate the peaks by (1) having sufficient range of control over p_c so that nearly pure Doppler

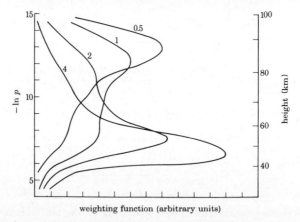

FIG. 3.4. Weighting functions for a vertical sounding PMR showing the dependence on cell pressure p_c (the figure on each curve is p_c in millibars). These curves were calculated (by C. D. Rodgers) using a more exact scheme than that used for Fig. 3.3.

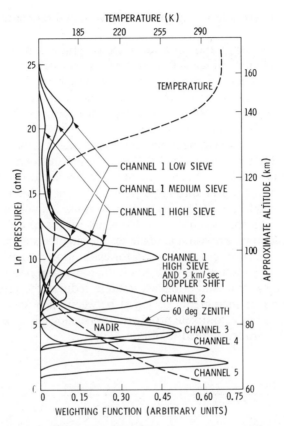

FIG. 3.5. Calculated weighting functions for the Pioneer Venus PMR, labeled Channel 1. The other channels (2–5) used conventional grating spectroscopy. A representative Venusian temperature profile is also shown. [From Taylor *et al.*, 1979.]

and pure Lorentz weighting functions can be measured separately, and (2) working with differences of weighting functions, rather than with the functions themselves, in the retrieval. The latter requires good instrumental SNRs to be successful, since it is necessary to work with the difference between two noisy radiance measurements. The process is further complicated by the fact that the atmosphere may be in thermal nonequilibrium, which means that the rate of emission of radiation is no longer given by the Planck function $B_v(T)$ but some other, more complex, function of temperature. This is known as the source function and is conventionally denoted by $J_v(T)$. Since equilibrium depends on collisions between molecules, J_v is also a strong function of pressure. Further discussion of this intricate and scientifically very interesting problem is beyond the scope of this chapter.

The reader is referred to Houghton *et al.* (1983) and references therein for this.

Since the exact shape and behavior of the weighting functions for PMRs are complicated and strongly affect the performance of a given instrument, techniques have been developed to measure weighting functions experimentally. These data are used to refine the calculated versions, which are seldom exact owing to small uncertainties in the spectroscopic parameters (line shapes, positions, and intensities).

The apparatus for weighting function measurements is shown in Fig. 3.6. It was originally developed by Abel (1966) and used and refined by Taylor *et al.* (1972), Curtis *et al.* (1974), and Jones (1983). The radiometer is mounted so as to view a hot source through a path of the gas to be measured by a particular channel. A multitraversal chamber is used, giving up to 10 m of path, and the gas can be cooled to 240 K by means of a cooling jacket around the chamber. Provision is made for viewing the source without the path, and the path without the source, for calibration purposes. This then allows the transmission of the path at a known pressure p to be measured. An automatic system using a ballast volume reduces the pressure in the chamber by equal increments of log p between each measurement of transmission. When a complete profile of τ versus log p has been obtained, the curve can be differentiated to obtain $K(p)$.

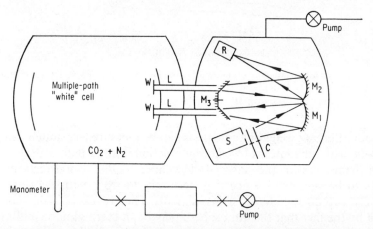

FIG. 3.6. Schematic diagram of an apparatus for the measurement of weighting functions. S is a source of thermal radiation, modulated by a chopper C; the flux is focused by a mirror M1 and light pipe L into a variable-pathlength, variable-temperature white cell containing the gas of interest (here CO_2 broadened by N_2) contained by windows W. The beam emerging from the white cell is focused by M_2 onto a receiver R, normally the flight PMR instrument. A third mirror M3 can be stepped into the beam, as shown, to provide a calibration point. A shutter in front of the source provides a second calibration point. [From Abel *et al.*, 1970.]

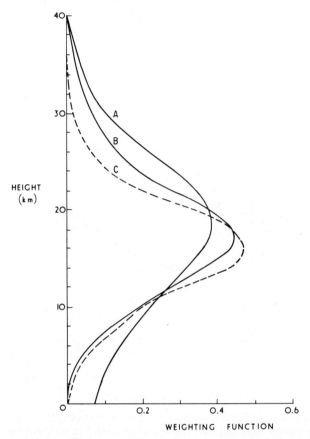

FIG. 3.7. Weighting functions for balloon radiometer: A, as calculated; B, as measured in the laboratory; and C, the measured function after correction for the atmospheric temperature profile. [From Taylor *et al.*, 1972.]

The first application of this technique to a PMR was by Taylor *et al.* (1972), who measured the single weighting function of the balloon proto-type. Figure 3.7 shows how the measured curve compares to that calculated using the approximations described above [e.g., Eqs. (3.4) and (3.5)]. Better agreement can be obtained using more rigorous calculations; for example, Curtis (1974) has described the calculation and measurement of weighting functions for the Nimbus 6 PMR (Fig. 3.8). He also examined the use of Doppler scanning, whereby the shape of the weighting function and the height of its peak can be adjusted using the Doppler shift introduced by the orbital velocity of the spacecraft rather than the cell pressure. Since the speed relative to the surface of a Nimbus satellite at 1000-km altitude is more than

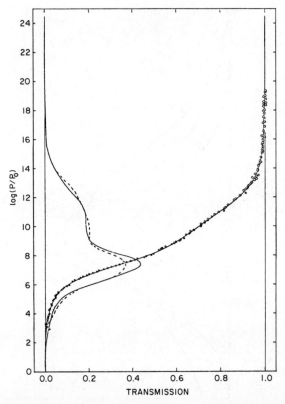

FIG. 3.8. Measurement in the laboratory of one of the Nimbus 6 PMR weighting functions. The individual measurements appear as points, to which a smooth curve of transmission versus pressure is fitted. This is differentiated to obtain the weighting function (solid curve). The calculated weighting function is shown (dashed) for comparison. [From Curtis, 1974.]

an order of magnitude greater than the mean molecular speeds at atmospheric temperature, Doppler scanning is achieved by viewing at a few degrees (actually 15° for Nimbus 6 PMR) to the nadir. The effect of these scans on the weighting functions is illustrated in Fig. 3.9.

The most recent PMR instruments have been limb viewing rather than nadir viewing, that is, they observe the atmosphere tangential to the surface rather than perpendicular to it. For these the weighting functions are quite different. Provided the cell pressure is not too low, so that the atmosphere is less than optically thick over the whole path, the geometry of the field of view and not the spectroscopic parameters (spectral band, etc.) largely determine the width and shape of the weighting functions (Fig. 3.10). Thus, arbitrarily high vertical resolution can be obtained, up to the limit dictated

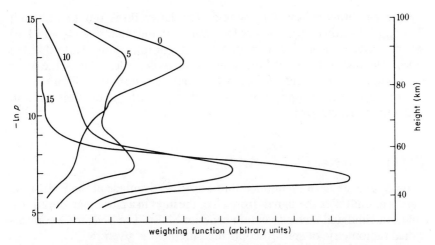

FIG. 3.9. Weighting functions for a vertical sounding PMR showing the effect of Doppler scanning. The number on each curve is the viewing direction in degrees from nadir.

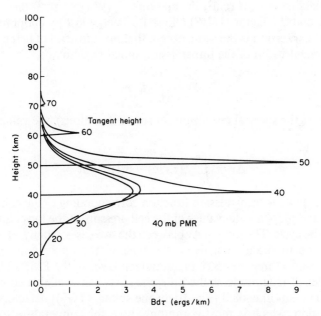

FIG. 3.10. Weighting functions for a PMR operating in the limb-scanning mode, with an angular field of view of 0.05° corresponding to 3.5-km vertical resolution at the tangent point. The cell length is 1 cm and its mean pressure is 40 mbar. [From C. D. Rodgers, unpublished work.]

by the curvature of the atmosphere. The latter turns out to be about 3–4 km. This still compares very favorably with the nadir case (10–15 km) when vertical resolution is a paramount consideration. Note that the horizontal resolution in the limb-viewing case is degraded from of the order of 10 km to several hundred, but this is usually less important than vertical resolution for many applications—hence the growth in emphasis on limb sounding in recent years.

C. Signal-to-Noise Ratio (SNR)

It has already been mentioned that a crucial advantage of the PMR is its ability to multiplex the signals from all of the lines in a particular vibration–rotation band and hence to obtain superior SNRs. The SNR for a conventional radiometric or spectroscopic measurement is given by

$$SNR = (1/2^{1/2})A\Omega\Delta\nu I_\nu(t^{1/2}/NEP) \tag{3.7}$$

where NEP (W Hz$^{-1/2}$) is the noise-equivalent power of the detector, t (sec) the dwell time, $\Delta\nu$ (cm^{-1}) the spectral bandwidth or resolution, Ω (sr) the angular field of view, A (cm^2) the aperture, I_ν (W cm^{-1} sr^{-1}) the incoming radiance, and the factor $(1/2^{1/2})$ allows for energy lost by chopping. For a PMR, the expression is the same except that now, instead of being equal to the equivalent width of the transmission function f_ν, that is,

$$\Delta\nu = \int_0^\infty f_\nu\, d\nu \tag{3.8}$$

(the same as the spectral resolution for simple functions), the value of $\Delta\nu$ is given by

$$\Delta\nu = \int_0^\infty f_\nu(\tau_\nu(p_c') - \tau_\nu(p_c''))\, d\nu \tag{3.9}$$

where f_ν is now the transmission function corresponding to the band-isolating filter and p_c', p_c'' are the values of the cell pressure at the lower and upper limits of the cycle. The ratio of $\Delta\nu$ between the two cases, when f_ν and p_c have been chosen to sound roughly equal levels in the upper atmosphere, is typically two to three orders of magnitude in favor of the PMR. This is the same order of magnitude as the difference between available cooled (e.g., Hg·Cd·Te) and uncooled [e.g., triglycine sulfate (TGS)] detectors for the 15-μm region, which is most commonly used for temperature sounding. Thus, in addition to the reduced complexity in obtaining the desired spectral resolution, the PMR had a SNR advantage which offers a qualitative gain in the detector technology needed.

For limb viewing, the field of view must be reduced from typically 1° (equivalent to about 20-km resolution from Nimbus orbit) to perhaps 0.1° (to get 5-km vertical resolution at the limb). This reduces Ω and hence the étendue of the instrument by about two orders of magnitude. Part of this can be recovered by the use of a larger telescope (i.e., by increasing A), but even so the use of uncooled detectors for limb observations is just adequate, even for a PMR.

A more useful quantity for assessing the ability of an instrument to measure temperature is the noise-equivalent temperature change (NET), defined by the equation

$$\frac{\Delta \nu}{2^{1/2}} A\Omega\tau_0 \frac{dB_\nu(T)}{dT} \epsilon\text{NET} = \frac{\text{NEP}}{t^{1/2}} \qquad (3.10)$$

where ϵ is the emissivity of the atmosphere and B the Planck function of its temperature T at the wave number of observation ν. NET is then the smallest change in T which can be detected above the instrument noise in a measurement lasting t sec. This is a function of altitude and modulator setting (cell pressure) as well as T itself; the measurements are generally useful when NET is less than about 1 K. The Nimbus 6 PMR and the Nimbus 7 Stratospheric and Mesospheric Sounder (SAMS) achieved NETs down to about 0.1 K; the Improved Stratospheric and Mesospheric Sounder (ISAMS) is expected to have NETs of around 0.02 K.

For composition measurements, an even more useful quantity is noise-equivalent emissivity (NEE); this is defined by

$$(\Delta \nu/2^{1/2})A\Omega\tau_0 B_\nu(T)\text{NEE} = \text{NEP}/t^{1/2} \qquad (3.11)$$

TABLE 3.2

CALCULATED NOISE EQUIVALENT EMISSIVITIES FOR ISAMS[a]

Gas in modulator	Equivalent width (cm^{-1})[b]	Planck function $\times 10^6$ $(\text{W cm}^{-1}\ \text{sr}^{-1}$ at 240 K)	Detector NEP[c] $(\text{W Hz}^{1/2})$	NEE[d]
CO_2	0.16	6.6	1×10^{-12}	0.003
H_2O	0.10	0.3	8×10^{-13}	0.1
NO	0.06	0.10	7.4×10^{-14}	0.04
NO_2	0.15	0.33	3.2×10^{-13}	0.02
N_2O	0.17	1.4	1.0×10^{-12}	0.01
CH_4	0.05	1.0	1.0×10^{-12}	0.07
CO	0.08	0.03	6.9×10^{-14}	0.1

[a] See Table 3.6 for spectral passbands.
[b] For a cell pressure of 1 mbar and length of 1 cm.
[c] Mercury cadmium telluride at 70 K except for CO and NO, which are lnSb at 70 K.
[d] For a single 2-sec sample.

NEE is the smallest change in emissivity (directly related to abundance of the species under observation; see Section 3.5.B) which can be measured in t sec. Table 3.2 shows some calculated values of NEE for ISAMS as examples of the current state of the art in composition measurements by remote sensing.

D. REJECTION OF OVERLAPPING SPECIES

As well as selecting only the strongest (or some other) part of each spectral line, to give weighting functions with desirable properties, the PMR will also strongly discriminate against overlapping lines of other species. The fact that spectral bands are seldom isolated is a serious problem for conventional radiometers, particularly since the overlapping species is often H_2O, O_3, or some other highly variable constituent whose influence is difficult to correct in the data analysis. Even the PMR often cannot eradicate the problem entirely. Let us consider some examples of specific cases. The most important encountered so far are (1) ozone overlap with the 15-μm band of CO_2, used for temperature sounding; (2) mutual overlap between methane (CH_4) and nitrous oxide (N_2O) near $7\frac{1}{2}$ μm, since these are the most useful bands for abundance measurements of these species; (3) overlap of the nitrogen dioxide (NO_2) band by water lines near 6.3 μm.

Figure 3.11 shows the relative positions and intensities of the CO_2 and O_3 bands. The SAMS band-selecting filter includes all of both bands; it is found then that ozone contributes up to 15% of the wide-band signal but less than 1% for the PMR signal. The reason for the reduction, of course, is the fact that only those O_3 lines that correlate with the CO_2 lines contribute to the PMR signal. With its much greater sensitivity, ISAMS is able to use a narrower band-isolating filter (640–700 cm^{-1}) which ensures that the contamination by ozone is negligible for both the wide-band and PRM channels.

Figure 3.12 shows a calculated spectrum at low spectral resolution of the emission from the limb at 20-km altitude, in the region of the $7\frac{1}{2}$-μm methane and nitric oxide bands. These bands overlap strongly and cannot be completely separated by band-isolating filters even if they are quite narrow. In such cases the PMR greatly reduces but cannot eliminate the overlap problem; the degree to which CH_4 contributes to the N_2O signal, and vice versa, is illustrated in Fig. 3.13. It is necessary then to retrieve both species simultaneously with due allowance for the interaction; this has been done successfully for SAMS (see Section 3.5.B).

The case of NO_2 is a particularly interesting one, because the only useful band is buried in the ν_2 band of the H_2O near 6.3 μm. NO_2 is a difficult gas to retain for very long periods in a modulator cell, but considerable effort has been expended to make this possible for ISAMS in order to extract the NO_2

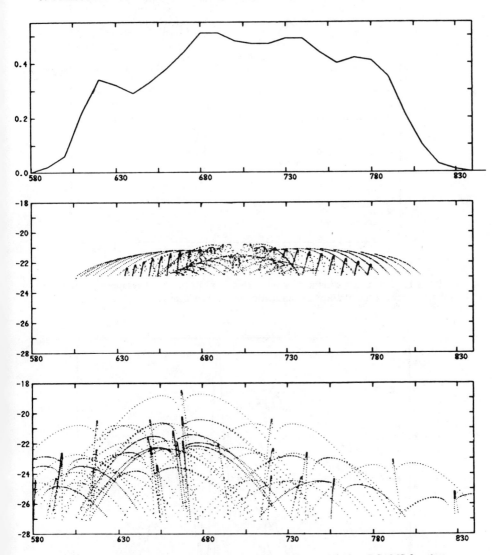

FIG. 3.11. (Top) Profile of the band-isolating filter used by Nimbus 7 SAMS for observations of the 15-μm CO_2 band; (center) line strengths for ozone in this spectral region; (bottom) the CO_2 line strengths. The ozone line strengths have been multiplied by 0.025, which is approximately the ratio between O_3 and CO_2 abundances in the mid-stratosphere; so their contributions may be directly compared. The ordinate is in units of cm^{-1} (mol cm^{-2})$^{-1}$ and the abscissa in cm^{-1}. [From J. J. Barnett, unpublished work.]

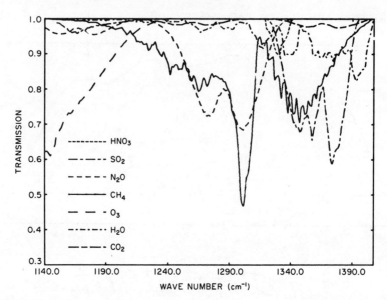

FIG. 3.12. Calculated spectra of seven minor constituents as they appear, at 1 cm^{-1} resolution, viewing the atmospheric limb at a tangent height of 20 km. [From R. L. Jones, unpublished work.]

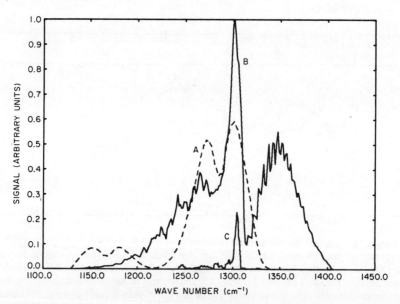

FIG. 3.13. Illustrating the efficiency of pressure modulator radiometry in separating the signatures from heavily overlapped bands of different species: A, the signal from N_2O viewed using an N_2O PMR; B, the signal from CH_4 viewed using a CH_4 PMR; C, the signal from CH_4 viewed using an N_2O PMR, all for limb viewing at a tangent height of 25 km. [From R. L. Jones, unpublished work.]

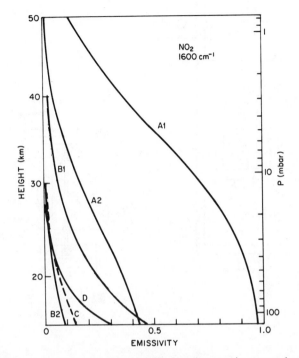

FIG. 3.14. Illustrating how pressure modulator radiometry improves the possibility for observing nitrogen dioxide in a spectral region contaminated by H_2O and collision-induced oxygen bands. The quantity plotted is the effective emissivity of the atmosphere at the limb for NO_2 with mixing ratios of 6 ppbv (A1) and 0.6 ppbv (A2), observed by a PMR with 1-cm cell length and 2-mbar cell pressure; B, same as A1 and A2 except the wide-band emission for $1590-1605$ cm^{-1} filter is shown; C, the wide-band emission for 4 ppmv H_2O; D, the wide-band emission for O_2.

signal and obtain accurate measurements of this key reactive member of the NO_x family. A completely revised modulator design, using titanium rather than beryllium – copper spider springs and external drive coils (cf. Section 3.3.A) has been developed for the purpose. Figure 3.14 demonstrates the extent to which interference by water vapor can be suppressed by the pressure modulation technique.

3.3. Techniques

A. PRESSURE MODULATORS

Several techniques for actually achieving the modulation of the pressure in the gas cell were tried by Taylor (1970) before the now-standard method

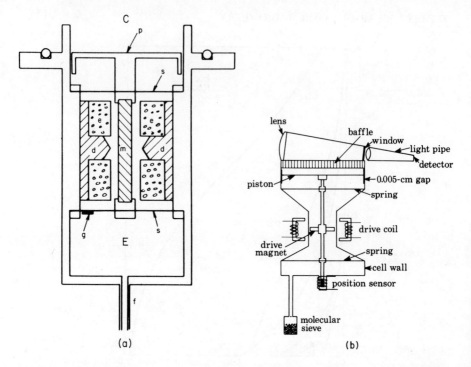

(a)

(b)

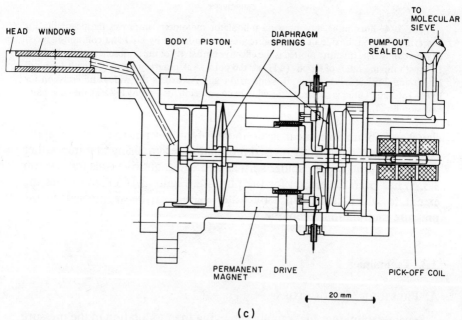

(c)

was evolved. A successful early version used a flexible diaphragm and a bass loudspeaker drive. Another used a magnetically suspended steel ball bearing inside a glass tube. However, greater depth of modulation (i.e., higher compression ratios) and better reliability were achieved by the arrangement in Fig. 3.15a. The piston has a deep skirt and a very small clearance (~0.005 cm) inside the bore. This is sufficient to prevent significant leakage past the piston by gas viscosity alone, without any piston rings or other rubbing contact. A large stroke (~1 cm) is achieved by having very positive lateral location of the piston using flat beryllium–copper spider springs. The piston was driven electromagnetically by incorporating a permanent magnet into the shaft and surrounding it with cross-connected coils. The coils were fed by the amplified signal from a piezoelectric chip soldered to one arm of the lower spider spring. This closed-loop arrangement ensured that the piston ran always at its resonance frequency, to give maximum amplitude for minimum power consumption and a means of measuring the pressure (Section 3.3.C).

The piezoelectric sensor was superseded for the Nimbus 6 satellite application by the electromagnetic position pick-off approach shown in Fig. 3.15b, which still used a moving magnet drive. In its current state of development, the pressure modulator uses a moving coil drive (Fig. 3.15c). It was found (Drummond *et al.,* 1980) that this gives better amplitude control and has the added advantage of being able to reverse the polarity of the coil to provide damping of the piston when the modulator is turned off. This prevents resonances from causing unwanted modulation in the deactivated units when several modulators share the same detector, as in SAMS. It also provides additional protection during launch, when there is a risk of damage due to violent excitation of the piston by the vibration of the launch vehicle.

There are numerous technical problems associated with the production of pressure modulators, paramount among which is the need for scrupulous cleanliness and elimination of all but the tiniest of leaks. Next is the requirement that the piston move very accurately in the bore, covering a linear distance of about 1 cm, while maintaining a clearance of only 0.005 cm. Finally, the materials used must be compatible with each other with regard to thermal expansion coefficients. This is not entirely possible at

---

FIG. 3.15. Evolution of the pressure modulator. (a) The 1969 balloon radiometer: p, piston; s, spider spring; m, permanent magnet; d, soft-iron former holding coils; g, piezoelectric pickoff; f, filling tube; E, electronics housing; C, gas cell. [From Taylor *et al.,* 1972.] (b) The 1976 Nimbus 6 PMR modulator. [From Curtis *et al.,* 1974.] (c) The 1978 Nimbus 7 SAMS modulator. [From Drummond *et al.,* 1980.]

the interface between the germanium windows on the gas cell and the modulator body; flexible glues have been developed which overcome this problem, although extra development was required to obtain chemical compatibility with CO_2 and other working gases. The body itself and the piston are made from titanium, which is strong, noncorrosive, and relatively light and can be machined to high tolerances. The modulator head and tail are bolted to the body and sealed by gold O rings. The piston is suspended on flat etched beryllium – copper spider springs 0.025 cm thick. These produce virtually no restoring force in response to longitudinal motion so long as the amplitude is small, but offer enormous resistance to sideways displacements, which would tend to cause the piston to rub against the bore.

The detailed design and manufacture of a pressure modulator (actually that for Pioneer Venus) has been described by Schofield (1980). He also describes a model for the "pumping effect," whereby the various flows inside the modulator (past the piston, and between the bore and the cell, etc.) result in a distribution of pressure cycles inside the modulator that have different amplitudes, phases, and degrees of harmonicity. In particular, the mean pressure and depth of modulation in the optical path are not the same as would be expected on the basis of static considerations. For the Pioneer Venus modulator in its "high-sieve-pressure" setting, the mean cell pressure was about 3% lower than the mean value of 9.336 mb over the sieve.

Another important detail is the fact that the gas in the modulator cell tends to cycle in temperature, as well as pressure, owing to adiabatic heating (Taylor, 1970). If the cycling were purely adiabatic, the temperature swing T would be

$$\Delta T = T\{1 - [1 - (\Delta V/V)]^{\gamma-1}\} \tag{3.12}$$

(Taylor, 1970) where $\Delta V/V$ is the compression ratio and γ the ratio of specific heats. This predicts values of ΔT of several tens of degrees for typical compression ratios. Such a temperature swing would result in an emission signal from the cell of the same order or larger than the atmospheric signal, and 180° out of phase with it. Small variations in cell temperature T or in piston amplitude (hence ΔV) would change this emission signal in a way that might be difficult to distinguish from the real signal. It is, therefore, very important to stabilize the modulator temperature and amplitude, and to monitor both to high precision. The emission signal can then be treated as an offset and calibrated out. It can also be eliminated by double chopping (Section 3.4.A).

In practice, the emission offset is not so large as implied above because conduction of heat to the cell walls can take place on a time scale comparable with the period of the piston, especially if the mean cell pressure is low. Schofield (1980) analyzed the situation where the cycling is intermediate between isothermal and adiabatic and obtained the curves in Fig. 3.16 for the Pioneer modulator. The amplitudes of the temperature swing range from about 1 to about 10 K, depending on sieve temperature setting, and are about 90° out of phase with pressure. The phase assists considerably in suppressing the offset in the electronics, and in practice there is no serious difficulty in calibrating out the residual, which was in the range 5–50% of

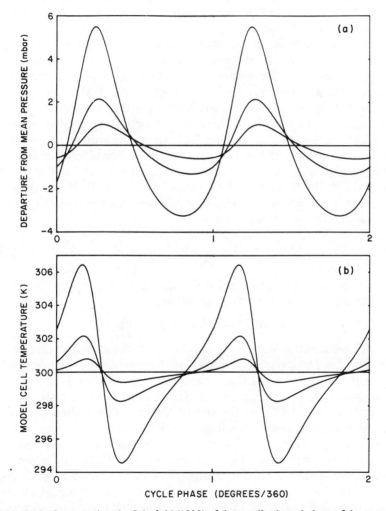

FIG. 3.16. Computations by Schofield (1980) of the amplitude and phase of the temperature and pressure cycles in the optical path of the Pioneer Venus PMR. (a) Model cell pressure cycles, departure from mean pressure. (b) Model cell temperature cycles, modulator temperature 300 K. Piston amplitude 1 cm, nominal pressure settings 9.336, 3.966, and 2.054 mbar.

the average signal from Venus, depending on sieve setting. This is particularly straightforward on the spin-stabilized Pioneer since a reference signal from space is obtained during every 12-sec rotation of the spacecraft.

B. Molecular Sieves

It has already been shown (Section 3.2.B) how the weighting functions depend on the mean cell pressure about which modulation occurs. If this pressure can be altered in flight, then different operational modes are possible—for example, for optimal sounding of different height ranges in the atmosphere. Molecular sieves have been developed to achieve this. These are materials with a matrix structure that traps a very large amount of the operating gas (typically 100–1000 times as much as is present in the modulator plus gas cell) and releases it in response to heating in such a way that the partial pressure above the sieve is a function of temperature only. A side benefit of the use of sieves is the fact that the reservoir provides a ballast supply of gas to prevent loss of pressure due to adsorption or small leaks.

The earliest sieve materials were zeolites which worked well with CO_2 and were used in the Nimbus 6 PMR (Curtis *et al.*, 1974). It can be shown (Morgan and Stapleton, 1971) that the pressure P above a quantity of sieve material depends on temperature as

$$P = \frac{K(T)}{A_{max}/A - 1} \tag{3.13}$$

where A is the mass of CO_2 per unit mass of zeolite, A_{max} its maximum capacity, and $K(T)$ an expression of the form

$$K(T) = \exp(C - \Delta E/RT) \tag{3.14}$$

with ΔE representing the energy change per mole accompanying absorption. For the particular zeolite used in Nimbus 6 and Pioneer PMRs, $C = 16.9$ and $E/R = 4730$ K (Morgan and Stapleton, 1971). From this it can be shown that 2 gm of zeolite (a typical amount) holds approximately 100 times as much CO_2 as the rest of the modulator when filled at its maximum working pressure (Schofield, 1980). Under conditions like these, where this ratio is large, A is independent of T, and the pressure above the sieve and hence in the gas cell is a function only of T. Figure 3.17 shows how cell pressure depended on sieve temperature for the Pioneer Venus PMR. Figure 3.18 shows the mechanical arrangement of the Venusian sieve—a typical application. A long, thin stainless-steel tube is used to connect the sieve to the modulator body so that sieve temperatures up to 70°C can be used without heating the gas in the cell appreciably. The use of foam

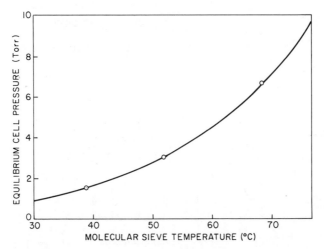

FIG. 3.17. Typical variability of cell pressure with molecular sieve temperature setting, in this case for carbon dioxide over a zeolite sieve. [From Schofield, 1980.]

insulation keeps the total power consumption, even at the warmest setting, below 0.5 W.

The molecular sieves being developed for ISAMS include two important improvements. First, zeolite has been discarded as the sieve material in favor of a silica matrix obtained by reducing organic silicates in a bomb calorimeter. The reason for this is that some of the more reactive species used in the SAMS modulator, especially nitric oxide, underwent chemical changes in which the zeolite acted as a catalyst. Tests so far show that this effect is small in silica, and the material should also be suitable for use with nitrogen dioxide. Second, the ISAMS sieves are mounted on individual cold patches which radiate to space, cooling the sieves to temperatures around $-50°C$ when no heater power is supplied. For high-pressure operation, the sieve and patch are electrically heated. This takes several watts of power, working against the radiative sink, but offers two advantages. The first is the ability to "empty" the cell by virtually freezing out the gases, thus gaining a potentially valuable calibration point. The second is the ability to store reactive gases longer at low temperatures. NO_2, in particular, can be stored as liquid N_2O_4 without the need for a sieve at all.

C. CALIBRATION

Next to radiometric calibration, which is accomplished by conventional means (views of cold space and of on-board blackbodies), the most impor-

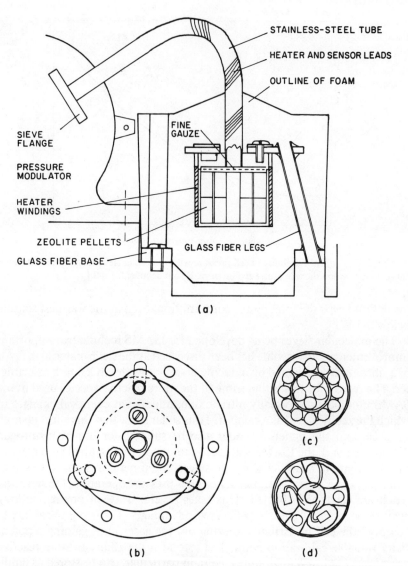

FIG. 3.18. Details of the Pioneer Venus molecular sieve design. (a) The molecular sieve; (b) glass fiber mount; (c) pellet geometry; (d) sensor configuration. [From Schofield, 1980.]

tant calibration variable is the cell pressure. Fortunately, this can be measured to high accuracy by monitoring the resonance frequency at which the piston in the modulator runs. This approach works because the spider spring suspension, which has tremendous resistance to sideways motion, provides very little in response to axial motion until the springs are near the end of their travel. Thus the restoring force on the moving piston is due in part to the compression of the gas. It follows that the resonance frequency depends on pressure as

$$\omega = \omega_0 + (P_c/Vm)^{1/2}A \tag{3.15}$$

(Taylor, 1970), where p_c is cell pressure, V is the volume above the piston (assumed small compared to the total volume), m the moving mass, and A the piston area. Thus, since the piston runs always at its resonance frequency (Section 3.3.A), measurement of ω and its inclusion in the telemetry gives a measurement of p_c which can be extremely accurate. On Pioneer Venus, for example, ω was monitored to 0.001 Hz over a 100-cycle average, and this yielded a value of p_c to within about 0.001 mbar. The limiting accuracy is due to the calibration of the pressure–frequency curve in the laboratory before flight. An occasional problem is a tendency for ω_0 to change, owing to aging or launch stresses. This is one reason for designing the most recent sieves to include the point $p_c = 0$ in their range (Section 3.3.B).

Other calibration requirements for PMR instruments are similar to those also needed by conventional radiometric instruments and are not described in detail. Calibration activities routinely performed on PMRs for space use include the following:

(1) radiometric calibration using standard blackbody sources;
(2) linearity measurements,
(3) spectral broadband measurement and spectral leak tests, using a monochromator,
(4) field of view measurements using point sources and collimated beams; and
(5) weighting function measurement using laboratory paths.

In addition to these, great importance is attached to regular in-flight calibration. The need for this can be greater for PMRs than for conventional radiometers owing to the need to monitor the various offsets to which PMRs are susceptible. In addition to the universal problem of thermal drift, due to temperature changes inside the instrument that can occur when the environment or even the scene being viewed changes, there is a thermal emission offset (Section 3.3.A) from the modulated gas and also a problem called motional chopping. The latter occurs when the field being viewed by the instrument has large gradients in it (as does the atmosphere at the limb) and the instrument field of view is modulated by mechanical vibrations in the instrument. A typical source of field-of-view modulation is small vibrations of reflecting components in the optics, induced by the motion of the piston in the modulator. It is not difficult to make the vibration very small, but the effect on the signal can still be large, because the *broadband* signal at the detector is modulated with the pressure modulation frequency, and so it has an equivalent width advantage of several orders of magnitude. The problem is tackled by

(1) minimizing motional chopping in the mechanical design,
(2) attempting to shift the phase of the remainder away from that of the modulator, and
(3) calibrating to check that any residual is constant.

For completeness, it is worth mentioning here a related complication. Bizarre effects can result in multimodulator instruments if two or more modulators are run at nearly identical or harmonic frequencies. In ISAMS, for example, with eight modulators, beats can be a serious problem. This has been overcome by a move away from the use of a few fixed molecular sieve settings to the quasi-continuous adjustment provided on ISAMS. This allows the modulators to be tuned independently even if their pressure – frequency responses change in orbit.

3.4. Instruments

A. Balloon Instruments

The first balloon-borne PMR was a simple, one-channel, nadir-viewing device built to test the principle and flown from Lark Hill, England, in August, 1970 (Taylor *et al.,* 1972). The modulator contained CO_2 at a pressure of 280 mbar and used a piezoelectric element, soldered to one of the spider springs, to obtain a position reference for use in the piston drive servoloop (Fig. 3.15a). Viewing vertically downward, the weighting function for a 6-cm cell at 280-mbar peaks near 16-km altitude, according to both theory and measurement (Fig. 3.2).

A more advanced balloon PMR was built by Challoner *et al.* (1978). The main purpose of this was to measure nitrogen oxides in the stratosphere, in particular, NO and NO_2, which play an important part in the photochemical cycle of ozone. The instrument uses moving magnet modulators similar to the Nimbus 6 design, viewing the atmosphere through Cassegrain fore-optics with a field of view of $0.5°$. A motor-driven scan mirror scans the atmosphere at angles close to the horizontal and also upward for a quasi-space view for calibration. Liquid-nitrogen-cooled InSb (for NO) and MCT (for NO_2) detectors are employed. A key feature of the balloon radiometer is its use of double chopping, whereby the PMR signal is taken from the side bands about a mechanical chopper running at a much higher frequency (195 Hz). This not only reduces $1/f$ noise in the signal, but also eliminates the emission offset (Section 3.3.A). NO_x measurements with the system are described by Drummond and Jarnot (1978) and Roscoe et al. (1981).

Recently, a new balloon instrument using pressure modulators of a novel design has been developed at the University of Toronto. The following brief description is by J. R. Drummond (personal communication, 1982). The modulator relies for its operation upon the use of a Ferrofluidic[1] seal to transfer the rotation of a shaft into the vacuum system with a low attendant power loss. The efficiency of the system allows the use of a nonresonant internal mechanism at the penalty of increased power dissipation. The drive consists of a flywheel/crank, connecting rod, linear motion shaft, and piston, which is sealed to the bore by a lightly sprung PTFE piston ring, all of which can be seen in Fig. 3.19. The whole unit is made almost entirely of aluminum with some stainless steel and PTFE. The bearing surfaces are made of Rulon,[2] a proprietary, PTFE-based, filled plastic.

The frequency of oscillation is about 17 Hz with a total electrical power consumption of about 100 W most of which is dissipated in the motor. Compression ratios of 5:1 have been obtained at gas pressures up to 25 mbar. Above 25 mbar the power consumption begins to rise and a more powerful motor would be required.

The system is capable of containing most gases, limited mainly by the ferrofluid (which may be tailored to most gases), the ball-bearing lubricant, and the metals used in the design.

The initial use of the modulator is in an experiment to measure carbon compounds in the stratosphere—particularly formaldehyde (CH_2O), methane (CH_4), and carbon monoxide (CO). The principal difficulty in these measurements is the low expected concentration and the stability of formaldehyde which polymerizes in the cell at an unacceptable rate (50% decrease in 10 min). To counteract the loss, the cell includes a formaldehyde generator consisting of an electrical heater embedded in paraformaldehyde powder. Paraformaldehyde decomposes into formaldehyde and a small amount of water at temperatures above about 100°C. The water vapor is eliminated by absorption on a calcium sulfate dryer leaving the formaldehyde gas in the modulator.

The three-channel pressure-modulator instrument will be flown from a

[1]Ferrofluidic is a registered trademark of the Ferrofluidics Corporation.
[2]Rulon is a registered trademark of the Dupont Corporation.

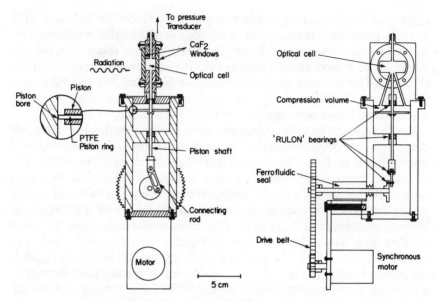

FIG. 3.19. The pressure modulator designed at the University of Toronto for the 1983 balloon campaign. [From J. R. Drummond, unpublished work.]

10 million cubic foot balloon launched from the Canadian Centre for Space Science facility in Gimli, Manitoba, in the summer of 1983.

The importance of the compounds measured arises from the oxidation of methane and the possible anthropogenic influences on the oxidation chain. Schematically the chain proceeds as

$$CH_4 \rightarrow CH_2O \rightarrow CO \rightarrow CO_2$$

with attendant production of H_2O and H_2 (see Enhalt and Tonniben, 1979). Since H_2O is active chemically in ozone processes and the CO_2 is active chemically and radiatively, this chain can influence the stratosphere in the long term if a sustained methane source is produced by the troposphere, which is the case. In turn, the major sources of tropospheric methane (cattle and swamplands) are landbased and subject to anthropogenic influence through farming and land management schemes, and it therefore follows that this chain forms a way in which man's activity can influence the stratosphere.

By measuring the magnitude and diurnal variations of the "stable" products of the methane decomposition chain, it will be possible to obtain information regarding the rate of decomposition and to compare this with the computed rate of injection of methane into the stratosphere. It will also be possible to obtain more reliable estimates of the rate of production of H_2O, H_2, and CO_2 from methane.

B. NIMBUS

Selective chopper radiometers were flown on Nimbus 4 and 5, launched in 1970 and 1972, respectively, and PMRs on Nimbus 6 (1976) and Nimbus 7 (1978). The Nimbus 6 PMR was a two-channel nadir-viewing instrument which measured temperatures in the mesosphere (50–90-km altitude). A particular feature was the use of Doppler scanning and molecular sieves together to "tune" the weighting functions for different types of observation (Curtis *et al.*, 1974). The two channels differ from each other only in the lengths of the modulator cells, the first being 1 cm long and intended to observe the range from 60 to 90 km above the surface and the second 6 cm long to observe the 40–60-km region. Table 3.3 shows the various cell-pressure settings which were provided, and Table 3.4 the radiometric performance obtained.

Figure 3.20 shows a block diagram of one of the two channels. A gold-coated plane mirror is used either to direct the field of view downward, toward the atmosphere, or to view cold space or an internal reference blackbody for calibration purposes. The stepper motor which selects the view is itself mounted in jeweled bearings in order to obtain the ±15° Doppler scan. After passage through the modulator cell (Section 3.3.A), the radiation from the target is incident on a detector assembly consisting of a lens, a condensing light pipe, and a TGS pyroelectric bolometer with

TABLE 3.3

NIMBUS 6 PMR: CELL CO_2 PRESSURE CORRESPONDING TO
VARIOUS TEMPERATURE SETTINGS ON THE SIEVES

Sieve setting	Channel 1		Channel 2	
	Sieve temperature (°C)	Cell pressure (mbar)	Sieve temperature (°C)	Cell pressure (mbar)
1	26.5	0.55	U[a]	U
2	34.8	0.90	26.5	0.66
3	43	1.48	37.5	1.24
4	51.3	2.43	48.5	2.32
5	59.5	4.0	59.5	4.34
6	105	>30	105	>30

[a] U, unthermostated.

TABLE 3.4

NIMBUS 6 PMR: NOISE EQUIVALENT TEMPERATURE FOR
DIFFERENT CELL MEAN PRESSURES

Path length (cm)	Extremes of pressure swing (mbar)	Equivalent[a] width (ΔW cm^{-1})	Noise equivalent temperature (K)
1	0.25/0.47	0.030	1.3
1	0.68/1.27	0.056	0.7
1	1.21/2.28	0.085	0.5
6	2.5 /4.0	0.35	0.11

[a] Calculated from equation $W = \int (\tau_1 - \tau_2) dv$ where τ_1 and τ_2 are the transmissions at frequency v of the gas in the cell at the extremes of pressure occurring in the modulation.

integral preamplifier. The output from this is passed through a low-noise amplifier and a synchronous filter into a phase-sensitive detector utilizing a reference waveform from the pressure modulator drive. The electronics for both radiometers consumes a total of less than 5 W, and the complete package weighs 12.5 kg.

The Stratospheric and Mesospheric Sounder (SAMS) on Nimbus 7 is the most advanced PMR instrument yet built and is described at some length. Further details may be found in the paper by Drummond *et al.* (1980).

The instrument consists of two modules: a sensor unit, 55 × 30 × 55 cm³ in size and 23.6 kg in weight, which contains the optics, modulators and other mechanisms, and detectors; and an electronics module, weighing 6.7 kg and drawing about 20 W of power. There are a total of six detectors and seven pressure modulators arranged as shown in Fig. 3.21. These view the atmosphere in three fields of view, each 1.6° × 0.16° (100 km × 10 km at the limb) in horizontal and vertical extent, respectively. Note that some of the channels share detectors and so cannot be used simultaneously; in particular, three modulators are in series with a single cooled InSb detector, and only one is turned on on any particular day. The InSb detector is thermally isolated from the structure and mounted upon a two-stage radiation cooler intended to reduce its temperature to around 160 K. In fact, the leakage of heat into the cooler has been greater than intended and the detector is running at nearer 180 K, with a consequently lower SNR than expected. This has been compensated by using zonal averages of the data for CO, NO, and 4.3-μm CO_2 measurements rather than single soundings.

The layout of the fore-optics and detector optics for SAMS is shown in Figs. 3.22 and 3.23. Radiation entering the instrument from the limb does so

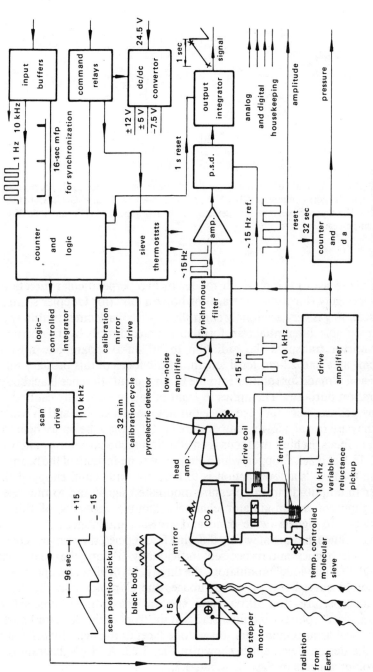

FIG. 3.20. Block diagram for the Nimbus 6 PMR. [From Curtis *et al.*, 1974.]

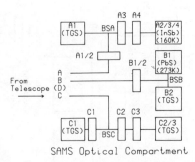

FIG. 3.21. Schematic of the Nimbus 7 SAMS channels. The rectangular boxes represent pressure modulators containing: A1/2, CO_2; A3, CO; A4, NO; B1/2, H_2O; C1, CO_2; C2, N_2O; C3, CH_4. The square boxes represent detectors of the types specified. The junctions BSA, B, C are dichroic beam splitters.

via a plane scan mirror, which rotates in two perpendicular directions to scan vertically (for limb coverage) or horizontally (for Doppler scanning). The scanning is very accurately controlled by feedback circuits utilizing two linear variable differential transformers actuated directly by the mirror. The scan mirror transmits the radiation to an off-axis parabolic mirror of 177-cm² area and 22-cm focal length. At the focus of this primary mirror, provision is made for rotating into the beam a small reference blackbody for calibration purposes. The optics in front of this are not fully calibrated by this procedure, since they see space but not the blackbody, and to compensate they are run at a lower temperature ($\sim 0°C$) than the optics behind the primary focus. Behind the focus is an elliptical secondary mirror and then a fast (245 Hz) black chopper, which chops only one-fortieth of the beam. The reason for this "shallow" action is to keep the wide-band chopped signal nearer in amplitude to the pressure-modulated signal and to increase the throughput of the modulator channels. Double chopping of this kind produces two signals (wide band and pressure modulated) on the same detector. Since they are at widely differing frequencies, they can be separated in the electronics and processed individually. Before the beam passes through the individual modulators, the three fields of view are separated by a compound curved mirror which images the ellipsoid onto the relevant detector aperture stop. Broadband spectral selection is achieved with dichroic beam splitters and filter stacks at the front of the detector housings. The optical arrangement that images one facet of the field-dividing mirror onto the detector element is shown in Fig. 3.23. A block diagram of the electronics appears in Figs. 3.24 and 3.25.

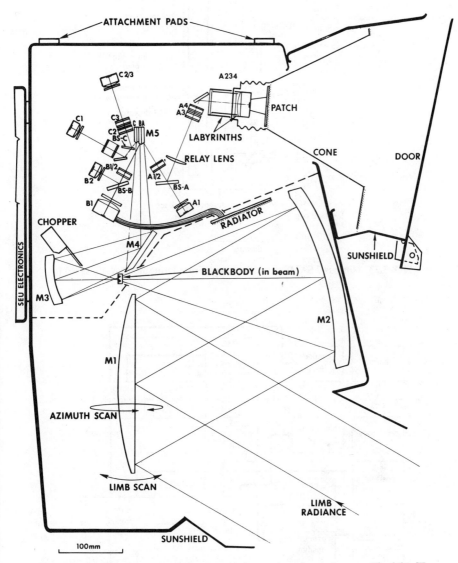

FIG. 3.22. Layout of Nimbus 7 SAMS. For a key to the abbreviations, see Fig. 3.21. [From Drummond *et al.*, 1980.]

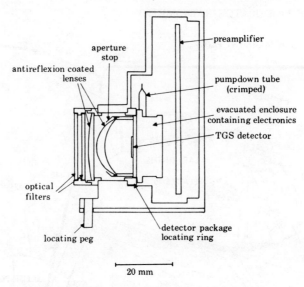

FIG. 3.23. Nimbus 7 SAMS detector optics. [From Drummond *et al.*, 1980).]

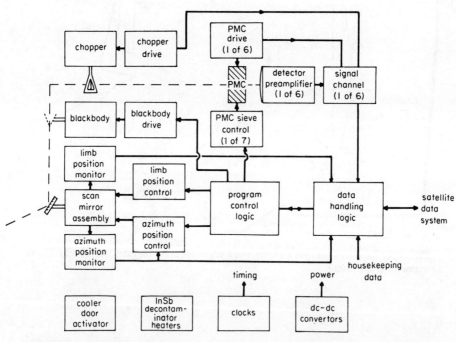

FIG. 3.24. Block diagram of Nimbus 7 SAMS electronic subsystems. [From Drummond *et al.*, 1980.]

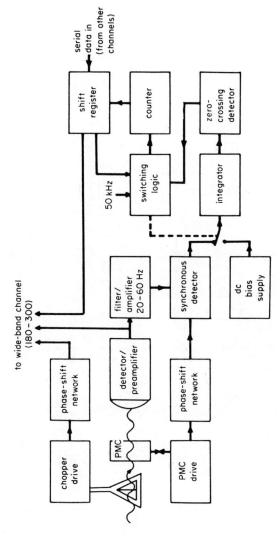

FIG. 3.25. Block diagram of the PMR half of a SAMS signal channel; the other half handles the wide-band signal. [From Drummond *et al.*, 1980.]

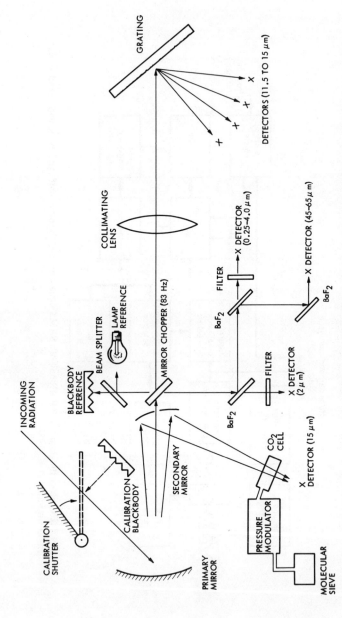

FIG. 3.26. Schematic of the Pioneer Venus Orbiter Infrared Radiometer showing the PMR at bottom left. [From Taylor *et al.*, 1979.]

C. Pioneer Venus

In 1978 a PMR was placed in orbit around the earth's planetary neighbor and near-twin, Venus, on board the NASA Pioneer Venus orbiter. The PMR was a subsystem within the Orbiter Infrared Radiometer temperature-sounding experiment (Taylor *et al.*, 1979), its purpose being to provide coverage of the highest atmospheric levels (100–130-km altitude), which were inaccessible to the conventional spectroscopic channels that made up the rest of the instrument. The Pioneer Venus application is the only one to date in which the PMR has been mounted on a spin-stabilized spacecraft. In this case the rotation rate was 5 rpm, or 1° every 30 msec. Clearly, dwell times much shorter than, for example, the 2 sec employed by SAMS had to be used in order to avoid serious smearing of the field of view on the planet. The best compromise between spatial resolution and SNR was obtained with an angular field of view of 5° and a dwell time of 180 msec. Since Pioneer approached to within 50 km of the level being observed at the lowest point in its orbit, the resulting best spatial resolution was about 10 km.

The layout of the optical system is shown in Fig. 3.26. The PMR channel was fed by an elliptical secondary mirror located near the focus of an off-axis parabolic primary mirror 5 cm in diameter. The latter had no need of pointing mechanisms or scan mirrors since the rotation of the spacecraft traced the field of view across the planet and also provided a space view once per spin. Full-scale calibration was obtained by means of a reflecting lightweight cover which was placed across the aperture at regular intervals of about 30 min. When in place, this caused the detector to view the interior of a black, thermostatically controlled cavity inside which the optics were also mounted. Four molecular sieve temperature settings were provided (Table 3.5), one of which was only to provide piston damping during the vibrational environment of an Atlas-Centaur launch.

TABLE 3.5

Molecular Sieve Settings for the Pioneer Venus PMR

Setting	Sieve temperature (°C)	Mean cell pressure (mbar)	PMC frequency (Hz)	Signal-to-noise ratio[a]
Low	3.70 ± 1.0	1	33.4 ± 0.1	12
Medium	50.7 ± 1.0	4	34.5 ± 0.1	27
High	67.2 ± 1.0	8	37.6 ± 0.1	54
Launch	~ 100	~ 20	0[b]	—

[a] For a blackbody target at 240 K and 200-msec dwell time.
[b] Critically damped.

D. UPPER ATMOSPHERE RESEARCH SATELLITE

The most recent and most powerful version of the PMR so far is the 12-channel Improved Stratospheric annd Mesospheric Sounder presently being developed for the first Upper Atmosphere Research Satellite (UARS). ISAMS exploits the much greater mass, space, and power resources of UARS relative to NIMBUS to employ active detector cooling for the first time, thereby obtaining an improvement in sensitivity of more than two orders of magnitude in most channels. The coolers, which were specially developed for this application, are in fact themselves developments of the pressure modulator principle. Nonrubbing pistons sealed by gas viscosity and suspended on spider springs drive a Sterling-cycle cooler using helium as the working fluid. Early versions, weighing about 4.5 kg, demonstrated a cooling power of 500 mW from a 80-K load into lab ambient when consuming 30 W of power, a very useful specification for ISAMS.

As the name implies, ISAMS has many similarities to SAMS. The main improvements, relative to the Nimbus instrument, may be summarized as follows:

(1) The improved performance that results from the use of cooled detectors. These make possible a design goal of a 200:1 SNR when viewing a 240-K blackbody for the 15-μm CO_2 channel, for example (Section 3.2.C).

(2) A revised scan mirror arrangement which permits viewing of the limb in either direction perpendicular to the spacecraft trajectory. This gives coverage of both polar regions (Section 3.5.D).

(3) A narrow field of view and a smaller aspect ratio, giving a footprint on the limb of approximately 3×15 km.

(4) Provision of a full-field object space calibration blackbody for better radiometric calibration.

(5) A new molecular sieve, offering improved chemical stability for NO and permitting the inclusion of an NO_2 PMR.

(6) Active stabilization of instrument temperature, and chopping against cold space as a radiometric zero reference.

A further improvement, not directly associated with ISAMS but of great value, is the stability of the UARS spacecraft. Nimbus rocks in its orbit with an amplitude of about 1° (equivalent to 50 km of tangent height at the limb); the new platform is about two orders of magnitude better than this.

Figure 3.27 shows an ISAMS block diagram. The optical layout is similar to SAMS but much improved in detail. Table 3.6 lists the spectral bands and pressure modulators that are employed. The whole system, including electronics and coolers, is housed in a single unit measuring $102 \times 94 \times 86$ cm^3 which weighs 105 kg.

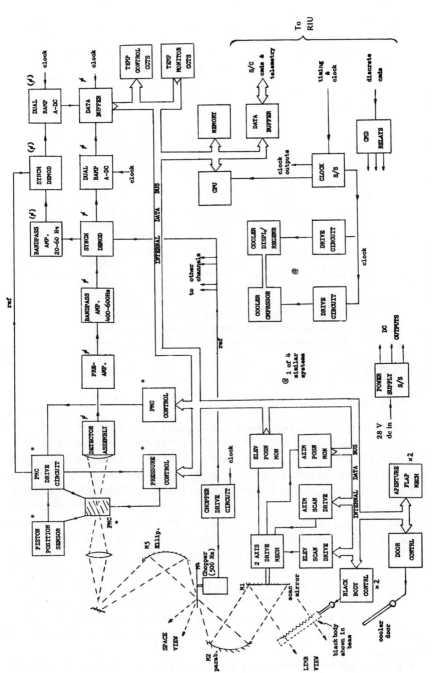

FIG. 3.27. Block diagram of the ISAMS being developed for UARS: (*) one of eight similar systems; (≠) one of eleven similar systems; [(≠)] one of nine similar systems; one pair of detector channels share same PMC; two detector channels do not include PMCs.

TABLE 3.6

Spectral Channels for the Improved Strateospheric and
Mesospheric Sounder

Channel designation[a]	Modulated gas	Isolation filter (cm^{-1})	Function[b]
A1	CH_4	1330–1400	Methane, wind
A2	N_2O	1230–1295	Nitrous oxide, wind
A3	CO_2[c]	690–715	Rotational temperature
A4	CO_2[c]	655–680	Vibrational temperature
B1	CO	2080–2220	Carbon monoxide
B2	H_2O	1500–1575	Water vapor
C1	NO	1840–1940	Nitric oxide
C2	NO_2	1592–1603	Nitrogen dioxide
C3	[d]	980–1070	Ozone
C4	[d]	860–900	Nitric acid
C5	CO_2	640–700	Pressure, wind

[a] The letters designate fields of view. These are 2 km wide in the vertical direction and separated by 1 km with A at the top.

[b] Where a species is stated an abundance measurement is implied

[c] Channels A3 and A4 share the same modulator.

[d] Broadband measurements only.

3.5. Applications

A. Temperature

The Nimbus 6 PMR was entirely devoted to measurements of temperature in the mesosphere, a region for which previously only sporadic measurements by rockets had been available. The availability for the first time of global-scale maps therefore revealed many interesting features of the region (e.g., see Houghton, 1978). Figures 3.28 and 3.29 illustrate a day in 1976 for which large eddy amplitudes were present over the North Pole; note particularly the reversal in phase between the two levels illustrated so that the hot center at 85 km lies directly on top of the cold center at 50 km.

The limb-viewing pressure modulator radiometer on Nimbus 7 (SAMS) measures the temperature field from about 10- to about 90-km altitude; an example for a day in 1981 is shown in Fig. 3.30. Note how the North Polar regions are warmer than lower latitudes by 10–20 K at some levels in the stratosphere (in spite of the fact that it was then winter in the Northern Hemisphere), while the reverse behavior occurs at higher levels, in the mesosphere.

Rather similar behavior was observed in the atmosphere of Venus (Fig. 3.31), although there are no large seasonal effects on that planet, and the

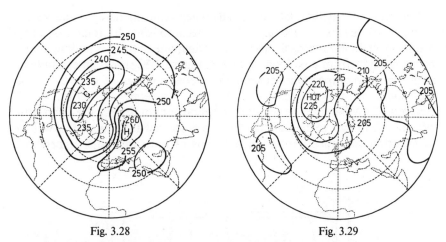

Fig. 3.28   Fig. 3.29

FIG. 3.28. Temperature field in the Northern Hemisphere at a height of about 42 km, as measured by the PMR on Nimbus 6 (channel 2115) on 7 February 1976.

FIG. 3.29. As Fig. 3.28, but for the second PMR channel (3000) measuring at about 85-km altitude. Note the phase reversal in the wave surrounding the pole.

mechanisms at work are probably not the same. The PMR data on Venus were crucial for obtaining, among other things, the information that the mean equator-to-pole temperature gradient reverses near 90-km altitude, which has profound implications for the circulation of the atmosphere (Taylor *et al.*, 1981).

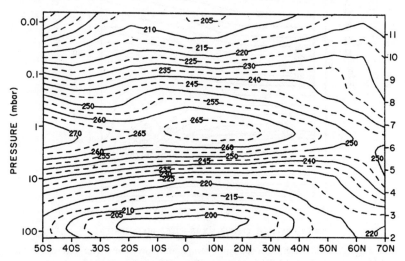

FIG. 3.30. A zonal mean cross-section of temperature (in kelvins) measured by the SAMS on Nimbus 7 on 5 February 1981. [From Barnett *et al.*, 1981.]

Validation of satellite data, especially when radically new techniques are being employed, is a vital step. This is accomplished by intercomparing results from different sensors, preferably when one of them is making direct measurements from a balloon or rocket. Figure 3.32 shows an example of such an intercomparison between the global analysis of data from the radiosonde network, prepared at the Free University of Berlin, and a Nimbus 7 SAMS map. The agreement is good but not perfect; the discrepancies are due in part to the way the data are processed and mapped, as well as to experimental uncertainties in both sets of measurements. Experience

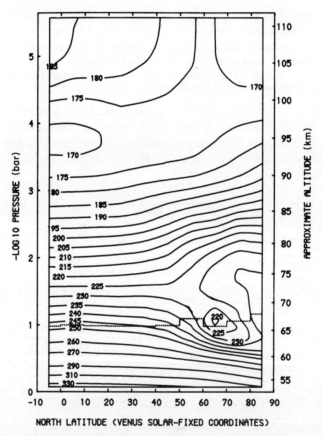

FIG. 3.31. A zonal mean cross-section of temperature on Venus, averaged over the period from 4 December 1978 to 14 February 1979. [From Taylor *et al.*, 1981.]

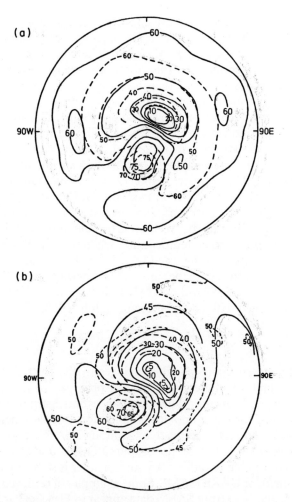

FIG. 3.32. A preliminary comparison between SAMS temperature measurements (---) at (a) 30 mbar (~25 km) (b) 10 mbar (~30 km), with conventional data (—) from radiosondes processed at Berlin Free University. [From Barnett *et al.*, 1981.]

predicts that gradual refinements will reduce the differences to perhaps 1–2 K. Validation for temperatures measured at higher levels and for composition measurements is more difficult owing to the paucity of independent data with which to compare.

The problems associated with retrieving temperature structure in low-pressure regions where local thermodynamic equilibrium (LTE) no longer applies have already been mentioned (Section 3.2.A). For the 15-μm CO_2 band, LTE breaks down below the region near the mesopause when kinetic temperatures assume their lowest values anywhere in the atmosphere. The temperatures corresponding to the vibrational energy levels of the CO_2 molecule are even lower because there are insufficient collisions between the molecules to excite the vibrational upper state. The *rotational* states of the molecule, however, require far fewer collisions in order to maintain an equilibrium population, and so these are in LTE to much greater altitudes. The PMR can be used to measure rotational, as well as vibrational, temperatures and hence to obtain valuable information on the energetics of the mesopause region. The approach (Holt, 1978) is to measure emission from the 15-μm band simultaneously in two spectral intervals, one containing lines corresponding to transitions between states of low rotational energy and the other high. The ratio between these two measurements is related in a known way to the rotational temperature, while their sum depends on the vibrational temperature in the usual way. In the LTE region (below about 70 km) both temperatures are the same. This experiment will be performed for the first time by the ISAMS on UARS, since useful accuracies (1 – 2 K) can only be obtained with cooled detectors (Holt, 1978).

B. COMPOSITION

Increased concern about possible changes in the earth's climate have stimulated a surge of interest in chemical processes in the atmosphere, particularly those which control the abundances and distributions of ozone, water vapor, and carbon monoxide. Exploratory measurements of H_2O, CH_4, CO, N_2O, and NO were made by Nimbus 7 SAMS, and much more comprehensive studies of these species, plus NO_2, O_3, and HNO_3 (the latter two by conventional filter radiometry since neither is stable in a modulator cell), are planned for UARS ISAMS. Some examples of retrieved abundance fields for CH_4 and N_2O from SAMS data appear in Figs. 3.33 and 3.34. The interpretation of these observations must take account of transport as well as chemical processes. Generally the approach is through detailed comparisons with computerized theoretical models which attempt to incorporate all of the relevant physics and chemistry. Qualitative differences between the CH_4 and N_2O distributions (especially at high latitudes in the winter hemisphere) suggest that chemical processes are significant even for long-lived species such as these.

A very useful way to study the performance of a composition-measuring channel in the design phase of an experiment is by the use of the concept of *effective emissivity E.* This is defined simply as the ratio between the

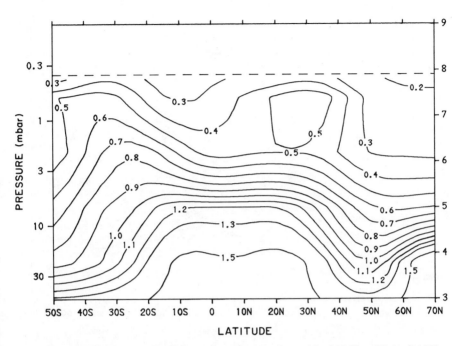

FIG. 3.33. Zonal mean distribution of methane as observed by SAMS on 23 April 1979. [From Jones, 1982.]

calculated emission from a particular species observed at a given altitude z above the limb, and the emission which would result from a blackbody at the same temperature as the atmosphere at level z. Figure 3.14 shows some curves of E versus height for NO_2 as it will be measured by ISAMS. Three different modulator cell pressures are shown; the curves described as wide band correspond to the measurements made with the modulator when the instrument behaves as an ordinary filter radiometer. The advantage of the PMR as a means of increasing effective emissivity, especially at higher altitudes, can be seen. This is even more pronounced with species that have a substantial abundance in the mesosphere, for example, H_2O (Fig. 3.35). The improvement in E by reducing p_c has to be traded off against SNR, which also depends on p_c as described above. However, the trade-off is easily calculated from the known SNR, SNR_{ref} obtained when viewing the reference blackbody at temperature T_{ref} since

$$SNR = SNR_{ref} \times E \times [B(T)/B(T_{ref})] \qquad (3.16)$$

where T is the mean temperature of the atmosphere in the field of view and

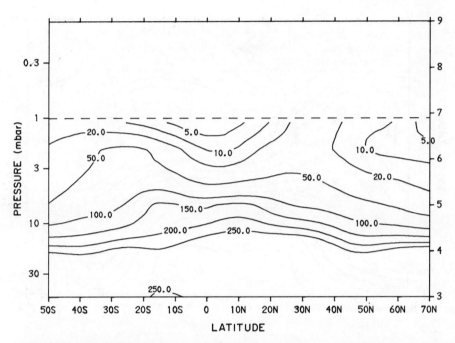

FIG. 3.34. Zonal mean distribution of nitrous oxide as observed by SAMS on 21st April 1979. [From Jones, 1982.]

$B(T)$ is the Planck function at the effective wave number of the channel. A further useful quantity is the *noise-equivalent emissivity* (NEE), which is the value of E for which SNR in Eq. (3.16) is equal to unity. Returning to the example of NO_2, the NEE for $p_c = 1$ mbar, and the other parameter, as specified for ISAMS, is calculated to be 0.02 for one 2-sec sample. If it is noted also that NEE is approximately proportional to p_c, then curves of this kind can be used to plan observing sequences and to estimate the accuracy of the abundances to be retrieved.

C. Pressure

All limb-viewing instruments need to obtain pressure information, along with temperature and composition, in order to fix the vertical scale to which these other parameters are referred. Drummond *et al.* (1980) note that, for the specific case of SAMS viewing at a level where the effective emissivity is 0.5, a change of signal corresponding to $\Delta\epsilon = 0.01$ (equivalent to a change in mixing ratio of about 6%) could also result from a change in the level being

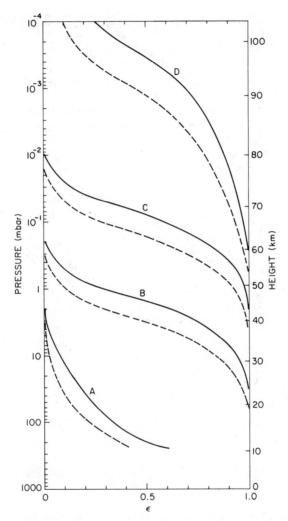

FIG. 3.35. The calculated effective emissivity of water vapor, illustrating the effect of varying cell pressure p_c. Curve A is the wide-band signal; for the other curves $p_c = 6$ mbar (B), 0.3 mbar (C), and 0.03 mbar (D). The full line is for a mixing ratio of 5 ppmv in the atmosphere, the dashed line for 1.25 ppmv.

viewed of 0.15 km. The latter is equivalent to a change in pressure at the tangent point of about 2% or a change in the viewing direction in roll of only 0.003°. Although UARS will be much better, Nimbus spacecraft suffer unpredictable fluctuations in roll with an amplitude of the order of 1°. It was necessary, therefore, to deduce pressure rather precisely (to within about 1%) from the measurements themselves.

The PMR lends itself particularly well to the solution of this problem because of its property of measuring pressure modulator and wide-band

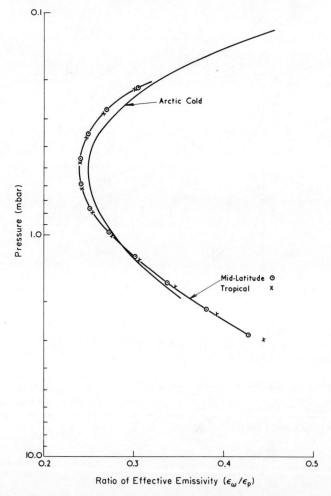

FIG. 3.36. Ratio of the wide band to the pressure modulator effective emissivity as a function of tangent height pressure for three very different model atmospheres, illustrating how this ratio may be used to determine the pressure.

signals in the same field of view simultaneously. The ratio of the two signals is found to be a strong function of tangent point pressure, but to depend only very weakly on temperature (Fig. 3.36; see also Drummond *et al.*, 1980; Barnett *et al.*, 1981). At the level where the ratio is most sensitive to the pressure, it can be determined to about 2% using a statistical temperature profile. When the retrieved temperature profile is used in an iterative scheme, the reference pressure determination can be improved to about 1% accuracy.

The very much higher SNRs available from the new generation of PMRs with cooled detectors, such as ISAMS, offer the promise of pressure measurements to accuracies of a fraction of 1%. At the same time, the spacecraft will be much more stable and have more accurate reference systems, using sun and star trackers, which can place the tangent height relative to the surface to within a few tens of meters. This does not eliminate the need for a pressure measurement by the instrument, of course, because the pressure at a given altitude normally fluctuates by several percent. Instead, it offers the possibility for producing maps of pressure on a constant height surface, which would be of great interest to the meteorologist. The performance in this respect of the UARS, which represents the current state of the art for meteorological instrument pointing, is rather marginal in terms of pressure retrievals. Absolute pointing accuracies of about 0.01° are expected, which translates to a pressure uncertainty of some 6%. However, it is not clear to what extent the residual pointing error will consist of a systematic component which can be calibrated out by reference to radiosondes. It may not be possible to achieve the desired accuracy of measurement of pressure versus height of 1% or better for some years yet, but clearly the goal is almost within reach.

D. Winds

Any relative velocity along the line of sight of a PMR will result in a Doppler shift of the lines in the cell relative to those in the atmosphere. In a hypothetical extreme case the modulated lines could move entirely clear of the atmospheric emission lines, and the signal would then fall to zero. The Doppler shift corresponding to typical orbital speeds of around 7000 m sec^{-1} for Nimbus or UARS is enough to shift the lines relative to each other by many Doppler linewidths, since the latter corresponds to the thermal velocity distribution of the molecules, which at a typical middle atmosphere temperature of 240 K averages about 300 m sec^{-1}. For this reason both SAMS and ISAMS view the limb at right angles to the spacecraft velocity vector, with provision for a "Doppler scan" of a few degrees (actually 15° for SAMS and 10° for ISAMS) in azimuth. The scan mirror in ISAMS is programmed to keep this angle such that the component of spacecraft velocity just cancels the velocity of the atmosphere owing to the rotation of the earth. The latter is, of course, latitude dependent and requires an azimuth scan of amplitude about 4° to obtain a continuous null.

In addition to this predictable source of Doppler shift, there is a contribution due to the motion of the atmosphere relative to the surface. At certain levels this can be 100 m sec⁻¹, or even higher, which shifts the null point by 1°. If the instrument can scan and locate the null point (by finding the azimuth angle at which the signal is maximum) to an accuracy substantially better than 1°, then a useful measurement of wind velocity along the line of sight becomes possible. Figure 3.37 illustrates how the effective emissivity of the atmosphere (Section 3.5.B) depends on azimuth angle for one of the ISAMS 15-μm channels. This shows, as would be expected intuitively, that the sensitivity to wind increases with increasing Doppler shift as the strong centers of the atmospheric lines move into the steep wings of the PMR lines. The sensitivity also tends to increase with decreasing pressure as the atmospheric lines become less pressure broadened, up to the height where even the line centers start to become optically thin when the signal falls off again.

The detailed performance depends on factors such as cell length and pressure, as well as on species and wavelength. It is convenient to define a noise-equivalent wind speed (NEWS) as

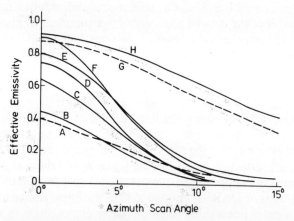

FIG. 3.37. Dependence of the effective emissivity on azimuth away from 0° (which is the normal to the spacecraft velocity vector): 1° introduces a line-of-sight velocity of approximately 100 m sec⁻¹. Curves A and G assume 3 mbar of N_2O in the modulator and tangent heights of 40 and 34 km; corresponding values for the other curves: B, 0.5 mbar of $C^{13}O_2^{16}$ at 95 km; C, 1 mbar of $C^{13}O_2^{16}$ at 77 km; D, as for curve B, but at 83 km; E, as for curve C, but at 65 km; F, as for curve B, but at 70 km, H, as for curve C, but at 50 km.

$$\text{NEWS} = \frac{\Delta I}{\partial I/\partial v} \quad \text{m sec}^{-1} \tag{3.17}$$

where I is radiance, ΔI the system noise, and v the line-of-sight wind. NEWS is then the smallest change in v that can be discerned above the instrument noise level, analogous to NET for temperature (Section 3.2.C). Values of NEWS of about 1 m sec.$^{-1}$ are found from curves similar to those of Fig. 3.37, assuming the instrumental parameters from the design for ISAMS (Section 3.4.D). This assumes, however, that the spacecraft is perfectly stable. In fact it is likely to contribute about 1 m sec^{-1} of additional noise owing to pointing uncertainties of the order of 0.01° in all three axes. A measurement time of 120 sec has been assumed, during which various points (60 in all) of the signal-versus-azimuth curve (Fig. 3.37) are sampled. To minimize the effect of atmospheric temperature and composition fluctuations, the scan would best be arranged to "freeze" on a particular location at the limb while the spacecraft travels past.

An important fundamental limitation inherent in this approach to wind

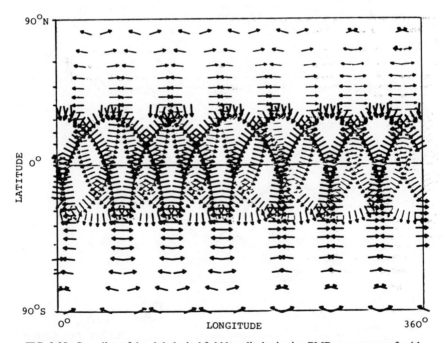

FIG. 3.38. Sampling of the global wind field by a limb-viewing PMR on a spacecraft with a 54° inclination orbit over the course of a day. The arrows show the direction of the vector whose magnitude would be measured. For clarity, only every second orbit is shown, and only alternate vectors plotted. Figure by J. J. Barnett.

measurement is its restriction to a single component of the wind velocity vector, that perpendicular to the spacecraft velocity. Thus, only the zonal component of the wind is available from a polar orbit and only the meridional component from an equatorial orbit. For a satellite in an orbit of intermediate inclination such as UARS ($i = 57°$), the direction of the vector alters continuously and, in fact, quite good sampling of the global wind field is produced over the course of a day (Fig. 3.38). Nevertheless, it clearly would be desirable to measure both horizontal components simultaneously, and a method for doing this using a PMR has been suggested by McCleese and Margolis (1982). Their technique involves the use of an electrooptical phase modulator (Yariv, 1971) to introduce an adjustable frequency shift into the incoming radiation. This device is a crystal of cadmium telluride, to which a very-high-frequency alternating voltage is applied. It has the effect of moving some of the energy of an incoming spectral line into side bands, whose displacement from the input line is equal to the modulation frequency. If the latter can be as high as 500 MHz, then the shift is large enough

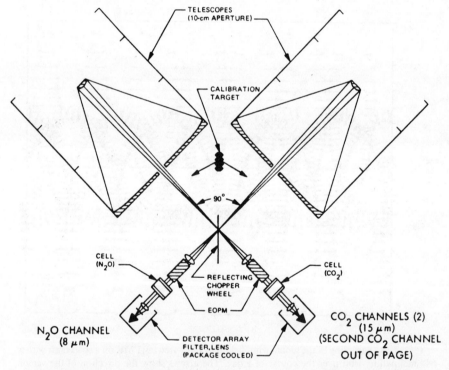

FIG. 3.39. Conceptual design for a dedicated wind-measuring experiment based on PMRs. [From McCleese and Margolis, 1982.]

to cancel completely the Doppler shift at viewing angles 45° to a typical spacecraft velocity of 7.5 km sec^{-1}. In this way a component of v can be measured at 45° to either side of the direction at right angles to the orbital motion, and the complete horizontal vector obtained globally with the two components at a point separated in time by only a few minutes. A further advantage is that the electrically induced shift can be chosen so that the measurements are always made on the steepest part of the radiance-versus-frequency shift curve (cf. Fig. 3.37), thus gaining sensitivity. The proposed experimental configuration is shown in Fig. 3.39.

E. RESONANCE FLUORESCENCE MEASUREMENTS

In the upper atmosphere, collisions between molecules are sufficiently infrequent that absorption of a solar photon may be followed by reemission at the same wavelength but in a different direction. At lower levels the probability is high that the absorption will be followed by collisional quenching. The fluorescence process is extremely interesting to the atmospheric scientist because of the insight it can give into physical processes taking place at the mesopause and above; since the sun is such a bright source, it also offers an opportunity for measuring the abundance of species such as H_2O, which are in such small quanitities at these levels they are difficult to observe any other way. The PMR is an ideal device for observing fluorescence since it discriminates against background sources such as Rayleigh scattering. The SAMS on Nimbus 7 (Section 3.5.B) measured the abundance of mesospheric water by this technique and showed that the mesosphere is much drier than the stratosphere (Drummond *et al.*, 1981). Figure 3.40 shows SAMS measurements of mixed fluorescence and thermal emission from the 4.3-μm band of CO_2; fluorescence accounts for most of the difference between the day and night profiles.

F. OCCULTATION MODE

Occultation mode is a second method (cf. Section 3.5.E) for using the sun as a powerful source to observe trace constituents in the upper atmosphere. In this approach the PMR views the sun directly (or via a diffusing plate) and makes measurements during sunset or sunrise as the spacecraft passes behind the limb as seen from the sun. So far, occultation measurements with a PMR have not been made from a spacecraft, but a balloon-borne version for measuring HCI profiles is under development and has flown twice (H. K. Roscoe, personal communication). Calculations have shown that CO_2, H_2O, and O_2 profiles could be measured in the earth's upper atmosphere or nearer the surface on Mars with a relatively simple instrument.

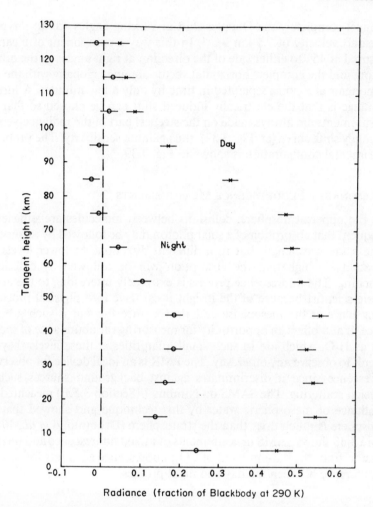

FIG. 3.40. Observations by Nimbus 7 SAMS of mixed thermal and resonance fluorescence emission from carbon dioxide in the 4.3-μm band. The curve for nighttime shows the thermal component alone. [From Barnett *et al.*, 1980.]

G. PLANETARY ATMOSPHERES

Some mention has already been made above of the Venusian temperature maps obtained by the PMR on the Pioneer orbiter. These remain the only observation of a planet other than the Earth made by this technique, but several others have been studied and their implementation is a matter of active planning in Europe and the United States.

The next logical application and that which has been receiving the most attention is the use of a PMR to map water vapor on Mars. This is a major scientific question since the relationship between subsurface, polar cap, and atmospheric moisture bears heavily on the history and future evolution of the climate of the planet. The measurements are very difficult because the atmosphere of Mars is cold and thin and the amounts of water vapor it can

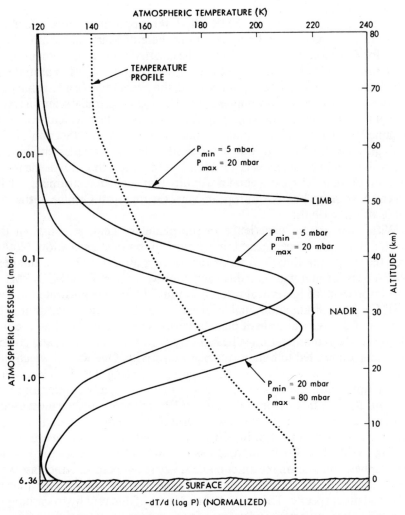

FIG. 3.41. Weighting functions for limb and nadir views of the atmosphere of Mars by a CO_2 PMR: gas, $C^{12}O_2^{16}$; cell length, 10 cm; $\Delta v = 610-625$ cm^{-1}. [From D. J. McCleese, unpublished work.]

hold are small compared to Earth, typically just a few tens of precipitable microns corresponding to mixing ratios of the order of a few parts per million. Considerable success was achieved by the NASA Viking orbiter which carried a near-IR, high-resolution spectrometer for water mapping. However, there remains an urgent need for a thermal instrument with the capability of making measurements independent of solar illumination and with less susceptibility to airborne dust. It is an application to which a PMR is ideally suited.

At the same time, a CO_2 PMR offers the opportunity to explore the temperature structure of the upper atmosphere of Mars, as has now been done for Earth and Venus. Apart from the fact that such measurements have never been made on Mars above the highest level (about 35-km altitude) at which conventional sounding can be used, the posession of a good data base on all three terrestrial atmospheres is another highly desirable scientific goal.

Figure 3.41 shows the weighting functions for Mars which would be obtained by an instrument similar to that on Pioneer Venus (Section 3.4.C), with an H_2O PMR added. Calculations show that the smallest amount of water that could be detected is less than 1 ppm, or less than 1% of the mean amount present. There is a good possibility that such an instrument will be flown to Mars on board a European Mars Geophysical Orbiter in the late 1980s or early 1990s.

With their greater experience in the planetary field, scientists in the United States have been examining a more ambitious application. Noting that the weighting functions for nadir viewing are rather broad, the next NASA Mars orbiter will probably carry limb-viewing H_2O and CO_2 PMRs. The improvement in vertical resolution thus obtained is illustrated in Fig. 3.41. Very important additional information on the vertical distribution of water and the vertical scale of planetary waves can be obtained as a result. However, the radiometer must have a very narrow field of view, and cooled detectors are needed to obtain sufficient sensitivity. One way in which this can be accomplished (with a weight penalty) is by using closed-cycle coolers.

The upper atmospheres of the outer planets, especially Jupiter and Saturn, are also candidates for study using PMRs. In these cases the most useful working gases are the hydrocarbons, especially methane, acetylene, and ethane. The results of weighting function calculations for Saturn are shown in Fig. 3.42. The PMR approach is found to be most useful for the stratospheric regions on the outer planets, where temperatures increase with height owing to absorption of sunlight in the near-IR absorption bands of CH_4 and other species. The relative abundances of different hydrocarbons in this region are important indicators of the photochemical activity going on in the region. For these observations not only the detectors but also the modulators themselves need to be cooled, to reduce the IR background flux.

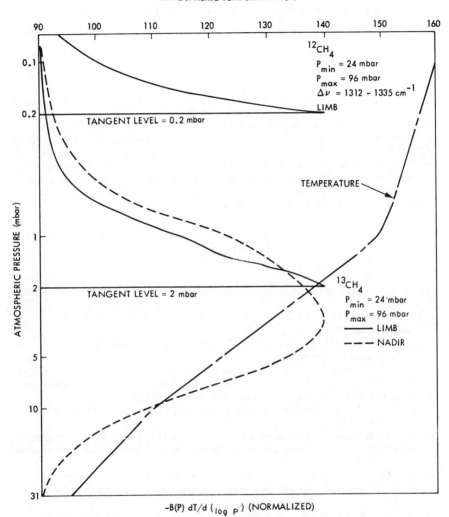

FIG. 3.42. Weighting functions for limb and nadir views of the atmosphere of Saturn by methane PMRs with the specifications shown on the figure. [From D. J. McCleese, unpublished work.]

This raises new problems of maintaining tolerances and electronics design which must be solved before such an experiment is implemented.

ACKNOWLEDGMENTS

The development of the PMR and its successful application to numerous important atmospheric studies have come as the results of more than 16 years of dedicated effort by many people. Special credit belongs to Professor J. T. Houghton, FRS, who introduced the concept of the PMR and was the architect of the satellite experiments described in this article. I am grateful to him and to J. J. Barnett, J. R. Drummond, R. L. Jones, C. D. Rodgers, D. J. McCleese, J. T. Schofield, and J. G. Whitney for permission to use unpublished material and for supplying figures. The space experiments described herein were sponsored by the U.K. Science and Engineering Research Council and conducted in collaboration with the U.S. National Aeronautics and Space Administration.

REFERENCES

Abel, P. G. (1966). Observations of infrared emission in the atmosphere. Ph.D. Thesis, Oxford University.
Abel, P. G., et al. (1970). The Selective Choppes Radiometer for Nimbus D. *Proc. R. Soc. London,* A320, 35–55.
Barnett, J. J. et al. (1981). The stratosphere and mesospheric sounder on Nimbus 7. Two year report. *Atmos. Phys. Memo.* 81.1.
Challoner, C. P., Drummond, J. R., Houghton, J. T., Jarnot, R. F., and Roscoe, H. K. (1978). Infrared measurements of stratospheric composition. 1. The balloon instrument and water vapour measurements. *Proc. Soc. London, Ser. A* 364, 145–149.
Curtis, P. D. (1974). Measurements of Temperature in the Upper Atmosphere Using Satellite Instruments. Ph.D. thesis, Oxford University.
Curtis, P. D., Houghton, J. T., Peskett, G. D., and Rodgers, C. D. (1974). Remote sounding of atmospheric temperature from satellites. V. The pressure modulator radiometer for Nimbus F. *Proc. Soc. London, Ser. A* 337, 135–150.
Drummond, J. R., and Jarnot, R. F. (1978). Infrared measurements of stratospheric composition. II. Simultaneous NO and NO_2 measurements. *Proc. R. Soc. London, Ser. A* 364, 237–254.
Drummond, J. R., Houghton, J. T., Peskett, G. D., Rodgers, C. D., Wale, M. J., Whitney, J., and Williamson, E. J. (1980). The stratospheric and mesospheric sounder on Nimbus 7. *Phil. Trans. R. Soc. London, Ser. A* 296, 219–241.
Drummond, J. R., Davis, G. R., and Mutlow, C. T. (1981). Satellite measurements of H_2O fluorescence in the mesosphere. *Nature (London)* 294, 431–433.
Enhalt, D. H., and Tonniben, A. (1979). Hydrogen and carbon compounds in the stratosphere. *Atmos Ozone: Its Variations Hum. Influence, Proc. NATO Adv. Study Inst., 1979* pp. 129–151.
Holt, C. E. (1978). Spectroscopic observations of atmospheric composition. M.Sc.Thesis, Oxford University.
Houghton, J. T. (1978). The stratosphere and mesosphere. *Q. J. R. Meteorol. Soc.* 104, 1–29.

Houghton, J. T., and Taylor, F. W. (1973). Remote sounding from artificial satellites and space probes of the atmospheres of the Earth and planets. *Rep. Prog. Phys.* **36,** 827–919.

Houghton, J. T., Taylor, F. W., and Rodgers, C. D. (1983). "Remote Sounding of Atmospheres." Cambridge Univ. Press, London and New York.

Jones, R. L. (1983). Spectroscopic measurements on minor atmospheric constituents. Ph. D. Thesis, Oxford University.

McCleese, D. J., and Margolis, J. S. (1982). "Gas Correlation Wind Sensor." NASA/JPL Rept. (Unpublished.)

Morgan, J. T., and Stapleton, C. B. (1971). A technique for controlling the pressure of CO_2 in the Nimbus F Radiometer. Rutherford Lab. Rept. RHEL/R216 HMSO 91-40-0-0.

Roscoe, H. K., Drummond, J. R., and Jarnot, R. R. (1981). Infrared measurements of stratospheric composition. III. The daytime changes of NO and NO_2. *Proc. R. Soc. London, Ser. A* **375,** 507–528.

Schofield, J. T. (1980). Remote sounding of the Venus atmosphere. Ph.D. Thesis, p. 326. Oxford University.

Taylor, F. W. (1970). Radiometric measurements of atmospheric temperature. Ph.D. Thesis, p. 76. Oxford University.

Taylor, F. W., Houghton, J. T., Peskett, G. D., Rodgers, C. D., and Williamson, E. J. (1972). Radiometer for remote sounding of the upper atmosphere. *Appl. Opti.* **11,** 135–141.

Taylor, F. W., *et al.* (1979). Infrared radiometer for the Pioneer Venus orbiter. 1. Instrument description. *Appl. Opt.* **18,** 3893–3900.

Taylor, F. W., Schofield, J. T., and Bradley, S. P. (1981). Pioneer Venus atmospheric observations. *Phil. Trans. R. Soc. London, Ser. A* **303,** 215—223.

Yariv, A. (1971). "Introduction to Optical Electronics." Holt, Reinhart, & Winston, Inc., New York.

Chapter **4**

Fourier Self-Deconvolution in Spectroscopy

JYRKI K. KAUPPINEN

DEPARTMENT OF PHYSICS
UNIVERSITY OF OULU
OULU, FINLAND

4.1. Introduction

Infrared (IR) spectroscopic techniques have developed rapidly in the last few decades, and it is now possible to obtain instrumentation that will routinely produce high signal-to-noise-ratio spectra with an instrumental resolution much narrower than the linewidth. This is particularly so in the case of condensed-phase spectra, where the intrinsic linewidths are generally

SPECTROMETRIC TECHNIQUES, VOL. III

of the order of 2 cm^{-1} or greater. Further, the most recently developed top-of-the-line instruments come with high-capacity storage devices and powerful minicomputers.

However, despite these advantages, the spectroscopist is limited in his ability to probe the structure of instrumentally unresolvable multicomponent band contours. Such band contours are routinely encountered in condensed-phase spectra and, at the Doppler limit, in gas-phase spectra.

In spectroscopy, the observed spectrum $E_w(v)$ is always the convolution of the instrumental profile $W_0(v)$ and the real spectrum $E(v)$ defined by the following convolution integral

$$E_w(v) = W_0(v) * E(v) = \int_{-\infty}^{\infty} W_0(v')E(v - v') \, dv' \qquad (4.1)$$

where v is the wave number (cm^{-1}).

If we know the instrumental function $W_0(v)$, we can calculate $E(v)$ from the observed spectrum $E_w(v)$. This operation is generally called *deconvolution*, that is, we *deconvolve* $E_w(v)$ with $W_0(v)$. However, the shape of $W_0(v)$ occasionally makes deconvolution impossible.

There are a few methods for calculating $E(v)$ from $E_w(v)$, such as pseudo-rotation (Jones *et al.*, 1967) and Van Cittert's iterative method (Van Cittert, 1931). However, the most elegant way to solve this problem is to apply the Fourier transforms (Betty and Horlick, 1976; Ferrige and Lindon, 1978; King and Bower, 1980; Kauppinen *et al.*, 1981a), defined as

$$E(v) = \int_{-\infty}^{\infty} I(x)e^{i2\pi vx} \, dx = \mathcal{F}\{I(x)\}$$

$$I(x) = \int_{-\infty}^{\infty} E(v)e^{-i2\pi vx} \, dv = \mathcal{F}^{-1}\{E(v)\} \qquad (4.2)$$

where $\mathcal{F}\{\ \}$ and $\mathcal{F}^{-1}\{\ \}$ are the Fourier transform and the inverse Fourier transform, respectively. The variable x of the interferogram $I(x)$ is in centimeters, if v is given in centimeter^{-1}. The spectrum is assumed to be even; that is, $E(-v) = E(v)$. According to the convolution theorem (Bracewell, 1965), the convolution in the Fourier domain (x domain) is simply multiplication, and from Eq. (4.1) it ensues that

$$\mathcal{F}^{-1}\{E(v)\} = \mathcal{F}^{-1}\{E_w(v)\}/\mathcal{F}^{-1}\{W_0(v)\} \qquad (4.3)$$

and the desired spectrum

$$E(v) = \mathcal{F}\{\mathcal{F}^{-1}\{E(v)\}\} \qquad (4.4)$$

In numerous practical examples deconvolution is used for resolution enhancement. If the spectrum $E(v)$ consists of lines with a line-shape function $E_0(v)$, the lines in the recorded spectrum $E_w(v)$ are always wider than $E_0(v)$ because convolution always broadens the lines, which is a general behavior of convolution. Hence, the resolution enhancement in deconvolution is evident. The efficiency of the resolution enhancement depends on the relative widths of $W_0(v)$ and $E_0(v)$.

Fourier self-deconvolution is a method whose main purpose is efficiency in resolution enhancement, with a complete loss of information on the line shape. It is evident that *self-deconvolution* by the observed line-shape function

$$E_{0w}(v) = W_0(v) * E_0(v) \qquad (4.5)$$

gives the maximum resolution enhancement. In theory, the lines following self-deconvolution by $E_{0w}(v)$ are infinitely narrow Dirac delta functions. In conventional deconvolution we deconvolve by $W_0(v)$, which results in the line-shape function $E_0(v)$. Owing to noise in the experimental spectra, this operation is only possible to a certain extent. In other words, before self-deconvolution we must smooth the experimental spectrum with a smoothing function $W(v)$. Smoothing and self-deconvolution together change the line-shape function from $E_{0w}(v)$ to $W(v)$.

The technique is well suited to the cases in which the instrumental resolution is much higher than the spectral resolution, that is, $W_0(v)$ is much narrower than $E_0(v)$. This is the case, for example, in condensed-phase spectroscopy and in very-high-resolution Doppler-limited gas-phase spectroscopy.

In this chapter we study the behavior of Fourier self-deconvolution in the case of noisy experimental spectra and illustrate the method with simulations and examples. We also discuss in detail the optimal use and the practical limitations of this technique and suggest some applications.

4.2. Basic Theory

Let us assume that the real spectrum $E(v)$ consists of the lines with a line-shape function $E_0(v)$. Hence, the line-shape function in the recorded spectrum $E_w(v)$ is $E_{0w}(v) = W_0(v) * E_0(v)$ according to Eq. (4.5). Smoothing with $W(v)$ and self-deconvolution in the Fourier domain are based on the following formula:

$$E'(v) = \mathscr{F}\left\{\frac{\mathscr{F}^{-1}\{W(v)\}\mathscr{F}^{-1}\{E_w(v)\}}{\mathscr{F}^{-1}\{E_{0w}(v)\}}\right\} \qquad (4.6)$$

where $E'(v)$ is called the self-deconvolved spectrum. In the Fourier domain, division by $\mathscr{F}^{-1}\{E_{0w}(v)\}$ accomplishes self-deconvolution, and multiplication (apodization) by $\mathscr{F}^{-1}\{W(v)\}$ results in smoothing with $W(v)$. The whole operation given in Eq. (4.6) replaces the line shape $E_{0w}(v)$ with $W(v)$ in $E'(v)$. This is easily demonstrated in the case where

$$E_w(v) = AE_{0w}(v - v_0) \tag{4.7}$$

According to Eq. (4.6), we have

$$
\begin{aligned}
E'(v) &= \mathscr{F}\left\{\frac{\mathscr{F}^{-1}\{W(v)\}A\mathscr{F}^{-1}\{E_{0w}(v - v_0)\}}{\mathscr{F}^{-1}\{E_{0w}(v)\}}\right\} \\
&= \mathscr{F}\left\{\frac{\mathscr{F}^{-1}\{W(v)\}A\exp(-i2\pi v_0 x)\mathscr{F}^{-1}\{E_{0w}(v)\}}{\mathscr{F}^{-1}\{E_{0w}(v)\}}\right\} \\
&= \mathscr{F}\{\mathscr{F}^{-1}\{AW(v - v_0)\}\} = AW(v - v_0)
\end{aligned}
\tag{4.8}
$$

where

$$\mathscr{F}^{-1}\{E_{0w}(v - v_0)\} = \mathscr{F}^{-1}\{E_{0w}(v)\}\exp(-i2\pi v_0 x) \tag{4.9}$$

according to the shift theorem (Bracewell, 1965). Hence, Eq. (4.8) indicates that Fourier self-deconvolution replaces the line shape $E_{0w}(v)$ with $W(v)$. This is illustrated in Fig. 4.1. We also see from Eq. (4.8) that Fourier self-deconvolution cannot alter the frequency v_0 and the line intensity A. The main purpose of Fourier self-deconvolution is precisely to reduce the

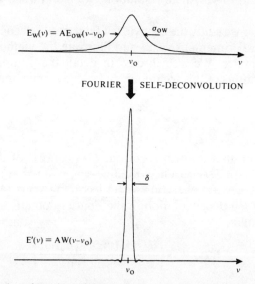

FIG. 4.1. Illustration of Fourier self-deconvolution operation in the wave-number domain.

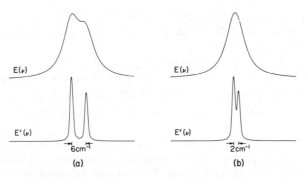

FIG. 4.2. Fourier self-deconvolution of band contours comprised of two overlapped 8-cm^{-1}-wide Lorentzian lines with relative intensities of 1 and 0.75. In (a) the lines are 6 cm^{-1} apart; in (b) they are 2 cm^{-1} apart. Self-deconvolution improves the spectral resolution by a factor of 5.3, and the half-width is now 1.5 cm^{-1}.

half-widths (full width at the half-height of the line) of the lines. The efficiency of this resolution enhancement is given by a factor

$$K = \sigma_{0w}/\delta \qquad (4.10)$$

where σ_{0w} and δ are the half-widths of $E_{0w}(v)$ and $W(v)$, respectively.

Figure 4.2 shows two simulated band contours $[E(v)]$ composed of two Lorentzian lines $[E_0(v)]$ with half-widths of 8 cm^{-1} and relative intensities of 1 and 0.75. The instrumental resolution is assumed to be infinite; that is, $W_0(v) = \delta(v)$ and $E_{0w}(v) = E_0(v)$. The lines are 6 cm^{-1} apart in Fig. 4.2a and 2 cm^{-1} apart in Fig. 4.2b. Fourier self-deconvolution was carried out according to Eq. (4.6) with (apodization)

$$\mathcal{F}^{-1}\{W(v)\} = [1 - (|x|/L)]^2 \qquad (4.11)$$

where L is 0.8 cm, giving (Kauppinen et al., 1981a)

$$K = \sigma_{0w}/\delta = 8 \text{ cm}^{-1}/1.5 \text{ cm}^{-1} \approx 5.3$$

This represents an improvement of spectral resolution by a factor of 5.3. In both cases we can recover the frequencies of the component lines; in the first example (Fig. 4.2a) we can also recover the relative integrated intensities of the lines.

In practice, the K value is limited by the noise in the recorded spectrum $E_w(v)$ and also by the instrumental resolution, so that

$$K \lesssim K_0 = \sigma_{0w}/\delta_0 \qquad (4.12)$$

where δ_0 is the half-width of the instrumental profile $W_0(v)$.

Figure 4.3 demonstrates stepwise the procedure of Fourier self-deconvolution in the v and x domains. Random white noise is also separately included in the illustration.

If we know the line-shape function $E_{0w}(v)$ in the recorded spectrum $E_w(v)$, the only option is the desired line shape $W(v)$. However, the signal-to-noise ratio in the self-deconvolved spectrum $E'(v)$ is strongly dependent on the shape and half-width of $W(v)$. This is easy to understand if we look at Fig. 4.3.

In practice, the most important thing in Fourier self-deconvolution is to know the rate of decrease in the signal-to-noise ratio as a function of K. Hence, the behavior of the noise in Fourier self-deconvolution is the main topic of the next chapter.

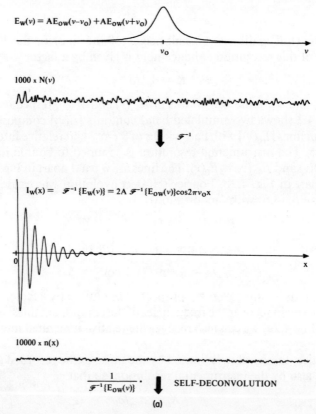

FIG. 4.3. Illustration of the various steps (a–c) of the Fourier self-deconvolution procedure.

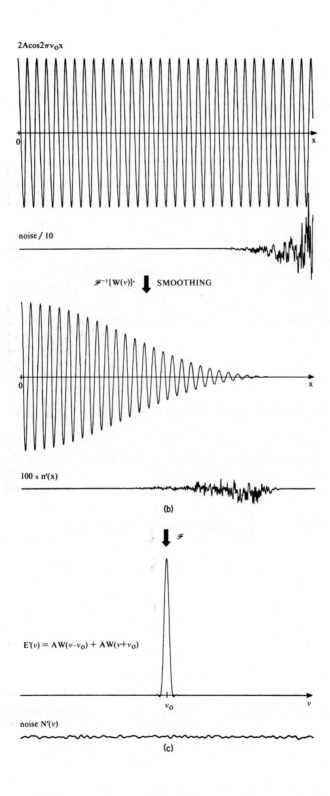

$2A\cos 2\pi\nu_0 x$

noise / 10

$\mathscr{F}^{-1}\{W(\nu)\}\cdot$ SMOOTHING

$100 \times n'(x)$

(b)

$\mathscr{F}$

$E'(\nu) = AW(\nu-\nu_0) + AW(\nu+\nu_0)$

ν_0 ν

noise $N'(\nu)$

(c)

4.3. Signal-to-Noise Ratio in Fourier Self-Deconvolution

A. GENERAL FORMULAS

The aim of this chapter is to derive the ratio Q, by which Fourier self-deconvolution decreases the signal-to-noise ratio. This ratio is given by

$$Q = \frac{(S/N)'}{S/N} \tag{4.13}$$

where S/N is the signal-to-noise ratio before and $(S/N)'$ after Fourier self-deconvolution. Generally, the ratio Q depends on K, $W(v)$, and $E_{0w}(v)$. First we derive a general formula for Q (Kauppinen et al., 1981b).

We assume a random white noise spectrum $N(v)$ and its inverse Fourier transform $n(x)$, called a noise interferogram. Further, we assume $N(v)$ and $n(x)$ to be even and real. Using Parseval's relation (Bracewell, 1965), the noise power spectrum $N^2(v)$ and the noise power interferogram $n^2(x)$ are related by

$$\int_{-\infty}^{\infty} N^2(v)\, dv = \int_{-\infty}^{\infty} n^2(x)\, dx \tag{4.14}$$

Experimental considerations will generally limit the integrals to the ranges $(-v_m, v_m)$ and $(-L_m, L_m)$, respectively. However, in the Fourier domain (interferogram) limitation takes place via a function $S(x) = \mathscr{F}^{-1}\{V(v)\}$, where $V(v)$ is the intrinsic smoothing function of the recording system affecting the noise and $S(x) = 0$ when $|x| > L_m$. Accordingly, we can express the noise power spectrum $N_S^2(v)$ as

$$\int_{-v_m}^{v_m} N_S^2(v)\, dv = \int_{-\infty}^{\infty} S^2(x) n^2(x)\, dx \tag{4.15}$$

In the case of random white noise, $n^2(x)$ varies much more rapidly than $S^2(x)$, and hence

$$\int_{-v_m}^{v_m} N_S^2(v)\, dv = \lim_{L \to \infty} \frac{1}{2L} \int_{-L}^{L} n^2(x)\, dx \int_{-\infty}^{\infty} S^2(x)\, dx$$

$$= \overline{n^2} \int_{-\infty}^{\infty} S^2(x)\, dx \tag{4.16}$$

Thus the root mean square (rms) of the noise in the spectrum recorded via smoothing with $V(v) = \mathcal{F}\{S(x)\}$ is given by

$$\sqrt{\overline{N_S^2}} = \sqrt{(\overline{n^2}/v_m)} \int_0^\infty S^2(x)\,dx \tag{4.17}$$

where $(\overline{n^2})^{1/2}$ is the rms value of the noise in the interferogram without smoothing with $V(v)$.

If we do not know $V(v)$ or $S(x)$, we can approximate $S(x)$ by taking the inverse Fourier transform of part of the noise in the recorded spectrum $E_w(v)$. The envelope of this interferogram is $S(x)$, as shown in Fig. 4.4. However, in all the cases the digitization interval Δv truncates the function $S(x)$ at $X = 1/2\Delta v$.

In Fourier transform spectroscopy the situation is simpler, because the function $S(x)$ is the weighting function applied to the recorded interferogram or only a boxcar function with a truncation point at $x = L_0$. If the aperture broadening is small compared to the truncation broadening,

$$S(x) = \mathcal{F}^{-1}\{V(v)\} \approx \mathcal{F}^{-1}\{W_0(v)\} \tag{4.18}$$

In the grating instruments, $S(x)$ is close to the absolute value of the

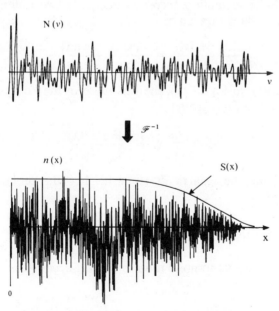

FIG. 4.4. Estimation of the noise transfer function.

electronic transfer function, typically a low-pass filter. However, a boxcar is a good approximation of $S(x)$ in this case.

A signal S, defined as a line height, is given by

$$
\begin{aligned}
E_{0w}(0) &= \mathcal{F}\{\mathcal{F}^{-1}\{W_0(v)\}\mathcal{F}^{-1}\{E_0(v)\}\}|_{v=0} \\
&= \int_{-\infty}^{\infty} \mathcal{F}^{-1}\{W_0(v)\}\mathcal{F}^{-1}\{E_0(v)\} \exp(i2\pi 0 x)\, dx \\
&= \int_{-\infty}^{\infty} \mathcal{F}^{-1}\{W_0(v)\}\mathcal{F}^{-1}\{E_0(v)\}\, dx \\
&= \int_{-\infty}^{\infty} A_0(x)I_0(x)\, dx
\end{aligned}
\tag{4.19}
$$

where

$$
A_0(x) = \mathcal{F}^{-1}\{W_0(v)\}, \qquad I_0(x) = \mathcal{F}^{-1}\{E_0(v)\}
\tag{4.20}
$$

Now we can express the signal-to-noise ratio of the recorded spectrum as

$$
\frac{S}{N} = \frac{E_{0w}(0)}{\sqrt{\overline{N_S^2}}} = \frac{\sqrt{v_m}}{\sqrt{n^2}} \frac{\int_{-\infty}^{\infty} A_0(x)I_0(x)\, dx}{\sqrt{\int_0^{\infty} S^2(x)\, dx}}
\tag{4.21}
$$

In Fourier self-deconvolution, according to Eq. (4.6), we multiply the signal and the noise in the x domain by

$$
\frac{\mathcal{F}^{-1}\{W(v)\}}{\mathcal{F}^{-1}\{E_{0w}(v)\}} = \frac{A(x)}{I_{0w}(x)} = \frac{A(x)}{A_0(x)I_0(x)}
\tag{4.22}
$$

Hence, according to Eq. (4.17), the rms noise in the Fourier self-deconvolved spectrum $E'(v)$ is given by

$$
\sqrt{\overline{N_S'^2}} = \frac{\sqrt{n^2}}{\sqrt{v_m}} \sqrt{\int_0^{\infty} \frac{A^2(x)S^2(x)}{A_0^2(x)I_0^2(x)}\, dx}
\tag{4.23}
$$

On the other hand, the signal in $E'(v)$ is the height of the smoothing function $W(v)$ expressed as

$$
W(0) = \int_{-\infty}^{\infty} A(x) \exp(i2\pi 0 x)\, dx = \int_{-\infty}^{\infty} A(x)\, dx
\tag{4.24}
$$

Accordingly, the signal-to-noise ratio in the self-deconvolved spectrum is given by

$$
(S/N)' = \frac{W(0)}{\sqrt{\overline{N_S'^2}}} = \frac{\sqrt{v_m}}{\sqrt{n^2}} \frac{\int_{-\infty}^{\infty} A(x)\, dx}{\sqrt{\int_0^{\infty} [A^2(x)S^2(x)/A_0^2(x)I_0^2(x)]\, dx}}
\tag{4.25}
$$

Now we can derive the ratio Q by which self-deconvolution decreases the signal-to-noise ratio. According to Eqs. (4.21) and (4.25), the general expression of Q is

$$Q = \frac{(S/N)'}{S/N} = \frac{\int_{-\infty}^{\infty} A(x)\, dx \sqrt{\int_0^{\infty} S^2(x)\, dx}}{\sqrt{\int_0^{\infty} [A^2(x)S^2(x)/A_0^2(x)I_0^2(x)]\, dx} \int_{-\infty}^{\infty} A_0(x)I_0(x)\, dx} \quad (4.26)$$

B. PRACTICAL FORMULAS

In this section we apply the general Eq. (4.26) to the case of a Lorentzian line shape

$$E_0(v) = \frac{\sigma_0/2\pi}{v^2 + (\sigma_0/2)^2} \quad (4.27)$$

when the instrumental resolution is much higher than the spectral resolution, that is, $\delta_0 \ll \sigma_0$ or $E_{0w}(v) \approx E_0(v)$. The Fourier transform of the line shape is

$$I_0(x) = \mathcal{F}^{-1}\{E_0(v)\} = \exp(-\sigma_0 \pi |x|) \quad (4.28)$$

Further, we assume

$$S(x) = A_0(x) = \begin{cases} 1, & |x| \le L_0 \\ 0, & |x| > L_0 \end{cases} \quad (4.29)$$

which is quite valid in Fourier transform spectra with boxcar weighting of the interferogram and very narrow aperture broadening; this is also a good approximation in grating spectra. Now, according to Eq. (4.26),

$$\begin{aligned} Q_0 &= \frac{(S/N)'}{S/N} = \frac{\int_{-\infty}^{\infty} A(x)\, dx \sqrt{L_0}}{\sqrt{\int_0^{\infty} A^2(x)I_0^{-2}(x)\, dx} \int_{-\infty}^{\infty} A_0(x)I_0(x)\, dx} \\ &\approx \frac{\pi\sqrt{1.207 K_0 \sigma_0/2} \cdot \int_0^{\infty} A(x)\, dx}{\sqrt{\int_0^{\infty} A^2(x)\exp(2\pi\sigma_0 x)\, dx}} \end{aligned} \quad (4.30)$$

where we assume the instrumental resolution to be so high that there is only very small distortion of the peak height; that is,

$$\int_{-\infty}^{\infty} A_0(x)I_0(x)\, dx = E_{0w}(0) \approx E_0(0) = \frac{2}{\pi\sigma_0} \quad (4.31)$$

$$K_0 = \frac{\sigma_{0w}}{\delta_0} \approx \frac{\sigma_0}{\delta_0} = \frac{\sigma_0}{1.207/2L_0} \quad (4.32)$$

The ratio Q_0 depends on $A(x)$, K_0, and $K = \sigma_{0w}/\delta \approx \sigma_0/\delta$, where δ is the half-width of $W(v) = \mathcal{F}\{A(x)\}$. This is clearly seen in the explicit form of Eq.

(4.30) for a triangular $A(x)$ given by

$$A(x) = \begin{cases} 1 - |x|/L, & |x| \le L \\ 0, & |x| > L \end{cases} \tag{4.33}$$

On the basis of the fact that $\delta = 1.772/2L$, the explicit form of Q_0 is given by

$$Q_0(K, K_0) = \frac{\pi\sqrt{1.207 \times 1.772 K K_0 T}}{4\sqrt{-1 + 2[-(1/T) + (1/T^2)(\exp T - 1)]}} \tag{4.34}$$

where $T = 1.772\pi K$ and $K < K_0$. If triangular weighting $[S(x)]$ is used in the computation of the original Fourier transform spectrum $E_w(\nu)$, we only need to replace 1.207 by 1.772/3 in Eqs. (4.30) and (4.34).

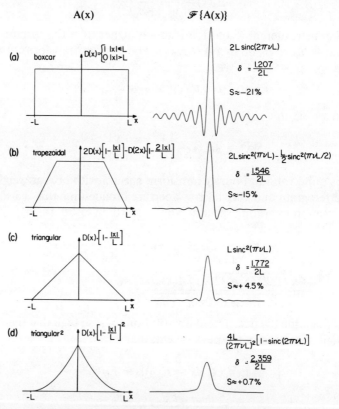

FIG. 4.5. The $A(x)$ functions (left-hand column) and the corresponding line-shape functions $\mathscr{F}\{A(x)\}$ (right-hand column) used in self-deconvolution. The half-width, $\delta = a/2L$, of the line-shape function and the relative magnitude s (%) of the strongest sidelobe of the line-shape function are listed in the right-hand column (Kauppinen et al., 1981b).

We have studied $Q_0(K, K_0)$ (Kauppinen *et al.*, 1981b) in the cases of the eight functions $A(x)$ shown in Fig. 4.5. The figure also shows the line-shape functions $W(v) = \mathcal{F}\{A(x)\}$ after Fourier self-deconvolution. Plots of Q_0 $(K, 5)$ versus K for the eight functions $A(x)$ are shown in Fig. 4.6 and listed in Table 4.1.

As is apparent from Eq. (4.30), any $Q_0(K, K_0)$ value can be obtained by the operation

$$Q_0(K, K_0) = (K_0/5)^{1/2} Q_0(K, 5) \qquad (4.35)$$

In practice, Table 4.1 can easily be used to estimate the signal-to-noise ratio $(S/N)'$ after Fourier self-deconvolution by multiplying the original signal-to-noise ratio S/N by the appropriate Q_0 value given in Table 4.1.

In the case of grating spectra with a good low-pass electronic filter, $S(x)$ is very close to a boxcar function and $A_0(x)$ is close to a triangular function.

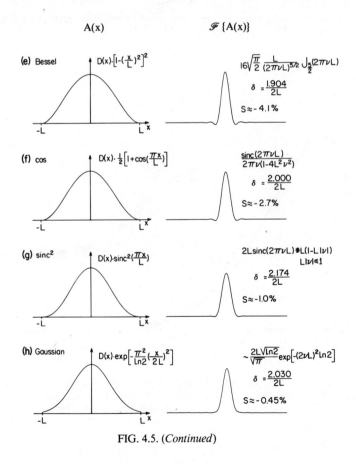

FIG. 4.5. (*Continued*)

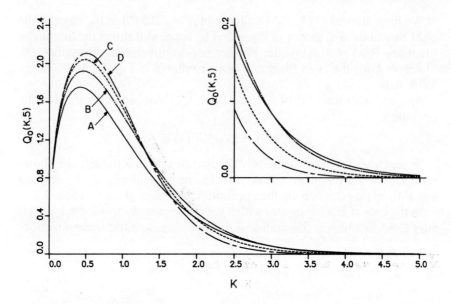

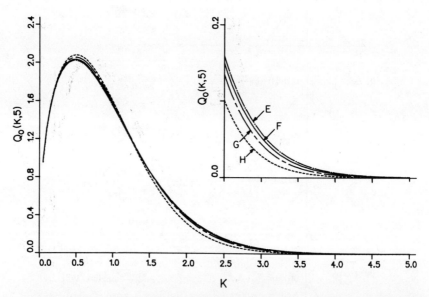

FIG. 4.6. $Q_0(K, 5)$ curves computed using Eq. (4.30) and the $A(x)$ functions shown in Fig. 4.5. Upper part—$A(x)$: A, boxcar; B, trapezoidal; C, triangular; D, triangular squared. Lower part—$A(x)$: E, Bessel; F, cos; G, sinc²; H, Gaussian (Kauppinen *et al.*, 1981b).

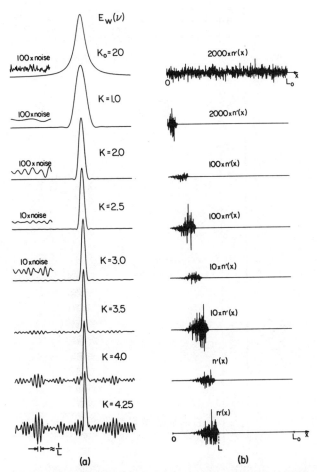

FIG. 4.7. (a) A Lorentzian line $E_w(\nu)$ (top) with random noise, $S/N \approx 2980$ and $K_0 = 20$, and self-deconvolved spectra with $K = 1.0, 2.0, 2.5, 3.0, 3.5, 4.0$, and 4.25 obtained using the sinc² function as $A(x)$. (b) The noise interferogram $n(x)$ (top) and the noise interferograms, $n'(x) = D(x) \cdot \text{sinc}^2(\pi x/L) \cdot \exp(\pi\sigma_0|x|)n(x)$, after self-deconvolution using the same parameters employed in (a). The source of the periodicity of about $1/L$ of the noise in (a) is clear from the noise interferograms $n'(x)$ (Kauppinen et al., 1981b).

Hence, we can use Table 4.1 on Eq. (4.30), if Eq. (4.31) is valid. In any case, however, we can use the general formula in Eq. (4.26).

The main difference between the Fourier transform and grating spectra is that in Fourier spectra $A_0(x)$ is usually applied to both the signal and the noise, whereas in the grating spectra $A_0(x)$ is applied to the signal and $S(x)$ (close to boxcar) to the noise.

TABLE 4.1.

Values of $Q_0(K,5)$ Computed Using Eq. (4.30) between $K = 0.5$ and 5.0 for the Eight Weighting Functions $A(x)$ Shown in Fig. 4.5[a]

K	Boxcar	Trapezoidal	Triangular	Triangular²	Bessel	Cos	Sinc²	Gaussian
0.5	1.74	1.92	2.04	2.11	2.02	2.04	2.05	2.08
0.6	1.68	1.88	2.01	2.08	1.99	2.00	2.02	2.05
0.7	1.59	1.80	1.93	2.01	1.91	1.93	1.95	1.98
0.8	1.49	1.70	1.82	1.90	1.81	1.82	1.85	1.87
0.9	1.37	1.59	1.69	1.76	1.68	1.70	1.72	1.74
1.0	1.26	1.46	1.54	1.60	1.55	1.56	1.58	1.59
1.1	1.14	1.33	1.39	1.43	1.40	1.41	1.43	1.43
1.2	1.02	1.21	1.24	1.26	1.26	1.27	1.28	1.27
1.3	0.917	1.09	1.10	1.09	1.12	1.13	1.13	1.11
1.4	0.816	0.968	0.957	0.935	0.986	0.989	0.990	0.962
1.5	0.723	0.859	0.830	0.790	0.862	0.861	0.858	0.820
1.6	0.638	0.757	0.713	0.661	0.747	0.744	0.737	0.692
1.7	0.560	0.663	0.609	0.546	0.643	0.637	0.627	0.578
1.8	0.491	0.578	0.516	0.447	0.549	0.542	0.529	0.477
1.9	0.428	0.502	0.435	0.363	0.467	0.458	0.443	0.390
2.0	0.373	0.434	0.365	0.292	0.394	0.385	0.369	0.317
2.1	0.324	0.373	0.305	0.233	0.331	0.322	0.305	0.255
2.2	0.281	0.320	0.253	0.185	0.277	0.267	0.250	0.204
2.3	0.243	0.274	0.209	0.146	0.231	0.221	0.204	0.162
2.4	0.210	0.233	0.173	0.114	0.191	0.182	0.166	0.128
2.5	0.181	0.198	0.142	0.0893	0.158	0.149	0.134	0.100

2.6	0.155	0.168	0.116	0.0694	0.130	0.122	0.108	0.0786
2.7	0.133	0.142	0.0947	0.0536	0.107	0.0988	0.0866	0.0612
2.8	0.115	0.120	0.0772	0.0413	0.0872	0.0801	0.0691	0.0475
2.9	0.0981	0.101	0.0626	0.0317	0.0711	0.0646	0.0549	0.0367
3.0	0.0840	0.0843	0.0508	0.0242	0.0578	0.0520	0.0435	0.0283
3.1	0.0718	0.0706	0.0410	0.0184	0.0468	0.0418	0.0343	0.0217
3.2	0.0613	0.0590	0.0331	0.0140	0.0379	0.0334	0.0270	0.0166
3.3	0.0523	0.0492	0.0267	0.0106	0.0306	0.0267	0.0212	0.0127
3.4	0.0446	0.0409	0.0214	0.00800	0.0246	0.0213	0.0166	0.00969
3.5	0.0380	0.0340	0.0172	0.00603	0.0198	0.0169	0.0129	0.00737
3.6	0.0323	0.0282	0.0138	0.00453	0.0158	0.0134	0.0100	0.00560
3.7	0.0275	0.0234	0.0110	0.00340	0.0127	0.0106	0.00779	0.00424
3.8	0.0233	0.0194	0.00878	0.00254	0.0101	0.00836	0.00603	0.00321
3.9	0.0198	0.0160	0.00701	0.00190	0.00805	0.00659	0.00465	0.00242
4.0	0.0168	0.0132	0.00558	0.00141	0.00640	0.00518	0.00359	0.00183
4.1	0.0143	0.0109	0.00444	0.00105	0.00508	0.00407	0.00276	0.00138
4.2	0.0121	0.00894	0.00352	0.000779	0.00403	0.00319	0.00212	0.00104
4.3	0.0102	0.00735	0.00280	0.000577	0.00319	0.00250	0.00162	0.000780
4.4	0.00866	0.00604	0.00222	0.000427	0.00252	0.00195	0.00124	0.000585
4.5	0.00734	0.00496	0.00176	0.000315	0.00199	0.00152	0.000947	0.000439
4.6	0.00620	0.00406	0.00139	0.000232	0.00157	0.00119	0.000721	0.000329
4.7	0.00524	0.00333	0.00110	0.000171	0.00124	0.000923	0.000549	0.000246
4.8	0.00443	0.00272	0.000867	0.000126	0.000974	0.000717	0.000418	0.000184
4.9	0.00374	0.00222	0.000684	0.0000924	0.000766	0.000556	0.000317	0.000138
5.0	0.00316	0.00182	0.000539	0.0000677	0.000601	0.000431	0.000240	0.000103

[a] From Kauppinen et al., 1981b.

215

In Fig. 4.6 the characteristic behavior of Q_0 when $K > 1.0$ is that it decreases rapidly and nonlinearly as a function of K. This is also demonstrated in Fig. 4.7 using the sinc² function as $A(x)$ and starting from a Lorentzian line with $K_0 = 20$, to which has been added random noise so that $S/N \approx 2980$. The spectrum $E_w(v)$ and the self-deconvolved spectra with $K = 1.0, 2.0, 2.5, 3.0, 3.5, 4.0,$ and 4.25 are shown in the left-hand column of Fig. 4.7. The signal-to-noise ratios $(S/N)'$, are 9280, 2440, 825, 266, 78.6, 22.6, and 11.4 for $K = 1.0, 2.0, 2.5, 3.0, 3.5, 4.0,$ and 4.25, respectively. These values are in good agreement with the values of 9420, 2200, 799, 259, 76.9, 21.4, and 11.1 calculated by multiplying $S/N = 2980$ by the corresponding Q_0 values (Eq. (4.35) and Table 4.1).

With high K values, Q_0 decreases nearly exponentially. This results from the dominance of the $[\int_0^\infty A^2(x) \exp(2\pi\sigma_0 x)\, dx]^{1/2}$ term in Eq. (4.30). This can be shown clearly in the case of a triangular $A(x)$ by using Eq. (4.34). With high K values

$$Q_0(K,K_0) \approx [(1.207\pi K_0)^{1/2} T^2/4\sqrt{2}] \exp(-T/2)$$

where $T = 1.772\pi K$.

It is evident in Fig. 4.7 that at high K values the noise is no longer random. Rather, those components having periodicities of about $1/L$ ($\approx \delta = a/2L$) dominate. The reason for this is apparent in the right-hand side of Fig. 4.7, which shows the interferograms of the noise following self-deconvolution, that is, multiplication by $D(x)$ sinc²$(\pi x/L)$ $\exp(\pi\sigma_0 |x|)$. After self-deconvolution the noise amplitude of the interferogram has a maximum just below L. This maximum results in periodicities of about $1/L$ in the noise of the self-deconvolved spectra.

Apart from the dependence of Q_0 on K, there is also a clear dependence on $A(x)$. At a fixed K in the range $0-2.5$, the extreme values of Q_0 only differ by a factor of about 2.2. At higher K the differences are much larger, being factors of about 4.6 at $K = 3$, 12 at $K = 4$, and 47 at $K = 5$ (Table 4.1). Hence, the higher K is, the more critical is the selection of $A(x)$. This dependence is illustrated in Fig. 4.8, where $E_w(v)$ from Fig. 4.7 has been self-deconvolved using $K = 4$ and each of the weighting functions $A(x)$, shown in Fig. 4.5. The difference of more than one order of magnitude between the results obtained with a triangular squared and a boxcar function is clearly shown. Also shown is the dominance of the strong sidelobes when boxcar weighting is used. Further, with high K values the signal-to-noise ratio $(S/N)'$ in the deconvolved spectrum is roughly proportional to the magnitude $|s|$ of the strongest sidelobe of $\mathcal{F}\{A(x)\}$ expressed as a percentage of the height of $\mathcal{F}\{A(x)\}$ in Fig. 4.5.

We find that the ratio

$$C = Q_0/|s| \tag{4.36}$$

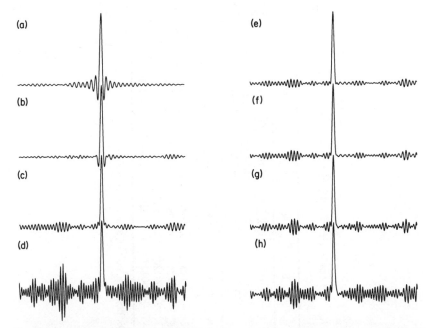

FIG. 4.8. Comparison of the effect of $A(x)$ on $(S/N)'$ starting from the spectrum $E_w(v)$ with $S/N \approx 2980$ shown in Fig. 4.7. The self-deconvolved spectra with $K = 4$ show significant differences in $(S/N)'$ depending on the $A(x)$ used: (a) boxcar; (b) trapezoidal, (c) triangular, (d) triangular squared, (e) Bessel, (f) cos, (g) sinc^2, (h) Gaussian. There is more than an order-of-magnitude difference in $(S/N)'$ between triangular squared and boxcar weighting (Kauppinen et al., 1981b).

is approximately constant. For example, at $K = 5$: $C_A = 0.015$, $C_B = 0.012$, $C_C = 0.012$, $C_D = 0.0097$, $C_E = 0.015$, $C_F = 0.016$, $C_G = 0.024$, and $C_H = 0.023$, where A–H refer to $A(x)$ in Fig. 4.5.

We have also measured experimentally (Kauppinen et al., 1981b) $Q_0(K, 20)$ values with $K = 1, 2, 3, 4,$ and 5 for the eight weighting functions $A(x)$ shown in Fig. 4.5. The results are given in Table 4.2, together with values predicted from Table 4.1 with the help of Eq. (4.35). The data show remarkable agreement, the maximum differences between observed and calculated $Q_0(K, 20)$ values being less than 10%. These differences are mainly due to small variations of the rms noise of the interferogram as a function of x_0 computed over a narrow region around x_0. This means that $(1/2L')\int_{x_0-L'}^{x_0+L'} n^2(x)\,dx$ is not constant when L' is a small fraction of the whole interferogram, and hence Eq. (4.16) is not completely valid.

The maximum practical K value, that is, maximum resolution enhancement, is approximately given by

$$K \geq \log_{10}(S/N). \qquad (4.37)$$

TABLE 4.2

THE OBSERVED AND CALCULATED VALUES OF $Q_0(K,20)$ WITH $K = 1-5$ FOR ALL EIGHT WEIGHTING FUNCTIONS $A(x)$ SHOWN IN FIG. 4.5[a,b]

K	$Q_0(K,20)$[c]	A	B	C	D	E	F	G	H
1	C	2.52	2.92	3.08	3.20	3.10	3.12	3.16	3.18
	O	2.41	2.77	3.04	3.09	2.94	3.02	3.10	3.18
2	C	0.746	0.868	0.730	0.584	0.788	0.770	0.738	0.634
	O	0.705	0.813	0.800	0.537	0.745	0.757	0.695	0.690
3	C	0.168	0.169	0.102	0.0484	0.116	0.104	0.0870	0.0566
	O	0.167	0.170	0.107	0.0485	0.119	0.107	0.0896	0.0619
4	C	0.0336	0.0264	0.0112	0.00282	0.0128	0.0104	0.00718	0.00366
	O	0.0356	0.0293	0.0109	0.00258	0.0126	0.0108	0.00771	0.00406
5	C	0.00632	0.00364	0.00108	0.000135	0.00120	0.000862	0.000480	0.000206
	O	0.00688	0.00386	0.00104	0.000143	0.00127	0.000859	0.000495	0.000210

[a] A, boxcar; B, trapezoidal; C, triangular; D, triangular squared; E, Bessel; F, cos; G, $sinc^2$; H, Gaussian.

[b] From Kauppinen et al., 1981b.

[c] C, calculated; O, observed.

For example, for S/N values of 10, 10^2, 10^3, 10^4, and 10^5 the maximum K values are 1, 2, 3, 4, and 5 which, with the Bessell function and $K_0 = 20$, give $(S/N)'$ values (from Table 4.2) of 31.0, 78.8, 116, 128, and 120, respectively.

As an example of the dependence of Q_0 on $A(x)$ in the case of a real spectrum we have self-deconvoluted the IR spectrum of chlorobenzene in the C–H stretching region. Figure 4.9 shows the results (Kauppinen *et al.,* 1981b) in the cases of the eight different weighting functions $A(x)$. The original spectrum $E_w(v)$ (top) was recorded with a DIGILAB FTS-11 Fourier transform spectrometer, with an instrumental resolution of about 1.2 cm^{-1} ($L_0 = 0.50$ cm) and with $(S/N) \approx 3000$. In self-deconvolution we used $\sigma_{0w} \approx \sigma_0 = 9.8$ cm^{-1} and $K = 4$ for all $A(x)$. We find there is more than one-order-of-magnitude difference between the signal-to-noise ratio obtained with boxcar and triangular squared weighting, and almost one-order-of-magnitude difference between trapezoidal and triangular squared

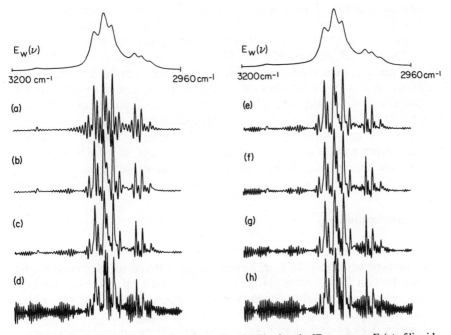

FIG. 4.9. Comparison of the effect of $A(x)$ on $(S/N)'$ using the IR spectrum $E_w(v)$ of liquid chlorobenzene in the C–H stretching region. The self-deconvolved spectra for all eight weighting functions, $A(x)$, were computed using $\sigma_{0w} \approx \sigma_0 = 9.8$ cm^{-1} and $K = 4$: (a) boxcar, (b) trapezoidal, (c) triangular, (d) triangular squared, (e) Bessel, (f) cos, (g) sinc^2, (h) Gaussian. The deconvolved spectra show that the half-widths of the lines differ since some lines indicate overdeconvolution, that is, negative sidelobes. The figure verifies a dependence of $(S/N)'$ on the weighting functions, $A(x)$, similar to that shown in Fig. 4.8 (Kauppinen *et al.,* 1981b).

weighting. Also, all signal-to-noise ratios $(S/N)'$ calculated using $(S/N) = 3000$ and $K_0 = 8$ (Eq. (4.35)) and the corresponding Q_0 values from Table 4.1 are in good agreement with the values derived from the self-deconvolved spectra. This figure shows that it is easy to reduce the spectral linewidth by a factor of 4 using a proper weighting function $A(x)$, in our Fourier self-deconvolution method.

4.4. Fourier Self-Deconvolution and Even-Order Derivatives

Another approach to resolution enhancement is the computation of the even-order derivatives of the recorded spectrum often used in spectroscopy. We have studied (Kauppinen *et al.*, 1981c) the computation of the first-order derivatives of spectra applying the Fourier transforms and demonstrated a few advantages of Fourier self-deconvolution compared with the derivative spectra. Figure 4.10 compares the even-order derivative and self-deconvolved spectra computed from a noisy Lorentzian line. As we can see, the second, fourth, and sixth derivatives result in the fixed K values of 2.7, 3.9, and 5.3, respectively, and in strong negative sidelobes of the fixed line shape. In Fourier self-deconvolution, however, both the K value and the line shape $W(v)$ are continuously selectable. Hence, we can eliminate the troublesome strong negative sidelobes of the line as shown in Fig. 4.10b. The signal-to-noise ratios $(S/N)'$ in all of the derivative and self-deconvolved spectra are approximately the same at the same K values. Hence, the signal-to-noise ratios of the derivative spectra change, as a function of K, in much the same way as do those of the self-deconvolved spectra.

4.5. Applications

The results presented in the preceding section demonstrate that the signal-to-noise ratio $(S/N)'$ in Fourier self-deconvolved spectra is highly dependent on K and, particularly at higher K values, on $A(x) = \mathcal{F}^{-1}\{W(v)\}$. The optimal combination depends on the purposes and criteria of application, and hence no general "optimal set" of conditions can be defined. However, we can outline an approach to performing Fourier self-deconvolution through the following steps:

(1) Estimate (S/N), σ_0, and $K_0 = \sigma_{0w}/\delta_0 = \sigma_0/\delta_0$ from the observed spectrum $E_w(v)$.

(2) Select the signal-to-noise ratio $(S/N)'$ required in the self-deconvolved spectrum $E'(v)$.

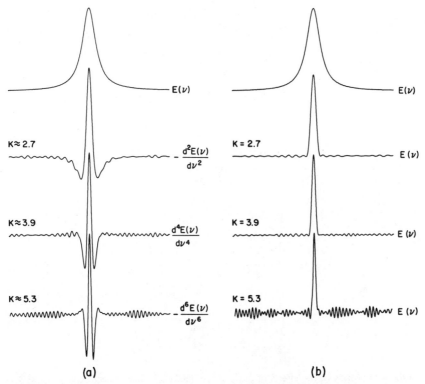

FIG. 4.10. Noise behavior in even-order derivation and self-deconvolution. (a) a Lorentz-ian line $E(v)$ with $(S/N) = 200$ and the second, fourth, and sixth derivatives of the Lorentzian lines with (S/N) of 200, 2000, and 20,000, respectively. (b) Self-deconvolved spectra of the corresponding noisy Lorentzian lines when using K values 2.7, 3.9, and 5.3 (Kauppinen *et al.*, 1981c). Reprinted with permission, Copyright © 1981 American Chemical Society.

(3) Select $A(x)$ (in Fig. 4.5 A, B, C, . . .) so that the strongest sidelobe of $\mathscr{F}\{A(x)\} = W(v)$ will be approximately equal to the peak-to-peak value of the noise in the self-deconvolved spectrum; that is,

$$(S/N)' \approx 1/|s| \qquad (4.38)$$

(4) Find K so that [Eq. (4.35)]

$$Q_0 = \frac{(S/N)'}{S/N} = \left(\frac{K_0}{5}\right)^{1/2} Q_0(K, 5) \qquad (4.39)$$

where $Q_0(K, 5)$ is the values of Q_0 in Table 4.1 in the column of the selected $A(x)$.

(5) According to Eq. (4.10), the derived K value defines the truncation

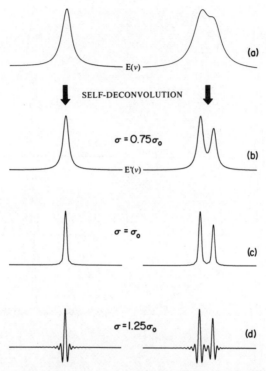

FIG. 4.11. Study of the effects of an incorrect half-width in self-deconvolution. (a) The spectra shown in Figs. 4.2a and 4.3a are deconvolved using triangular squared weighting and $L = 0.8$ cm. (b) Deconvolution with a 25% underestimation of the half-width. (c) Deconvolution with the correct half-width. (d) Deconvolution with a 25% overestimation of the half-width (Kauppinen *et al.*, 1981a).

point L in $A(x)$ with the help of the following equation (see Fig. 4.5):

$$K \approx \frac{\sigma_0}{\delta} = \frac{\sigma_0}{a/2L} = \frac{2L\sigma_0}{a} \qquad (4.40)$$

An alternative approach to steps (4) and (5) is to increase K stepwise, starting from a low K value, until the desired condition is achieved. A good example of this procedure is the left-hand side of Fig. 4.7.

The only parameter that might be difficult to estimate from the observed spectrum is the half-width σ_0. If there exists a single line in the observed spectrum, we can measure the half-width σ_{0w} of this line and use it as σ_0. This is a good approximation when the instrumental resolution is high ($K \ll K_0$). However, the main purpose of Fourier self-deconvolution is its application to overlapped bands or lines. In this case the correct value of σ_0 can be determined from a series of spectra resulting from self-deconvolution with small K and with Lorentzian shapes having different half-widths (σ_0). Underestimation of the half-width σ_0 results in a self-deconvolved spectrum which still has a line shape close to the Lorentzian and a resolution lower than that predicted on the basis of the K value. On the other hand, overestimation of σ_0 results in large negative sidelobes and a slightly higher resolution. We can illustrate this by using the spectra in Figs. 4.2a and 4.3a, both of which have a half-width σ_0 of 8 cm^{-1}. In Fig. 4.11 we show the results of self-deconvolution with 0.75 σ_0 (Fig. 4.11b), with σ_0 (Fig. 4.11c), and with 1.25 σ_0 (Fig. 4.11d). The weighting function was triangular squared with $L = 0.8$ cm.

Experimentally, we frequently encounter cases where the half-widths differ. In such cases we self-deconvolve with a Lorentzian line corresponding to the narrowest line, thus avoiding the effects of overdeconvolution shown in Fig. 4.11. However, it is not very serious to use a slightly incorrect half-width in Fourier self-deconvolution, because only the line shape after self-deconvolution is different from the theoretical one, $W(v) = \mathcal{F}\{A(x)\}$. There are no distortions in the integrated intensity and frequency of the lines due to the incorrect half-width.

Figure 4.12 shows an example of Fourier self-deconvolution in practice.

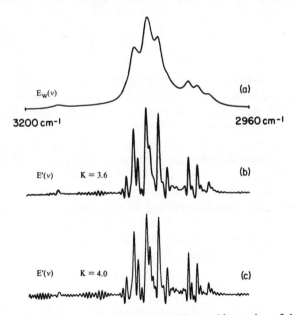

FIG. 4.12. Fourier self-deconvolution of the C–H stretching region of the spectrum of chlorobenzene with a 9.8-cm^{-1}-wide Lorentzian line. (a) Experimental spectrum with an instrumental resolution of 1.2 cm^{-1} and a signal-to-noise ratio S/N of about 3000. (b) Self-deconvolved spectrum with a Bessel-type weighting function and $K = 3.6$. (c) Self-deconvolved spectrum with a Bessel-type $A(x)$ and $K = 4$.

In Fig. 4.12a we show the real spectrum $E_w(v)$ of chlorobenzene in the C–H stretching region. This spectrum is the same as in Fig. 4.9, and it has been recorded with a DIGILAB FTS-11 Fourier transform spectrometer with an instrumental resolution of about 1.2 cm^{-1} ($L_0 = 0.50$ cm) and $S/N \approx 3000$. Fourier self-deconvolution was performed as explained in steps (1)–(5). We assume a Lorentzian line shape and estimated $\sigma_0 = 9.8$ cm^{-1}, giving $K_0 \approx \sigma_0/\delta_0 \approx 9.8/1.2 = 8.2$. We self-deconvolved the observed spectrum $E_w(v)$ with two different K values using a Bessel-type weighting function $A(x)$ shown in Fig. 4.5e. In Fig. 4.12b we see the case in which the truncation point L in $A(x)$ is 0.35 cm. Hence, according to Eq. (4.40), we obtain $K = 2L\sigma_0/1.904 \approx 3.6$, and according to Eq. (4.39) the signal-to-noise ratio

$$(S/N)' = (S/N)(K_0/5)^{1/2}Q_0(K,5)$$

$$= 3000(8.2/5)^{1/2}0.0158 \approx 61$$

which is in good agreement with $(S/N)'$ measured from Fig. 4.12b. Figure 4.12c shows the result of Fourier self-deconvolution when the truncation point L in $A(x)$ is 0.39 cm. Now the calculated values of K and $(S/N)'$ are 4.0 and 25, respectively. This is an optimal case when a Bessel-type $A(x)$ is used.

Next we introduce a few applications of the Fourier self-deconvolution technique.

A. PURE MATERIALS

As shown in the two experimental examples, self-deconvolution of a band contour in a condensed-phase spectrum permits the determination of the positions and integrated intensities of the component bands, and the identification of bands not evident in the unresolved spectra.

When using the self-deconvolution method with gas-phase spectra, it is possible to improve the effective spectral resolution beyond the Doppler limit (e.g., using conventional methods: Pliva *et al.*, 1980; Pliva and Pine, 1982), provided that the instrumental resolution is higher than the Doppler width. In such cases the self-deconvolution technique is particularly easy to apply, as all lines in Doppler-limited spectra have approximately the same half-width. This width can usually be explicitly determined from the spectrum or estimated on the basis of theory.

B. MIXTURES

Self-deconvolution of the spectrum of a mixture may, at a minimum, permit the identification of the frequencies of the component bands and hence the components. With conditions under which the bandwidths are similar in magnitude, the degree of improvement of spectral resolution may be sufficient to determine the percentage of each component in the mixture directly, using the integrated band intensities and reference values from spectra of pure samples.

C. BAND FITTING

Self-deconvolution permits one to place a realistic value on the maximum number of bands (lines) that can be fitted to a contour and obtain initial estimates of the peak positions, relative intensities, and half-widths. The user may then constrain parameters within appropriate limits or check the final result to ensure that the values obtained are consistent with the result obtained by self-deconvolution.

We made a test to confirm the result of self-deconvolution. We measured manually the peak heights and frequencies of all the lines stronger than the noise level in Fig. 4.12c. After that we added all the observed lines replaced by Lorentzian lines 9.8 cm^{-1} wide, resulting in the spectrum which was very close to $E_w(v)$ in Fig. 4.12a, with an uncertainty less than the noise level in $E_w(v)$. Fourier self-deconvolution includes no assumption concerning the number of lines in a spectrum, while in band fitting such an assumption is required. This is the most important advantage of Fourier self-deconvolution compared with band fitting.

D. PARAMETER-DEPENDENT STUDIES

Frequently, it is of value to study the behavior of a system as a function of an external parameter such as temperature, pressure, concentration, or solvent. The spectral changes are often subtle, and if bands are overlapped, it is by no means clear whether the changes result from variations in frequency, half-width, intensity, or a combination of these factors. Self-deconvolution of a series of spectra can resolve this problem. For example, while studying the thermotropic behavior of lipids, we observed changes in the complex carbonyl stretching band. We were able to determine (Cameron *et al.*, 1983) that the band has three strong components, none of which was instrumentally resolvable, and that as the temperature is varied, the components change in both intensity and frequency.

E. BAND SEPARATION

Finally, we introduce an intriguing application of self-deconvolution. From the self-deconvolved spectrum we can separate a single line and carry out the inverse process on this line or on the residual spectrum, that is,

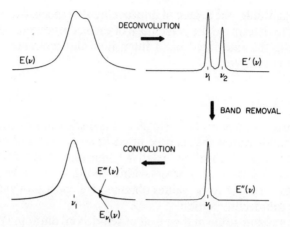

FIG. 4.13. Illustration of the band-separation procedure. The original $[E(v)]$ and self-deconvolved $[E'(v)]$ spectra are those shown in Fig. 4.2a. E''' results from convolution of $E''(v)$ with the original deconvolution function. Superimposed on $E'''(v)$ is $E_{v_1}(v) = [\sigma_0/2\pi]/[(\sigma_0/2)^2 + (v - v_1)^2]$, the line used in the generation of $E(v)$ (Kauppinen *et al.*, 1981a).

convolution with the deconvolution function. The result is the original line or spectrum no longer overlapped, even if the line shape used in the deconvolution is not the true line shape.

In Fig. 4.13 we show a simulation study of this process, using the observed spectrum $E(v)$ shown in Fig. 4.2a. First we deconvolve the spectrum by multiplying the corresponding interferogram by $[1 - (|x|/L)]^2 \exp(\sigma_0\pi|x|)$ and then transforming back to $E'(v)$. We then remove the line at v_2 and obtain $E''(v)$, that is, a single line at v_1. We then convolve $E''(v)$ with the original deconvolution function by multiplying the corresponding interferogram by $1/[1 - (|x|/L)]^2 \exp(\sigma_0\pi|x|)$, and obtain the spectrum $E'''(v)$ by taking the Fourier transform of the result.

Superimposed on $E'''(v)$ is shown the original Lorentzian $E_{v_1}(v)$ used in generating $E(v)$. There is a very good correspondence except for slight differences in the region where the band removal was carried out.

F. CONVENTIONAL DECONVOLUTION AND OTHER APPLICATIONS OF FOURIER TRANSFORMS

Fourier transforms are very useful in several modes of processing spectral data (Kauppinen *et al.*, 1981d). Usually the process can be expressed by the following equation:

$$E'(v) = \mathcal{F}\{B(x)\mathcal{F}^{-1}\{E_w(v)\}\} \tag{4.41}$$

where we can find the following operation between $E_w(v)$ and $E'(v)$:

(1) *Fourier self-deconvolution with $E_{0w}(v)$ and smoothing with $\mathcal{F}\{A(x)\} = W(v)$, if*

$$B(x) = A(x)/\mathcal{F}^{-1}\{E_{0w}(v)\} \tag{4.42}$$

(2) *Smoothing (Kauppinen et al., 1982) with $\mathcal{F}\{A(x)\} = W(v)$, if*

$$B(x) = A(x) \tag{4.43}$$

(3) *Derivation (kth order) and smoothing (Kauppinen et al., 1982), if*

$$B(x) = A(x)(2\pi i x)^k \tag{4.44}$$

(4) *Deconvolution with the instrumental function $W_0(v)$ and smoothing with $\mathcal{F}\{A(x)\} = W(v)$ (e.g., Jansson et al., 1970; Halsey and Blass, 1977; Braund et al., 1980), if*

$$B(x) = A(x)/\mathcal{F}^{-1}\{W_0(v)\} \tag{4.45}$$

This is the case in which the instrumental resolution is low ($\delta_0 \gtrsim \sigma_0$) and the instrument function $W_0(v)$ strongly distorts the recorded spectrum. In practice, it is useful to apply weak smoothing, for example, a boxcar $A(x)$ with a very large truncation point L, in order to keep $|B(x)| < \infty$.

We must bear in mind that deconvolution does not work correctly in all cases. For example, if there is a region in the Fourier domain where $\mathcal{F}^{-1}\{W_0(v)\} = A_0(x) = 0$, then $|B(x)| \rightarrow \infty$ and the computation of deconvolution fails. In the region where $A_0(x) = 0$ in convolution, the signal (information) is multiplied by zero, which means that we loose the signal completely and there is no way to get the information back. This is demonstrated in Fig. 4.14, where the instrumental function $W_0(v)$ is a sinc^2 function, which is valid in grating instruments with very narrow slits. As we see, the gratings truncate the signal at $x = L$ in the Fourier domain. In the case of a real spectrum, there exists a noise interferogram $n(x)$ in the region where $x > L$. In order to prevent an infinite (boundless) increase of the noise in deconvolution, where $n'(x) = n(x)/A_0(x)$ and $A_0(x) = 0$ when $x > L$, we must use smoothing by $A(x)$, which truncates the noise at $x = L$. Usually our aim in deconvolution is to compute $E_0(v)$ from $E_{0w}(v)$, but now, owing to the truncation of $A_0(x)$, the result is $E'(v) = 2L \ \text{sinc}(2\pi v L) * E_0(v)$ instead of $E_0(v)$. However, $E'(v)$ is much closer to $E_0(v)$ than $E_{0w}(v)$; for example, the relative distortions (Kauppinen et al., 1982) of peak heights in $E_{0w}(v)$ and $E'(v)$ are -34 and -15%, respectively.

Another good example of a case in which neither deconvolution nor self-deconvolution work correctly is truncation of the recorded interferogram in Fourier transform spectroscopy. The instrument function $W_0(v)$ is

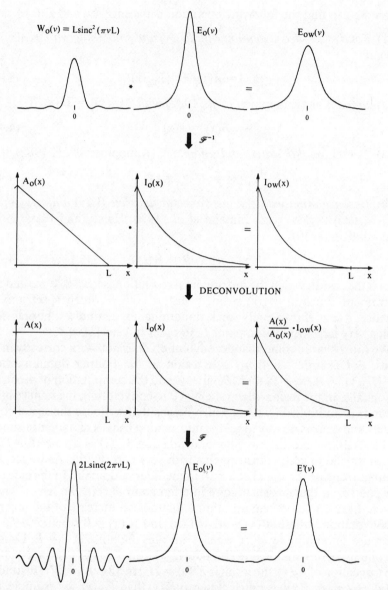

FIG. 4.14. Demonstration of a case in which deconvolution with an $L\,\mathrm{sinc}^2(\pi\nu L)$ function fails. The result is $2L\,\mathrm{sinc}(2\pi\nu L) * E_0(\nu)$ instead of $E_0(\nu)$.

now $2L_0 \text{ sinc}(2\pi vL_0)$, that is, the Fourier transform of a boxcar weighting function with the truncation point at $x = L_0$. This is valid if the aperture broadening is small. Consequently, deconvolution with the instrument function $2L_0 \text{ sinc}(2\pi vL_0)$ does not work in Fourier transform spectroscopy. But Fourier self-deconvolution works correctly up to a resolution of about $1.2/2L_0 = \delta_0$. However, overdeconvolution (see Fig. 4.11d) gives a slightly narrower line with very strong negative sidelobes. In other words, one cannot compute the spectrum with a resolution higher than the instrumental resolution in Fourier transform spectroscopy.

G. Fourier Complex Self-Deconvolution

Fourier complex self-deconvolution (Kauppinen and Moffatt, 1983) is self-deconvolution where the line shape function $E_{0w}(v)$ can be asymmetric and more complicated than in self-deconvolution. However, the line shape $W(v)$ after complex self-deconvolution is symmetric, as demonstrated in Fig. 4.15. In complex self-deconvolution in Eq. (4.6) we have

$$\mathcal{F}^{-1}\{E_{0w}(v)\} = \text{Re}(x) + i\,\text{Im}(x) \qquad (4.46)$$

where $\text{Re}(x)$ and $\text{Im}(x)$ are the real and imaginary parts of $\mathcal{F}^{-1}\{E_{0w}(v)\}$, respectively. Hence the method is based on the equation

$$E'(v) = \mathcal{F}\left\{ \frac{[\text{Re}(x) - i\,\text{Im}(x)]\,\mathcal{F}^{-1}\{W(v)\}}{[\text{Re}(x)]^2 + [\text{Im}(x)]^2}\mathcal{F}^{-1}\{E_w(v)\} \right\} \qquad (4.47)$$

We find that there is complex weighting in the Fourier domain resulting in a complex interferogram $I'(x)$, which gives a real spectrum

$$E'(v) = \mathcal{F}\{I'(x)\}$$

An example of this method is shown in Fig. 4.16. The line shape $E_{0w}(v)$ of the synthesized noisy spectrum $E_w(v)$ consists of three partly overlapped

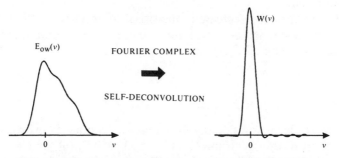

FIG. 4.15. Basic operation in Fourier complex self-deconvolution.

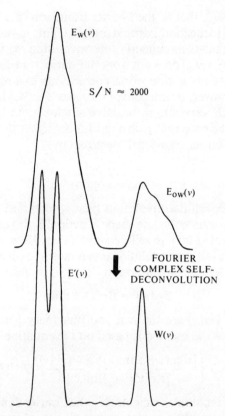

FIG. 4.16. Simulation example of Fourier complex self-deconvolution. Spectrum $E_w(v)$ consists of three lines with the shape of $E_{0w}(v)$.

Lorentzian lines. The spectrum $E_w(v)$ has been synthesized so that there are three "lines" with the shape of $E_{0w}(v)$ and two of them are overlapped. However, after Fourier complex self-deconvolution all three "lines" are clearly resolved.

The behavior of the decrease of the signal-to-noise-ratio $(S/N)'$ is quite similar to the case in self-deconvolution. Hence, the most prominent feature is the rapid decrease of $(S/N)'$ as a function of K.

4.6. Summary

Fourier self-deconvolution involves a multiplication of the inverse Fourier transform of the spectrum $E_w(v)$ by $A(x)/\mathscr{F}^{-1}\{E_{0w}(v)\}$ and the Fourier transform back to the spectrum $E'(v)$. The multiplication by $1/\mathscr{F}^{-1}\{E_{0w}(v)\}$

results in self-deconvolution, and $A(x)$ determines the line-shape function $W(v) = \mathcal{F}\{A(x)\}$ in $E'(v)$. The key to a successful application of this method is the successful determination of these two factors.

The line-shape function $E_{0w}(v)$ çan be empirically determined from the spectrum $E_w(v)$, or it is approximately $E_0(v)$, which is known on the basis of the theory. In several cases $E_0(v)$ can be approximated by a Lorentzian line with a half-width determined empirically.

The control of the line shape through $A(x)$ is equally critical. By selecting a satisfactory line shape $\mathcal{F}\{A(x)\}$, we avoid strong negative sidelobes which have plagued many of the previous attempts at deconvolution. We then control the noise and the spectral resolution, that is, $(S/N)'$ and K, by selecting the truncation point L in $A(x)$. These two choices result in a decrease of the intensity information [since $S/N > (S/N)'$] and an increase of frequency information (since $K > 1$). The amount of information does not change in self-deconvolution.

In practice, the degree of resolution enhancement that can be achieved is limited by a few factors. In the case in which $\mathcal{F}^{-1}\{W_0(v)\}$ and $\mathcal{F}^{-1}\{E_0(v)\}$ are positive throughout the Fourier domain, there are two practical limits in self-deconvolution and deconvolution. These are as follows: *the signal-to-noise ratio (S/N),* which limits the maximum practical K value $[\approx \log_{10}(S/N)]$ or truncates at $x = L$ in $A(x)$ and *an encoding interval Δv* in digitization of the spectrum. This truncates the signal in the Fourier domain at $X = 1/2\Delta v$. Thus the narrowest possible line after self-deconvolution or deconvolution is $2X \operatorname{sinc}(2\pi vX)$ with a half-width of $\approx 0.6/X$. If one of the functions $\mathcal{F}^{-1}\{W_0(v)\}$ and $\mathcal{F}^{-1}\{E_0(v)\}$ is zero in the Fourier domain when $x > X_0$, *this truncation limits* the half-width of the narrowest possible line to the value of $0.6/X_0$ via convolution with $2X_0 \operatorname{sinc}(2\pi vX_0)$ in the same way as shown in Fig. 4.14. Since truncation takes place in all three of these limits, the practical limit is precisely the one that gives the smallest truncation point (L, X, X_0) or the widest sinc function.

Finally, it might be emphasized that this Fourier self-deconvolution technique is generally applicable to any spectrum (IR, UV-visible, fluorescence, Raman, NMR, etc.). In most of the practical spectra the lowest limit is caused by the noise $[K = \log_{10}(S/N)]$, which is controlled via smoothing with $\mathcal{F}\{A(x)\}$. Thus, the most important key to a successful application of Fourier self-deconvolution is an optimal selection of $A(x)$.

ACKNOWLEDGMENTS

I warmly thank Mr. V. M. Horneman for his assistance in the preparation of the figures. I am also grateful to the Academy of Finland for the financial support.

REFERENCES

Betty, K. R., and Horlick, G. (1976). *Appl. Spectrosc.* **30**, 23.
Bracewell, R. M. (1965). "The Fourier Transform and Its Applications." McGraw-Hill, New York.
Braund, D. B., Cole, A. R. H., Cugley, J. A., Honey, F. R., Pulfrey, R. E., and Reece, G. D. (1980). *Appl. Opt.* **19**, 2146.
Cameron, D. G., Kauppinen, J. K., Casal, H. H., and Mantsch, H. H. (1983). To be published.
Ferrige, A. G., and Lindon, J. C. (1978). *J. Magn. Reson.* **31**, 337.
Halsey, G., and Blass, W. E. (1977). *Appl. Opt.* **16**, 286.
Jansson, P. A., Hunt, R. H., and Plyter, E. K. (1970). *J. Opt. Soc. Am.* **60**, 596.
Jones, R. N., Venkataraghavan, R., and Hopkins, J. W. (1967). *Spectrochim. Acta Part A* **23A**, 925, 941.
Kauppinen, J. K., and Moffatt, D. J. (1983). To be published.
Kauppinen, J. K., Moffatt, D. J., Mantsch, H. H., and Cameron, D. G. (1981a). *Appl. Spectrosc.* **35**, 271.
Kauppinen, J. K., Moffatt, D. J., Cameron, D. G., and Mantsch, H. H. (1981b). *Appl. Opt.* **20**, 1866.
Kauppinen, J. K., Moffatt, D. J., Mantsch, H. H., and Cameron, D. G. (1981c). *Anal. Chem.* **53**, 1454.
Kauppinen, J. K., Moffatt, D. J., Mantsch, H. H., and Cameron, D. G. (1981d). *High Resolut. Mol. Spectrosc., Colloq., 7th, 1981* Paper C3.
Kauppinen, J. K., Moffatt, D. J., Mantsch, H. H., and Cameron, D. G. (1982). *Appl. Opt.* **21**, 1866.
King, J., and Bower, D. I. (1980). *C.R.—Conf. Int. Spectrosc. Raman, 7th, 1980* pp. 242–243.
Pliva, J., and Pine, A. S. (1982). *J. Mol. Spectrosc.* **93**, 209.
Pliva, J., Pine, A. S., and Willson, P. D. (1980). *Appl. Opt.* **19**, 1833.
Van Cittert, P. H. (1931). *Z. Phys.* **69**, 298.

Chapter **5**

Improved Resolution of Spectral Lines Using Minimum Negativity and Other Constraints

SAMUEL J. HOWARD*

DEPARTMENT OF PHYSICS
THE FLORIDA STATE UNIVERSITY
TALLAHASSEE, FLORIDA

---

* Present address: Code 332, NORDA, NSTL Station, Mississippi 39529.

SPECTROMETRIC TECHNIQUES, VOL. III

5.1. Introduction

It is desirable to display experimental data in a form most easily interpreted by the human observer. Also, a different form may provide easier comparison or more convenient mathematical manipulation and a simpler theoretical treatment. For these reasons, further processing of experimental data is becoming a commonplace procedure in most laboratories. The researcher is most often interested in only a few parameters of the data and would like a clear and unambiguous display of those quantities. To satisfy these needs, the form of the recorded data usually must be altered in such a way that the informational content of the data is not unduly affected. Some particular "altered forms" that the reader is probably already familiar with are the Fourier transform, the Laplace transform, contrast and edge enhancement, differentiation of the data, and smoothing. The particular transform or operation applied is chosen according to the aspect which is to be emphasized.

To give an important example of the advantages of a different form of the data, consider the infrared (IR) spectral lines obtained from Fourier transform spectroscopy (FTS) data. Only limited interpretation is allowed for the interferogram taken with a Michelson interferometer. One cannot locate or measure in any quantitative fashion the electromagnetic spectral components until the Fourier transform is taken to separate out the various components into distinct "lines."

Another important example concerns the pictures taken of the earth from satellites, such as the LANDSAT data. One of the major goals of scientists is the discerning of various features on the earth's surface (such as forest, crops, desert, ocean, ice). Ways of differentiating these features automatically by pattern recognition techniques is one focus of current research. The quantitative comparison of many of the features of interest is often greatly facilitated by the taking of some data transform, the Fourier transform being one example. Edge enhancement is also helpful for the emphasis of certain features in these types of data.

Apodization is another example of form alteration that is often applied to spectroscopy data. The purpose of apodization is to remove the ambiguity in electromagnetic spectral lines. Many artifacts around spectral lines, such as sidelobes or "ringing," often extend a considerable distance away from each of these sharply peaked functions to overlap with adjacent sharply peaked lines. Apodization is effective in removing the artifacts but has the disadvantage of broadening the lines. The spectral lines often represent physically discrete components. When these discrete components are not closely spaced, apodization yields a less ambiguous result on the whole. The location and intensity of each individual line can be more accurately measured.

Resolution improvement is another type of form alteration that is effective in separating merged spectral lines, thereby also removing much of the ambiguity in spectral quantities. (Note that resolution improvement often involves the bringing in of additional information, as well as the altering of the form of the present data.) Resolution improvement is more fully discussed in succeeding sections.

Other than the difficulty of clearly displaying the desired information in the data, there are operations that occur naturally when recording the data that have the effect of reducing the information in the data. This results in the introduction of "deviations" from the true values of the quantity of interest and lead to "experimental error." The errors not only have the effect of "hiding" the quantities in the data desired to be observed, but also render ineffective many possible mathematical operations or transformations by introducing much larger errors into the output.

It is the nature of our physical world that the deviations imposed on the recorded data have a component described as *random*. Much of this component can be traced to the thermodynamic nature of our physical world, in which every bit of matter in the universe, including ourselves, is made up of very small discrete subunits called atoms; it is the inherent property of these atoms (and combinations of them known as molecules), when taken as a group, to move and bounce around in a random fashion because of the independence of their motions.

The other component of the error is often described as *systematic*. Many systematic errors have the fortunate property of being correctable quantitatively when they are known, or if there is some prior knowledge of how they come about, as opposed to the random component, which can only be ameliorated by "averaging" processes. Many of the degradation processes that affect images and most recorded data are classified as systematic errors. For many of these cases the error may be expressed as a function known as the *impulse response function*. Much mathematical theory has been devoted to the description of this function and to correction of the degradation due to its influence. A model common to degradation of nearly all recorded data and based on convolution with the impulse response function and superimposed random fluctuations (known generically as *noise*) is presented. This model forms the basis of nearly all restoration problems, and in this work it is applied to the improvement of IR spectroscopy data.

Systematic errors cannot be discussed generally, as most are peculiar to a particular experiment or its related apparatus. However, random or *statistical* phenomena are common to nearly all experimental data and have generated a large body of mathematical theory, from which we draw occasionally. Random or statistical measurements cannot be treated quantitatively but must be discussed in terms of "probabilities." For this reason, exact solutions cannot be obtained in the presence of random noise, only those that are "most probable." Thus optimal solutions must be based on statistical criteria.

5.2. The Fourier Transform

Because of its interpretation and the simplicity of many mathematical expressions of physical processes under the Fourier transform, Fourier analysis is an important tool in the scientists's arsenal. The interpretation of the values given by the Fourier transform as the amplitudes of sinusoidal waves of varying frequencies is very important to the development of optics and quantum mechanics.

The Fourier transform of a function of a single variable, let us say x, is indicated by $\mathcal{F}\{f(x)\}$ and is defined as

$$\mathcal{F}\{f(x)\} \equiv \int_{-\infty}^{\infty} f(x)e^{-i2\pi\omega x}\,dx = F(\omega) \qquad (5.1)$$

where $i = (-1)^{1/2}$. The inverse Fourier transform, indicated by $\mathcal{F}^{-1}\{F(\omega)\}$, is defined as

$$\mathcal{F}^{-1}\{F(\omega)\} \equiv \int_{-\infty}^{\infty} F(\omega)e^{i2\pi\omega x}\,d\omega = f(x) \qquad (5.2)$$

To be transformable, it is only necessary that $f(x)$ be piecewise continuous and integrable. In the notation convention customarily used, lowercase letters denote the function and capital letters denote its Fourier transform. To give a brief synopsis of customary terminology: The Fourier transform of the data is often called its *Fourier spectrum*." Also, x is often referred to as the *spatial variable* and ω the *frequency*.

From a strictly mathematical viewpoint, the Fourier transform may be considered as simply another way of expressing the data, with one function replaced by a different function. In its discrete form, the Fourier transform replaces N independent pieces of information by N other independent pieces of information. The only important consideration is that no information is lost in the transformation. This may be proved by substituting Eq. (5.1) into Eq. (5.2) and simplifying. [Let primes denote the variable of integration in

Eq. (5.1) to avoid confusion.] This gives

$$f(x) = \int_{-\infty}^{\infty} \left[\int_{-\infty}^{\infty} f(x')e^{-i2\pi\omega x'} \, dx' \right] e^{i2\pi\omega x} \, d\omega \tag{5.3}$$

Assuming that the order of integration may be changed, we have

$$f(x) = \int_{-\infty}^{\infty} f(x') \, dx' \int_{-\infty}^{\infty} e^{i2\pi\omega(x-x')} \, d\omega \tag{5.4}$$

The integral on the right is not well defined, as the complex exponential contains oscillatory terms that extend to infinity unchanging instead of decreasing to zero. In mathematical parlance, it is not "square integrable." To evaluate this, and to do so in such a way as to provide insight into the problem, we first determine the integral with finite limits and then let the limits approach infinity to see what form the results will take. For finite limits we have

$$\int_{-L}^{L} e^{i2\pi\omega(x-x')} \, d\omega = \frac{1}{i2\pi(x-x')} [e^{i2\pi\omega(x-x')}]_{-L}^{L}$$

$$= \frac{1}{i2\pi(x-x')} [e^{i2\pi(x-x')L} - e^{-i2\pi(x-x')L}] \tag{5.5}$$

This in turn may be written

$$\int_{-L}^{L} e^{i2\pi\omega(x-x')} \, d\omega = \frac{1}{\pi(x-x')} \sin 2\pi(x-x')L$$

$$= 2L \frac{\sin 2\pi(x-x')L}{2\pi(x-x')L} \tag{5.6}$$

from the definition of the complex exponential. This may also be written

$$\int_{-L}^{L} e^{i2\pi\omega(x-x')} \, d\omega = 2L \operatorname{sinc} 2(x-x')L \tag{5.7}$$

The final result follows from the definition of the sinc function. For the general variable y,

$$\operatorname{sinc} y \equiv \sin \pi y / \pi y \tag{5.8}$$

The general functional form of the sinc function is shown in Fig. 5.1. Now when L approaches infinity, the total function above becomes higher and narrower, and approaches the spike function:

$$\delta(x-x') = \begin{cases} 0, & x \neq x' \\ \infty, & x = x' \end{cases} \tag{5.9}$$

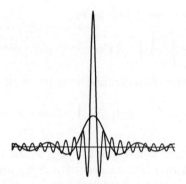

FIG. 5.1. Sinc function: The plots of the function $2L$ sinc($2Lx$) for two different values of L.

However, note the following property of our particular function as we integrate over it with the variable x':

$$\int_{-\infty}^{\infty} 2L \text{ sinc } 2(x - x') \, dx' = \int_{-\infty}^{\infty} \text{sinc } 2(x - x')L \, d[2L(x - x')] \quad (5.10)$$

On changing variables, letting $y = (x - x')2L$, we get

$$\int_{-\infty}^{\infty} \text{sinc } y \, dy = 1 \quad (5.11)$$

It is important to note that the final form of the integral is independent of L, so that the result would be true for any value of L, even infinite ones. With the additional property that its integral over infinite limits is unity, the spike function is known as the Dirac delta function,

$$\delta(x - x') = \begin{cases} 0, & x - x' \neq 0 \\ \infty, & x - x' = 0 \end{cases} \quad (5.12)$$

such that

$$\int_{-\infty}^{\infty} \delta(x - x') \, dx' = 1 \quad (5.13)$$

Note that when L is large, nearly all the contribution to the integral of the sinc function comes when x' is within a small neighborhood of x (x is, of course, treated here as a constant). Now let us see what this means when the expression within the integral is multiplied by some smooth function, $f(x')$. For L sufficiently large, $f(x')$ will vary little over the small region close to x in which the sinc function contributes to the integral. This means that the entire sinc function in this neighborhood is essentially multiplied by the value of $f(x')$ there [which is $f(x)$]. This implies that the value of the entire integral will be increased by this factor, the value of $f(x')$ close to $f(x)$. So instead of getting unity, we get (as $L \to \infty$)

$$\int_{-\infty}^{\infty} f(x')[2L \text{ sinc } 2(x - x')L] \, dx' = f(x) \tag{5.14}$$

Rewriting in terms of the Dirac delta notation, we have the very general result,

$$\int_{-\infty}^{\infty} f(x')\delta(x - x') \, dx' = f(x) \tag{5.15}$$

Substituting the results we have obtained back into the original problem, we have

$$f(x) = \int_{-\infty}^{\infty} f(x') \, dx' \int_{-\infty}^{\infty} e^{i2\pi\omega(x-x')} \, d\omega$$

$$= \int_{-\infty}^{\infty} f(x')\delta(x - x') \, dx' = f(x) \tag{5.16}$$

that is, the original function is recovered, verifying that no information is lost on taking the Fourier transform.

It is evident from the preceding discussion that some of the most interesting functions involved in Fourier analysis cannot be directly determined but must be obtained from a limiting process. This is a consequence of the basically sinusoidal nature of the complex exponential in the Fourier transform. The mathematical difficulties come about, of course, because each individual sinusoidal wave must, by definition, extend to infinity in an unchanging periodic pattern. There are other ways that the Dirac delta function may be derived from a limiting process. The treatment of the Dirac delta function and other interesting functions obtained from limiting sequences make up the mathematical theory of *generalized functions*. A more complete discussion of the Fourier transform and generalized functions is provided by Bracewell (1978), Papoulis (1962), Friedman (1956), and Lighthill (1970).

Because of their importance, some of the better known transform pairs and theorems of Fourier analysis are derived. Consider the rect function, defined as

$$\text{rect}(x/2L) = \begin{cases} 0, & |x| > L \\ \tfrac{1}{2}, & |x| = L \\ 1, & |x| < L \end{cases} \tag{5.17}$$

Taking the Fourier transform of this function, we have

$$
\mathscr{F}\left\{\mathrm{rect}\left(\frac{x}{2L}\right)\right\} = \int_{-\infty}^{\infty} \mathrm{rect}\left(\frac{x}{2L}\right) e^{-i2\pi\omega x} \, dx = \int_{-L}^{L} e^{-i2\pi\omega x} \, dx
$$

$$
= \frac{-1}{i2\pi\omega} [e^{-i2\pi\omega x}]_{-L}^{L} = \frac{1}{\pi\omega} \left[\frac{e^{i2\pi\omega L} - e^{-i2\pi\omega L}}{2i} \right]
$$

$$
= \frac{1}{\pi\omega} \sin 2\pi\omega L = 2L \frac{\sin 2\pi\omega L}{2\pi\omega L}
$$

$$
= 2L \, \mathrm{sinc} \, 2\omega L \qquad\qquad (5.18)
$$

Exactly the same result is obtained if the inverse Fourier transform is taken. Summarizing this transform pair,

$$
\mathscr{F}\{\mathrm{rect}(x/2L)\} = \mathscr{F}^{-1}\{\mathrm{rect}(x/2L)\} = 2L \, \mathrm{sinc} \, 2\omega L \qquad (5.19)
$$

Given the function $f(x)$ and its transform $F(\omega)$, let us see what happens to the transform when we shift the function by the amount a:

$$
\mathscr{F}\{f(x + a)\} = \int_{-\infty}^{\infty} f(x + a) e^{-i2\pi\omega x} \, dx
$$

$$
= \int_{-\infty}^{\infty} f(x + a)(e^{i2\pi\omega a} e^{-i2\pi\omega a}) e^{-i2\pi\omega x} \, dx
$$

$$
= e^{i2\pi\omega a} \int_{-\infty}^{\infty} f(x + a) e^{-i2\pi\omega(x+a)} \, d(x + a) \qquad (5.20)
$$

On changing variables, letting $y = x + a$, we get

$$
e^{i2\pi\omega a} \int_{-\infty}^{\infty} f(y) e^{-i2\pi\omega y} \, dy = e^{i2\pi\omega a} F(\omega) \qquad (5.21)
$$

The transform of the unshifted function is multiplied by the phase factor $\exp(i2\pi\omega a)$ to get the shifted result. Of course, the converse is true: Multiplying the spatial function by a phase factor will shift the function in the transform domain.

The addition theorem,

$$
\mathscr{F}\{f(x) + g(x)\} = \mathscr{F}\{f(x)\} + \mathscr{F}\{g(x)\} \qquad (5.22)
$$

follows directly from the distributive property of the integral. Proofs of all the important theorems and many interesting transform pairs may be found in Bracewell (1978).

5.3. Convolution

One very important characteristic of the Fourier transform is the simplicity of expression that is afforded to many physical processes by its application. Of particular interest to those involved in data enhancement and restoration are those processes that degrade optical images and line broadening effects in one-dimensional records such as spectroscopy and chromatography. Between the generation and recording of the data, there are many physical operations that act on the data and have the general effect of "broadening" every elementary element produced by the source. An example of this would be the emission line from a monochromatic source recorded by a grating spectrometer. Instead of the sharp line expected from a monochromatic source, the line recorded would be *broadened* owing to the width of the slits and the diffraction limit set by the width of the grating. The data that are recorded would then be the sum of all these broadened or *spread out* elements generated by the source (this is assuming that there is no interaction among the various elements, i.e., a *linear* response). In one dimension the general mathematical expression for this would be

$$h(x) = \int_{-\infty}^{\infty} f(s)g(x,s) \, ds \tag{5.23}$$

where s is the coordinate of the source, x is the coordinate of the recorded data, $f(s)$ is the intensity of the source at s, and $g(x,s)$ is the functional form in x of the intensity (this would be the electromagnetic intensity for spectroscopic quantities, but it could be mass distribution or almost any other quantity imaginable) due to the element (or wave number) of the source at the coordinate s. The variables x and s represent very general types of coordinates and could represent time, position, angle, wave number, etc. For IR spectroscopy data, they will usually represent wave number in units of centimeter^{-1}.

Mathematically, the above integral is known as the Fredholm integral of the first kind. If the function $g(x,s)$ is approximately shift invariant, that is, if it has the same functional form in x for every element in s, then we may write the much simpler expression

$$h(x) = \int_{-\infty}^{\infty} f(s)g(x - s) \, ds \tag{5.24}$$

which shows $g(x - s)$ as a function in x that is shifted by every element in s. This is the interpretation for nearly all physical applications. From a strictly mathematical point of view, however, $g(x - s)$ is interpreted as a function in s that is rotated or *convolved* 180° about every value of x on the s axis, multipled by the other function in s, $f(s)$, and integrated over s—hence its name, the *convolution integral*. The same result is obtained if the roles of f and g are interchanged, and the integration is generally described as the convolution of f and g, often indicated by $f * g$.

The preceding equation is found to be a good approximation to much experimental data of interest in the sciences. The function $g(x - s)$ is often called the *apparatus function*, or *machine function*, as it is usually the way the measuring device "smears" or broadens a single datum element entering the apparatus. In optics its two-dimensional counterpart is known as the *point-spread function*, as it is the way a single point of light (or generally any electromagnetic intensity) on the object is "spread out" or "smeared" in the image. Other names for $g(x - s)$ appropriate to the area of study are found in the literature. We use the designation *impulse response function*, as it is generally appropriate to all fields.

Upon taking the Fourier transform of the convolution, a much simpler mathematical expression is obtained:

$$\mathcal{F}\{h(x)\} = H(\omega) = \mathcal{F}\{f(x) * g(x)\}$$

$$= \int_{-\infty}^{\infty} \left[\int_{-\infty}^{\infty} f(s)g(x - s) \, ds \right] e^{-i2\pi\omega x} \, dx \qquad (5.25)$$

Assuming the order of integration may be changed, we have

$$\int_{-\infty}^{\infty} f(s) \, ds \int_{-\infty}^{\infty} g(x - s)e^{-i2\pi\omega x} \, dx = \int_{-\infty}^{\infty} f(s) \, ds[e^{-i2\pi\omega s}G(\omega)] \quad (5.26)$$

by direct application of the shift theorem. We have finally

$$G(\omega) \int_{-\infty}^{\infty} f(s)e^{-i2\pi\omega s} \, ds = G(\omega)F(\omega) \qquad (5.27)$$

and the convolution becomes a simple multiplication in the Fourier domain. Also, it may be shown that convolution in the Fourier domain is a multiplication in the spatial domain.

Because of the simplicity and the convenience of mathematical manipulation afforded by convolution and other mathematical expressions of closely related phenomena under the Fourier transform, a large body of mathematical theory has been developed treating this and related matters. Although the preceding equations concern the one-dimensional development, the generalization to two and higher dimensions is straightforward.

A closer relationship to the Fourier transform is afforded by optical images, as it may be shown that the diffraction pattern of two-dimensional images is the same as the two-dimensional Fourier transforms of these images. An excellent discussion of Fourier optics is provided by Goodman (1968). Another good treatment of Fourier analysis with optical applications is given by Papoulis (1968).

5.4. Deconvolution by Linear Methods

A. THE FOURIER APPROACH TO DECONVOLUTION

The simple expression for the convolution under Fourier transformation given by Eq. (5.27) suggests the quick and simple procedure for recovering the original appearance of the data by simply dividing through by $G(\omega)$, to obtain

$$F(\omega) = H(\omega)/G(\omega) \tag{5.28}$$

where, as before, $F(\omega)$ is the Fourier transform of the original data, $H(\omega)$ is the Fourier transform of the recorded data, and $G(\omega)$ is the Fourier transform of the impulse response function, often called the *transfer function*. It would seem now that all one would have to do to recover the original function, $f(x)$, is to take the inverse Fourier transform,

$$\mathcal{F}^{-1}\{F(\omega)\} = \mathcal{F}^{-1}\{H(\omega)/G(\omega)\} = f(x) \tag{5.29}$$

Since the degradation is expressed as a convolution, the inverse operation, which recovers the original function, is usually called *deconvolution*. However, there are several practical considerations that prevent such a trivial solution to the restoration problem.

The first consideration is that the impulse response function, $g(x)$, is often band-limited; that is, its Fourier transform, $G(\omega)$, is composed of only a low-frequency band of values. All higher frequencies are zero beyond a particular frequency, which we shall denote by $\omega = \Omega$. With a band-limited transfer function, multiplying $F(\omega)$ by $G(\omega)$, as in Eq. (5.27), brings $H(\omega)$ to zero at Ω. Attempted recovery of $F(\omega)$ by dividing $H(\omega)$ by $G(\omega)$, as in Eq. (5.28), results in zero divided by zero for all frequencies above Ω, a mathematically indeterminate case. Those frequencies in $F(\omega)$ above Ω thus seem to be lost to us forever. However, we find later that there is at least one physical constraint that will allow the complete spectrum beyond Ω to be recovered exactly (for noise-free data), as well as several constraints that will produce a reasonably good approximation to this high-frequency Fourier spectrum. However, many researchers are satisfied to recover only those frequencies up to Ω and set all values of ω beyond Ω to zero. This particular solution is known as the *principal solution,* as given by Bracewell and Roberts (1954).

The second, and more serious, consideration in all practical restorations is that experimental data are never completely free from noise and other error. A more realistic model of experimental data must include noise, which may be considered as additive:

$$h(x) = \int_{-\infty}^{\infty} f(s)g(x - s) \, ds + n(x) \qquad (5.30)$$

This model has proved sufficient for nearly all data of physical interest and is the starting point for nearly all theoretical treatments. Taking the Fourier transform of this we have

$$H(\omega) = F(\omega)G(\omega) + N(\omega) \qquad (5.31)$$

where $N(\omega)$ is the Fourier transform of the noise term. Solving for $F(\omega)$ we have

$$F(\omega) = H(\omega)/G(\omega) - N(\omega)/G(\omega) \qquad (5.32)$$

Analysis of Eq. (5.32) when $H(\omega)$ represents typical experimental data will give insight into most of the problems associated with practical deconvolution. In this analysis we assume that the noise term $n(x)$ is approximately Gaussian. The Fourier transform of normally distributed, or Gaussian, noise varies randomly both in magnitude and phase. However, it is noted that the envelope of the magnitudes is approximately constant over all frequencies of the Fourier spectrum. Because of the uncertainty principle of Fourier analysis, the broader the impulse response function $g(x)$, the narrower its Fourier spectrum $G(\omega)$. So if appreciable broadening of the data features occur, then $G(\omega)$ is usually quite narrow and tapers to small values rather quickly. For most cases then, the effect of the transfer function $G(\omega)$ on $H(\omega)$ generally is to cause a rapid tapering to small values, sometimes to a sharp cutoff at Ω, as discussed earlier. Whether or not the effect of the measuring instrument can be explicitly expressed as a convolution, all recording instruments generally exhibit an increasing lack of sensitivity at the higher frequencies of the Fourier spectrum, causing the informational content of the Fourier spectrum of the data of all recording instruments to taper eventually to very small values at the highest frequencies. Owing to the flat nature of the noise spectrum, that is, to the unchanging envelope of its spectral components, the (average) values of the noise spectrum will eventually surpass in magnitude the values of the spectral components of the information as one moves to the higher frequencies.

The reader should note that the gradual transition from information to noise, as one moves from the lower to higher frequencies in the Fourier spectrum, is the Fourier expression of the limitation of man's ability to measure accurately the various phenomena in the world around him. As is well known to anyone working in Fourier analysis, the finest details require the highest frequencies to represent them. The finest details also require the most precise measurements. When measurements are made to the limits of the ability of the measuring device, the recorded values are seldom the true values, but vary randomly about them, the (average) size of the deviations depending on how precisely the measurements are made. The Fourier spectrum reflects this inability to recover fine detail, as the highest frequencies are mostly noise, reflecting the randomness involved in making the most precise measurements. This Fourier relation thus tells us something very fundamental about man's relation to the world around him and his ability to know something of this world, but unfortunately we do not have time to explore the matter further here.

Getting back to the restoration problem, the seriousness of high-frequency noise in any practical restoration now becomes quite apparent. The transfer function $G(\omega)$, if not sharply terminated, tapers eventually to very small values in the high-frequency spectral region. Dividing $N(\omega)$, the Fourier transform of the noise, by these small values of $G(\omega)$, as must be done in Eq. (5.32), boosts these noise spectral components to enormous values, values much larger than any of the informational spectral components. So if we straightforwardly take the inverse Fourier transform in an attempt to recover the original appearance of the data, $f(x)$, we find that these large noise components have the effect of almost completely obscuring all information in the data. From Eq. (5.32) it follows that

$$\mathscr{F}^{-1}\left\{\frac{H(\omega)}{G(\omega)}\right\} = \mathscr{F}^{-1}\left\{F(\omega) + \frac{N(\omega)}{G(\omega)}\right\} = f(x) + \mathscr{F}^{-1}\left\{\frac{N(\omega)}{G(\omega)}\right\} \quad (5.33)$$

Examination of this equation makes it evident that if any semblance of the original appearance of the data is to be obtained, then something must be done to diminish the effect of the enormous second term on the right side of this equation. The reader should note, incidentally, that if $g(x)$ is assumed to be obtained with sufficient accuracy from theoretical considerations or direct measurement, and if $g(x)$ is not band-limited, then the simple model for the degradation that we have assumed tells us that noise is the sole obstacle to a complete recovery of the original function.

If we are to obtain further improvement, it is evident that additional information is needed. Any way of distinguishing the noise from the information in the data will be helpful. Also, it will be found later than any *a priori* knowledge of the original function is effective in recovering $f(x)$ in the presence of noise. There is one very important relationship between the noise and information in the data. It is the one we have just discussed. That is, the highest frequencies are nearly all noise. This is the reason that most restorations that involve smoothing are effective. It may be shown that smoothing operations leave the low frequencies relatively intact but that they strongly attenuate the highest frequencies, which, as we have discovered, are mostly noise.

When we examine Eq. (5.33), this relationship suggests the very direct operation of truncating the frequency spectrum before the noise term becomes excessively large. The next step is to determine the exact point of truncation. Unfortunately, there is no universal agreement on this. Many researchers determine the truncation point intuitively by an inspection of the results, which, of course, presumes some foreknowledge of the original appearance of the undistorted data. Another primarily intuitive criterion is that the cutoff frequency be chosen where the (average) values of the magnitude of the noise surpasses the magnitudes of the information component of the data. This presupposes some knowledge of the rms magnitude of the noise. However, this may be reasonably approximated by direct measurement of the noise values along some region of the base line where no information is known to exist, or by other means if this is not appropriate. There are more quantitative criteria for determining the truncation frequency of the Fourier spectrum. To determine the frequency that minimizes the mean square error between the resulting function and the original data $f(x)$ is one example. An elegant derivation of this, along with its simple result in terms of the rms of the noise and the signal, is given by Frieden (1975).

Regardless of the criterion used, however, simply truncating the spectrum does not produce the most satisfactory results. In the attempt to avoid retaining too much of the noise term, much of the information is usually truncated. Even if the data were noise free, this "truncation error" would be very undesirable, as a sharply terminated function produces many unwanted distortions in its Fourier transform. To treat this quantitatively, note that a truncated spectrum may be expressed as the multiplication of the spectrum by the rect function. Let us denote the truncation frequency by Ω_p. The low-frequency band defined is called the *processing bandwidth*. It should be evident that Ω_p must always be less than or equal to Ω (when Ω exists). We have the expression

$$\text{rect}\left(\frac{\omega}{2\Omega_p}\right) F(\omega)$$

Upon taking the Fourier transform of this, we have, by the convolution theorem,

$$\mathscr{F}^{-1}\left\{F(\omega)\,\text{rect}\left(\frac{\omega}{2\Omega_p}\right)\right\} = 2\Omega_p f(x) * \text{sinc}\, 2\Omega_p x \qquad (5.34)$$

Truncating the spectrum in the Fourier domain thus has the effect in the spatial domain of convolving the general function $f(x)$ with the sinc function. This is the reason why peaks obtained from a truncated Fourier spectrum are broadened with sidelobes or "ringing" around the peaks. Truncating the data function would also produce the same results in the frequency domain.

Many attempts to ameliorate truncation error involve multiplication of the Fourier spectrum by real symmetric functions, $W(\omega)$, called *windows;* explicitly, $W(\omega)H(\omega)$. Nearly all window functions involved in this operation are real, symmetric; are unity at the origin; and decrease in some smooth fashion to small values or zero at the cutoff frequency Ω_p. Upon multiplication, this type of window produces a more smoothly varying spectral function, which results in much more uniform peaks on taking the transform, with artifacts such as the sidelobes much reduced. However, a disadvantage is that the peaks are usually broadened.

In electrical engineering and many optical applications, window functions are usually called *filters.* The window function just described is called a *low-pass filter,* as it strongly attenuates the higher frequencies but leaves the low frequencies relatively intact. Windows that attenuate the low frequencies and emphasize the higher ones are called *high-pass filters.* The inverse of the transfer function, $1/G(\omega) = Y(\omega)$, is often called an *inverse filter.* In the case of deconvolution in which the product $H(\omega)Y(\omega)$ is formed, it almost always emphasizes the higher frequencies. Some ad hoc window functions that are often are applied to the data or their Fourier spectrum are the triangular window (often used for apodization), the ellipitcal arc, the *Hanning filter,* and the *Butterfield filter* (e.g., see Frieden, 1975; Gonzalez and Wintz, 1977).

There are several iterative methods of restoration that produce an ad hoc filtering effect for a finite number of iterations. The van Cittert method (van Cittert, 1931) is probably the best known of these. When it converges, it converges to the inverse-filtered estimate, $\mathcal{F}^{-1}\{H(\omega)/G(\omega)\}$, but behaves as a smoothing window in the frequency domain for any finite number of iterations. It may be shown that the noise increases linearly with every iteration (Frieden, 1975). Iteration is stopped before the noise becomes significantly large.

With noise in the data, we have the error due to both noise and information truncation when the spectrum is terminated. Choosing the truncation point further into the higher frequencies, we find the noise burden to be unbearable. Choosing the truncation point in the lower frequencies, we find the noise much reduced, but the truncation error now is unacceptable. Whatever the criterion used for determining the truncation point, it will be a trade-off between the two types of errors, and there will not be the most desirable restoration, as the original appearance of the data will still not be obtained. For further improvement, additional operations on the deconvolution model are needed. It is found that a carefully chosen window function will minimize the errors due to both noise and truncation. The general characteristic of such windows is that they are smoothly varying to minimize distortions such as the sidelobes and taper to small values or zero at Ω_p to reject the high noise level near cutoff, while preserving a close appearance to the original undistorted function. To produce an appearance close to the original function implies that some increase in resolution must occur. This means that values for these window functions must (smoothly) increase above unity for at least some frequency values beyond the dc component before dropping back eventually to zero to reject the noise.

Those filters enjoying the most widespread current use are derived from quantitative criteria. With the window function as an additional factor in the restoration, much greater flexibility is now allowed in a minimum mean-squared-error (mmse) criterion. Fixing the cutoff point at Ω and minimizing the expected value of

$$\left\langle \int_{-\Omega}^{\Omega} |F(\omega) - W(\omega)H(\omega)|^2 \, d\omega \right\rangle$$

we find that the desired window is given by

$$W(\omega) = \frac{G^*(\omega)\phi_0}{|G(\omega)|^2\phi_0 + \phi_n} \tag{5.35}$$

where the power spectrum of the signal is denoted by ϕ_0, and the power spectrum of the noise is denoted by ϕ_n. This is Helstrom's form (Helstrom, 1967) of the *Wiener least-squares filter,* and is widely known. Norbert Wiener's original smoothing filter (Goldman, 1953) is given by

$$W(\omega) = \phi_0/(\phi_0 + \phi_n) \tag{5.36}$$

Note that the above least-squares filter is based on statistical criteria and is the optimal filter in the presence of Gaussian noise. Including a sharpness constraint obtained by differentiating the inverse-filtered expression adds an additional factor to the above least-squares expression. Other constraints and approaches have produced a variety of filters that have been applied with some measure of success in many fields. See Frieden (1975) for further discussion of these interesting filters.

A window function that extends beyond Ω is often called an *extrapolating window.* Generally these functions extend to infinity. Slepian and Pollak (1961) developed an extrapolating window based on the constraint of finite extent that has had some applications in optics (Frieden, 1971).

The author developed an ad hoc extrapolating window that has been applied to the deconvolution of IR spectral lines with moderate success. The main motivation for the form of the filter was the observation that the Fourier transform of most smooth functions dies out in an approximately exponential fashion, with the envelope of the spectrum asymptotically approaching the spectral axis. It was the author's reasoning that perhaps if he could make the envelope of the universe-filtered spectrum fall off in an exponential sort of way, the magnitudes, at least, of these high-frequency components (which are mostly noise) would be closer to those of the original data, $F(\omega)$, and would exercise some improvement in the results. Even though this filter was moderately successful with the particular data to which it was applied, more quantitatively determined filters, such as the Wiener filter, produce better overall results generally.

This particular filter was applied to the deconvolution of a set of IR spectral lines with a Gaussian impulse response function. Slight, but observable, improvement was obtained. How much of this improvement was due to the magnitudes of the high-frequency components being close to the correct size, and how much was due to the remaining information in the high-frequency components, the author was unable to determine, however. Even though the *envelope* of the magnitudes of the noise components was very close to the *envelope* of the correct spectrum, the statistical variations about this envelope still kept the individual spectral values from being close to the true ones. Also, the phases were still completely random. These are the obvious causes of nearly all the artifacts and false features introduced, which offset nearly all the improvement brought about by the filter.

Actually, all linear operations on the data may be further generalized into one *net filter*. That this is true is especially apparent when one considers that even truncation is the same as multiplication by a rectangular window, the rect function. With all the abovementioned operations on the spectrum of the data, we have

$$W(\omega) \operatorname{rect}\left(\frac{\omega}{2\Omega_p}\right) \frac{H(\omega)}{G(\omega)} = \left[\frac{W(\omega)}{G(\omega)} \operatorname{rect}\left(\frac{\omega}{2\Omega_p}\right)\right] H(\omega)$$

$$= Y(\omega)H(\omega) \qquad (5.37)$$

where $Y(\omega)$ is the net filter that summarizes all possible (linear) operations on the recorded data. Thus

$$Y(\omega) = W(\omega)/G(\omega) \operatorname{rect}(\omega/2\Omega_p) \qquad (5.38)$$

Throughout this discussion we have assumed that the window functions applied in the Fourier domain were real and symmetrical. However, the impulse response function $g(x)$ is often asymmetrical, and phase factors would unavoidably be introduced into the expression for $G(\omega)$. If $g(x)$ is a simple and smoothly varying function, though, severe distortion generally does not result from the inclusion of these phase factors, and all the advantages of the aforementioned filters are usually preserved.

The considerable speed and simplicity of filters, in general, makes them appropriate for many real-time applications. However, by the uniqueness of the Fourier spectrum of a given data function, an exactly restored function can only be obtained by a restoration of those high-frequency spectral components that are missing or buried in the noise. The correct rendering of fine detail and significant improvement in resolution depends strongly on an accurate recovery of this high-frequency spectrum. In general, filters can do little to recover these high frequencies accurately, as the ratio of noise to signal in every spectral component is fixed, and there is nothing that a window function can do to change this ratio. One cannot reduce the noise without reducing the information also. This disadvantage of filters seems to be borne out in practice, as even the best filters produce results that are generally inferior to those produced by the better spectrum restoration schemes.

B. Direct Non-Fourier Deconvolution Techniques

So far in this discussion of restoration and enhancement of experimental data, the emphasis has been on Fourier methods of improvement. However, there are more direct ways of recovering the original appearance of the data from the convolution model as given by Eq. (5.24). The most straightforward way of performing deconvolution is not inverse filtering but the direct determination of the inverse of convolution in the spatial domain.

With sampled data, the convolution expressed in Eq. (5.24) becomes the discrete sum

$$h_i = \sum_{j=-\infty}^{\infty} f_j g_{i-j} + n_i \qquad (5.39)$$

which is a set of linear equations in the unknown discrete values of f. These equations may be written in matrix form. The functions h, f, and n would then be vectors, and g would be a matrix. In the presence of random noise, the statistically most probably solution would be obtained by operating on h with the inverse of the g matrix (e.g., see Gonzalez and Wintz, 1977). Other methods for solving a set of linear equations could also be applied. The presence of even a small amount of noise, though, results in a very unstable set of equations. See Frieden (1975) for a discussion of smoothing constraints and other regularizing procedures for increasing the stability of these equations.

The calculational efficiency of methods for determining meaningful solutions to these equations are seldom greater, however, than the efficiency of successful inverse-filtering methods, and the non-Fourier methods are not as extensively used.

It is interesting to note that if the discrete Fourier transform (DFT) of Eq. (5.39) is taken (assuming a finite number of equations), a multiplication of the transforms is also obtained for the discrete case:

$$H_n = F_n G_n + N_n \tag{5.40}$$

This expression is easily proved by substituting Eq. (5.39) into the DFT. If the DFT is cast in matrix form, and the matrix calculations carried out, G will take the form of a diagonal matrix. That is, the discrete Fourier transform presents us with a procedure for diagonalizing the matrix. This is one reason for the considerable efficiency of Fourier methods of deconvolution. Another important reason is the considerable calculational speed of the fast Fourier transform (FFT) computational algorithm (Cooley and Tukey, 1965) for calculating the DFT.

If an attempt were made to list all the references to the linear methods of restoration, both Fourier and non-Fourier, this list would be much too lengthy to justify its inclusion in this work. Extensive development is found in a number of fields of endeavor. Some textbooks that discuss primarily linear, as well as many nonlinear, methods of restoration are the following: Hall (1979), Pratt (1978), Andrews and Hunt (1977), Gonzalez and Wintz (1977), Papoulis (1977), Huang (1975), and Rosenfeld and Kak (1975). Most of these books discuss two-dimensional applications, but the theory is usually developed in one dimension. Extensive reference lists are included in several of these books.

5.5. Continuation of the Fourier Spectrum

Having decided that continuation of the Fourier spectrum offers the best possibility of a physically realistic restoration, we soon find that physical *constraints* are a necessary part of this restoration. As Harris (1964) pointed out, no unique way exists to extend the spectrum in the absence of additional information. It should be evident that constraints offer the only possibility for recovering the Fourier spectrum of band-limited data, as no information about the spectrum beyond Ω may be acquired from the convolution model. Placing limits on the values that the data or their Fourier spectrum may take will exercise some restriction on the spectrum. More generally, a constraint may be defined as any prior knowledge of the original function that may be applied to yield a function or its spectrum that is more probable. It is generally assumed that the more constraints that are available to apply to a particular restoration, the more probable, overall, are the resulting functions that are obtained. In practice, it is found that additional constraints usually contribute to further stability in the solution set of equations. Note that this runs counter to the influence of noise, which has the effect of rendering the values assumed less probable as the noise level increases. A more complete discussion of the error due to noise and a reduced low-frequency bandwidth for spectral restoration is given by Rushforth *et al.* (1982). There are many constraints, some much more quantitative than others, that have the possibility of application. Some constraints are peculiar to the particular data under investigation.

Most of the important physical constraints set well-defined limits to the data function (or its spectrum), beyond which the correct function is not allowed to go. An important example of this type of constraint is *nonnegativity,* whereby the correctly restored function is not allowed to extend below the zero-base-line limit and thereby take on nonphysical negative values. This is an appropriate constraint for optical quantities, as the electromagnetic intensity is always a positive quantity. This constraint could thus be applied to spectroscopy and optical images.

A fixed-limits constraint closely associated with this one is that of an *upper bound* limit to the values of the spatial function. This constraint would be appropriate for absorption spectroscopy and would be applied to render improvement in saturated IR spectral lines.

Another important constraint of fixed limits is that of *finite extent,* for which no deviations from zero are allowed for those intervals of the function over the spatial axis that lie outside the known extent of the original object. This constraint would be appropriate for spectroscopy in which the electromagnetic radiation in the bands outside the band of interest are filtered out. This constraint is also of considerable theoretical importance, as it may be shown that a complete restoration is effected for noise-free data. Data limited in space may be shown to have a spectral function that is analytic, which implies that the continued spectral function is unique (Harris, 1966; Wolter, 1961).

Another constraint of fixed limits that would apply to the Fourier spectrum is that of recovery of only a finite Fourier spectral band. This implies the restriction of all higher frequencies above this band to zero. As elimination or reduction of the highest frequencies leaves a much smoother result, this is often called a *smoothing* constraint. This type of constraint usually exercises some improvement in experimental data or their inverse-filtered result, as the higher frequencies of the Fourier spectrum for these cases are often predominantly noise. Some other important examples of this type of constraint are running means and convolution with a weighted function, such as that given by Savitzky and Golay (1964). The operations given in these two examples are linear and, as discussed in the previous section, may manifest themselves as filtering operations in the Fourier domain. So is the lone operation of simply truncating the Fourier spectrum. For the methods developed in this research, however, the recovery of a finite spectral band is bound up with the other constraints, and the resulting operations are not linear.

There are a number of interesting and effective constraints that, unfortunately, are appropriate only to specialized areas of study. Another constraint developed in this research that, although less quantitative than the ones previously mentioned, has the possibility of more general application is one based on prior knowledge of the apearance of the correctly restored function. This information was used to construct an artificial function that it was hoped would closely resemble the restored function. Specifically, it was hoped that this function's spectrum beyond the truncation frequency of the inverse-filtered estimate Ω_p would resemble the original spectrum of the undistorted function, so that it might be substituted onto the spectrum of the inverse-filtered estimate from Ω_p on to yield a complete set of spectral components that were reasonably correct. This procedure was successful in rendering much improvement to gas chromatographic data (Howard, 1978; Howard and Rayborn, 1980). The artificial function was created by measuring the heights, widths, and locations of the inverse-filtered peaks (the peaks representing the various chemical components in the sample) and constructing Gaussian functions with these parameters. Superimposing these Gaussian functions, which, of course, had no sidelobes or other artifacts, yielded the artificial function, which at least crudely resembled the correctly restored function for most cases. The disadvantage of this procedure is that it is very difficult to create an artificial function for the general case.If the peaks in the data above are not fairly well separated, it is very difficult to obtain the required parameters. This method thus has limited application.

Another constraint closely related to the one we have just discussed is that in which prior knowledge of the data and their associated impulse response function is sufficient to allow them to be adequately represented by analytic functions, such as power series. The noise (it is hoped) would not be present in the new (analytic) formulation. The deconvolution may then be calculated analytically. The correct restoration of the high frequencies is thus inherent in the method, which neatly avoids the noise problem associated with most practical restorations. From physical considerations, van de Hulst (1946) developed a series expression for the Voigt profile of spectral lines that allowed a successful analytic deconvolution to be performed. Morton and Rayborn (1979) successfully adapted this procedure to the deconvolution of molecular beam time-of-flight data. An independently developed but closely related method was used by Sheen and Skofronick (1974) to find an analytic function to correctly extend across the endpoints of molecular beam scattering data. Other examples may be found in the literature but are most often associated with specialized fields of study. As the most general types of data cannot be represented by an analytic function, these methods have limited application.

For the remainder of this discussion, some distinction is made between those restorations that affect the entire Fourier spectrum, and those in which the low-frequency band (or its associated spatial function) is held constant, and restoration of the remaining spectrum is made to this *region of support*. In the following discussion, these two general divisions are referred to, respectively, as the *former approach* and the *latter approach*.

All of the problems treated by the latter approach will fit the convolution model, with a modification of the way we customarily define the noise term, since a truncated spectrum may be expressed in the transformed domain as a convolution of the original function with the sinc function.

Experimentally obtained data always contain noise, and the highest frequencies cannot be determined by the inverse of convolution by either approach owing to insufficient information. For the general convolution model, the impulse response function may go to zero at Ω, as for diffraction-limited images, and information on all higher frequencies is lacking. When this is not the case, a sufficient number of high-frequency values may be recovered accurately enough to render a reasonable restoration when the noise level is low. However, more of the information in the lower frequencies is hidden as the noise level increases.

The information required to recover these high frequencies must be included in some way in the restoration procedure. In the former approach, which bases its restorations on the general convolution model, the techniques for restoration are nearly all iterative, and the information that comprise the constraints are included in each iteration to move the iterated function away from nonallowed values. In the latter approach (which cannot deal directly with the general convolution model) the fixed spectrum (or its associated spatial function) is used as a "base," the extrapolated spectrum (or its associated spatial function) is added to it, and the methods of restoration developed for this approach attempt to satisfy the constraints in some way for the total function.

It is apparent that the latter approach may be applied to a class of problems to which the former approach is not suited. For FTS data, for example, what is needed is a function to extend the interferogram, and modification or inverse filtering of the (finite) interferogram is seldom required.

The latter approach may also be applied to the general restoration problem (that is, with impulse response functions other than the sinc function) by lending to restoration in two distinct spectral bands. The most noise-free frequencies in the low-frequency band may be restored by inverse filtering. Using the FFT with discrete data, this operation may be performed very rapidly with modern digital computers, even if the entire spectrum is inverse-filtered. This is because only a term-by-term division is involved once the Fourier transform is taken. This restored low-frequency band may be used as the region of support for restoration of a high-frequency band by the latter approach. The smaller number of variables implied by the narrower band (compared to the former approach) needing to be restored also allows the calculations for this band to be performed very efficiently. Thus restoration in two distinct bands lends itself to extremely fast calculational procedures. However, the former approach lends itself to optimal restorations, as the entire spectrum interacts together in producing the final result. The latter approach (as yet) has no way of removing the residual noise in the low-frequency inverse-filtered band used as a region of support.

The emphasis in this research has been on methods that recover an additional spectral band, given the low-frequency band as a region of support. The interested reader will probably want to research the literature for further details about the former approach.

We next provide a more detailed treatment of those methods that restore an additional spectral band. To discuss this quantitatively, let $U(\omega)$ denote the fixed low-frequency spectral band and $V(\omega)$ the high-frequency band to be restored. By transforming, $u(x)$ would then be the fixed spatial function and $v(x)$ the spatial function formed from the high-frequency band. The purpose is to have the constraints satisfied (as best we know how) for the total function $u(x) + v(x)$ [or $U(\omega) + V(\omega)$, whichever expression is more appropriate]. It is, of course, only the high frequencies in $V(\omega)$ that vary until the constraints are best satisfied.

For the less quantitative constraints, iterative methods for determining $V(\omega)$ are usually the most appropriate. For the fixed-limits constraints, however, closed-form solutions are often possible. For fixed-limits constraints, exact numerical values may be assigned, at each value of the independent variable, to the deviations beyond the fixed limits into the nonallowed region. The desire is to minimize these nonallowed deviations in some fashion by varying $V(\omega)$ [or $v(x)$]. It is often possible to construct some function of these nonallowed deviations (often called a *penalty function*) that may be minimized to yield a unique solution for $V(\omega)$. A minimum mean-square-error (mmse) criterion would result in an integral over the square of the nonallowed deviations in the total function $u(x) + v(x)$ [or $U(\omega) + V(\omega)$], which would correspond to a sum-of-squares expression for discrete data. Integrating over the absolute value of the nonallowed deviations in the total function $u(x) + v(x)$ would be another expression that could be minimized, which would, of course, correspond to a sum of absolute values for discrete data. For the constraint of finite extent, one could minimize the maximum deviation of $u(x) + v(x)$ over those regions outside the limited extent of the original object.

Most present experimental data are acquired in sampled form, as this form is most easily processed by current methods. Modern digital computers are unmatched in speed and accuracy for calculation and manipulation of discrete data. If the Fourier transform of discrete data is desired, the FFT computational algorithm can calculate it with extreme rapidity. Furthermore, with sampled data, it is found that usually only a small number of discrete Fourier components are needed to represent adequately the spectral band to be restored. For these reasons, methods of restoration that only apply to discrete data are addressed further in succeeding sections.

There are numerous numerical techniques for minimizing the expressions for the nonallowed deviations discussed here. A very direct technique may be used to minimize the maximum deviation into nonallowed regions. A good discussion of these minimization techniques and listings of computer programs to implement many of them may be found in Bevington (1969). The sum-of-squares expression was adhered to in this research, as many of the required calculations could be carried out analytically *once and for all*. The sum-of-squares expression for some of the important constraints is formulated and details of the minimization procedure are carried out in Section 5.8.

Next we discuss some of the more significant methods of restoration that make use of the constraints mentioned earlier. These could not be mentioned with the constraints, as most of the researchers used several constraints for improvement. To provide at least some vestige of order, though, we begin with those methods that use all but the nonnegativity constraint.

Other than the nonnegativity constraint, probably the most important constraint applied to practical restoration of experimental data is the finite-extent constraint. A good review article on methods that use this constraint, along with the authors' own approach, is provided by Rushforth and Frost (1980). Here, the authors use a novel smoothing constraint, along with recovery of a finite spectral band in an iterative approach. An important early extrapolation scheme, based primarily on the analyticity of the Fourier spectrum implied by the constraint of finite extent, was presented by Harris (1964). The first restoration procedure based on this constraint that enjoyed extensive application was presented by Gerchberg (1974), with a method that iterates back and forth between the forward and inverse Fourier domains. The function band-limited due to an incomplete Fourier spectrum, is truncated so that all its values are now zero outside its known limited extent. Transforming to the Fourier domain, the spectrum is set back to its original (correct) values within the known bandwidth. Transforming back to the spatial domain, the resulting function is again truncated outside its limited extent, and the entire process is repeated. These iterations are continued until the error energy (sum of squared error values) has been sufficiently minimized. The FFT is used to manage the large number of calculations involved. Gerchberg's method was further generalized by Youla (1978). Even though almost all applications of this method have made use of the iterative procedure, Sabri and Steenaart (1978) have shown that a noniterative formulation may be developed. An interesting practical application of the iterative procedure was made by Tam and Perez-Mendez (1981) to two-dimensional tomographic images. Along with a smoothing constraint, these authors also applied other methods based on the finite-extent constraint to the limited-angle projection problem in tomography in this interesting paper. Another interesting application of the Gerchberg iterative algorithm to the limited-angle problem in tomography is provided by Sato *et al.* (1981). Maeda and Murata (1982) applied a modification of the Gerchberg algorithm to two-dimensional images, which they compared with the original Gerchberg algorithm. The modified procedure involved filtering and the use of prototype images (artificial or closely related images that incorporate prior information) in the iteration. A modification of the Gerchberg iterative procedure was made by Fienup (1980) in order to bring about more rapid convergence. This procedure was successfully applied to the reconstruction of computer-generated holograms and images. Further interesting theoretical discussion of Gerchberg's algorithm and closely related restoration problems may be found in the recent papers by Fienup *et al.* (1982), Montgomery (1982), Marks and Smith (1981), and Stark *et al.* (1981).

To mention some interesting noniterative restoration methods based on the finite-extent constraint, Rushford *et al.* (1982) successfully implemented a regularized singular-value decomposition (SVD) (e.g., see Lawson and Hanson, 1974) of the matrix formulation of the least-squares expression of the problem. A conjugate gradient descent (CGD) iterative algorithm (Hestenes, 1980) for solving the least-squares problem was also explored in this paper. Severcan (1982) also attempted to minimize the squared error by an SVD of the system matrix. Here the SVD representation was used to realize a pseudoinverse filter. A computationally very efficient method was developed by Howard (1981a) from the least-squares expression for the finite-extent constraint. Carrying out the analytic calculations results in a closed-form solution in the unknown discrete Fourier spectral components as given by the DFT. The only numerical calculations involved will then be the solving of the resulting linear equations in the unknown Fourier coefficients for each given data set. Matrix methods, such as the Gauss–Jordan matrix reduction, may be used to solve these linear equations. However, iterative methods, such as the Jacobi method, are more appropriate when the number of unknown coefficients to determine is large. Additional flexibility is provided by this method in that the number of Fourier coefficients one wishes to recover is completely arbitrary. This option of being able to recover a smaller spectral band is necessary for stability in the resulting linear equations when the noise and other errors in the data are appreciably large.

For those data sets in which both constraints may fittingly be applied, it is found that the constraint of nonnegativity is far more effective in producing physically correct restorations in the vast majority of cases. This constraint is very robust with regard to noise, as opposed to the finite-extent constraint. However, there are many research areas for which this constraint is not physically appropriate, and the finite-extent constraint is the only one that can aptly be applied. In spite of its effectiveness, no uniqueness proof for the nonnegativity constraint in continuing the Fourier spectrum has so far been presented, as has been done for the finite-extent constraint. In practice, most researchers use both constraints simultaneously, as well as all other constraints physically appropriate for their research area. Generally, the best restorations are produced with the most constraints applied, which bears out in practice what one would expect intuitively.

We next discuss those methods of restoration that are based on the general convolution model, in which all the information (constraints) that can be brought to bear is used in the restoring operations to recover the entire spectrum (or its corresponding spatial function) simultaneously. The theoretically optimal restorations are produced by these methods. Bearing this out, it is found in practice that all of the very best restorations are produced by the methods of this group. Some of these methods are discussed in detail. With one exception, the methods discussed are all iterative and consume much computer time. This single disadvantage makes nearly every one of them impractical for all but the simplest two-dimensional applications.

Two significant early papers that make use of the positivity constraint in solving the inverse problem from convolution are those by Biraud (1969) and Schell (1965). Biraud forces a positive output by defining the correctly restored function to be the square of some other real function and then attempting to find this so-defined real function. The iterative restoration is carried out in the Fourier domain, in which the function that is squared would become the convolution with itself (or autocorrelation). Formulating the squared error between this autocorrelation and the inverse-filtered estimate within the processing bandwidth, but demanding strict equality of the autocorrelation with the dc component of the data transform comprises

Biraud's definition of the problem. From this point, Schell and Biraud, each with his own iterative algorithm, determined their respective solutions to this problem. Spectral extrapolation is accomplished by the autocorrelation, as it defines values for the convolved spectral function up to twice the processing bandwidth. This spectral extrapolation method has been found to be most successful for impulse objects against a zero background.

Jansson et al. (1970), with a variation of the van Cittert method that includes a positivity and an upperbound constraint, has produced restorations for saturated IR spectral lines that, without question, are the best available at the present time. Jansson introduces a relaxation factor into the classical van Cittert iterative procedure that restrains the (spatial) function to remain between zero and the upper bound value. The success of this restoration procedure with experimentally obtained IR spectroscopy data has been further demonstrated in a book by Blass and Halsey (1981), which also includes some variations on this method developed by the authors. Kawata and Ichioka (1980a) recently applied Jansson's iterative procedure successfully to two-dimensional images. These authors also introduced a reblurring procedure into the basic Jansson algorithm (Kawata and Ichioka, 1980b).

Ioup (1981) developed a method based on van Cittert's iterative deconvolution and Morrison's (1963) iterative noise removal that produces spectral extrapolation with the ad hoc application of constraints. This was successfully applied to mass spectroscopy and molecular beam-scattering data.

The maximum entropy approaches of Burg (1967) and Frieden (1972) are based ultimately on the statistical properties of positive quantities, which would be the case for electromagnetic intensities. Maximum entropy for optical quantities follows from maximum likelihood; the solutions obtained are those most likely for the given sampled input data. Burg's solution is noniterative, with all the computational advantages that accrue from this. One matrix solution of a set of linear equations is followed by substitution of these outputs into other equations to get the solution values. Unfortunately, the arbitrary assumptions necessary to obtain this closed-form solution also make the equation set sensitive to noise error (e.g., see Frieden, 1975). The model assumed by Frieden requires an iterative solution but is more consistent with physical reality. Frieden, not satisfied with the loss of detail entailed in restorations produced by the more conservative criteria, such as mmse and maximum likelihood, subsequently came up with the more optimistic criterion of *maximum information* (Frieden, 1981). Sought is the signal that would relay a maximum of Shannon information (Shannon and Weaver, 1949) about itself into the recorded data. It is evident that more information would be carried by a better resolved solution, which is to be preferred over the more blurred result, such as would be given by the mmse criterion, which would, of course, be the Wiener-filtered estimate. Frieden also points out that "in the image-restoration case, the maximum information norm is equivalent to that of *minimum* likelihood of error in photon transitions from object to image planes." The positivity and other constraints are included in an additive penalty function in the formulation. Under certain conditions the maximum information estimate converges to the maximum entropy estimate. For optical images, it is found that the maximum information principle generally produces better results than does maximum entropy. Anyone interested in optimal methods should certainly try to keep up with Frieden in the literature!

This concludes our discussion of those restoration methods that attempt to improve the entire spectrum. In the remainder of this section we discuss some methods that extrapolate from a fixed low-frequency spectrum.

Mammone and Eichmann (1982a,b) used linear programming (LP) techniques to optimize solutions for constraints that could easily be formulated as equations or inequalities. They explored the minimization of the sum of squares, the sum of absolute values, and the maximum deviation. They found that the simplex LP algorithm (Hadley, 1962), which they adopted for use, restored the spectrum for the sum-of-absolute-values expression most efficiently. Positivity, finite extent, upper bound, and finite band recovered were the constraints used for improvement. SVD prefiltering was used for smoothing in the earlier paper.

In a natural extension of the Gerchberg iterative algorithm, Stark *et al.* (1982) introduced a nonnegativity constraint for further improvement. Restoration of a finite band was an additional constraint used. The authors investigated the convergence properties of this and the classical Gerchberg algorithm. They observed that the initial convergence of the present algorithm was much faster than Gerchberg's, but that this algorithm asymptotically approached the Gerchberg algorithm in the limit for a large number of iterations.

A novel smoothness constraint that was incorporated into a regularized matrix for the DFT formulation of the data was developed by Zhou and Rushforth (1982). A finite spectral band was recovered, but the smoothing constraint provided a more gradual transition to the spectral termination point, which produced much improved restorations. An iterative algorithm that computed a nonnegative result for a least-squares formulation (Lawson and Hanson, 1974) was applied for these restorations. Very good results were obtained for impulse objects.

From the DFT expression for the data, Howard (1981b) formulated a novel sum-of-squares expression for the negative deviations. The advantage of this particular sum-of-squares formulation was that minimization could be carried out analytically to result in a closed-form solution in the unknown discrete Fourier spectral components. The resulting equations, however, were nonlinear rather than linear, and the only presently known methods of solution are iterative. For solving these equations Howard adapted a variation of the method of successive substitutions, which allows a considerable simplification in the resulting numerical calculations. The resulting procedure, overall, is extremely economical in computational time. Further, the method is very versatile in that the finite-extent and upper bound constraints may be easily incorporated into the restoration procedure (along with the implicit constraints of minimum negativity and recovery of a finite spectral band) with only slight modification. A more detailed discussion of this method, along with the earlier one (Howard, 1981a) developed solely for the constraint of finite extent, is provided in Section 5.8.

The only methods of form alteration and data enhancement we have discussed so far are those that attempt to restore the original appearance of the data by determining the inverse of convolution, as given in Eq. (5.24). We have seen that the most advanced (nonlinear) methods of restoration involve the bringing in of additional information, as well as altering the present form of the data (by inverse filtering, etc.). Within the general context of form alteration, however, there are goals that are as important as the complete restoration of the quantity being measured. Altering the form to remove the ambiguity in the quantities of interest in the recorded data is one objective that is of considerable importance in many fields. For spectroscopy, we would want the resulting electromagnetic spectral lines recorded to be nonoverlapping so that desired parameters (such as wave number, intensity, and bandwidth) could be more accurately measured. Apodization and resolution improvement are two ways of removing the ambiguity in these lines. Apodization is more fully discussed when Fourier transform spectroscopy (FTS) data are treated. A detailed discussion of resolution improvement is provided in Section 5.6.

5.6. The Uncertainty Principle

The entire development of the restoration problem so far has been based on the model of convolution with additive noise. Convolution has the well-known effect of smoothing and broadening the blurring of all fine detail in the data. One would expect, then, that the restoration would always improve the resolution and restore the detail. However, there are many degrading effects that cannot be explicitly expressed as a convolution integral. If improved resolution only is considered the primary goal, then further insight is provided by examining other viewpoints. The *uncertainty principle* of Fourier analysis provides a very interesting perspective to this question. Letting Δx denote the standard deviation of the spatial function and $\Delta\omega$ the standard deviation of the spectral function, we must necessarily have

$$\Delta x\,\Delta\omega \geq 1/4\pi \qquad (5.41)$$

A proof of this relation may be found in Bracewell (1978). Consider a spatial distribution $f(x)$ and its spectrum $F(\omega)$, which come close to satisfying the equality in the above expression. We may take Δx and $\Delta\omega$ as measures of the width and hence of the resolution of the respective functions. To see how this relates to more realistic data, such as IR spectral lines, consider shifting the peak function $f(x)$ by various amounts and then superimposing all these shifted functions. This will give a reasonable approximation to a set of IR lines. To discuss quantitatively what is occurring in the frequency domain, note that the Fourier spectrum of each shifted function by the shift theorem is given simply by the spectrum of the unshifted function multiplied by a constant phase factor. The superimposed spectrum would then be

$$[1 + \exp(i2\pi\omega x_1) + \exp(i2\pi\omega x_2) + \cdots]F(\omega)$$

Where $x_1, x_2, \ldots$ are the amounts the spatial functions are shifted. As Δx becomes smaller, each peak becomes narrower; merged peaks become resolved. The $\Delta\omega$ of each superimposed peak would necessarily have to increase all by the same amount to satisfy the uncertainty principle. With the aid of the above relation, it is not too difficult to show that the superimposed Fourier spectrum is generally broadened also.

These arguments may be generalized to show that any overall increase in resolution is accompanied generally by a broadening of the Fourier spectrum. This seems to be borne out in practice, as almost any operation that alters the magnitude of the high frequencies relative to the low frequencies affects the resolution. Broadening the Fourier spectrum or boosting the higher frequencies relative to the lower frequencies generally improves resolution and increases the detail, and narrowing the Fourier spectrum or reducing the highest frequencies almost always reduces the resolution and exercises smoothing. This is apparently the reason for the success of such ad hoc methods as zeroing the dc component and lowest frequencies of the Fourier spectrum, of ad hoc high-pass filters, and of the unconstrained van Cittert method for the improvement of resolution. However, it needs to be pointed out that any boosting of the higher frequencies relative to the lower frequencies in an effort to improve resolution must be done in a meaningful way, and not with random magnitudes and phases such as one would get by the addition of random noise. Actually, multiplication by the simple window functions discussed earlier is one example of a meaningful way. These windows only affect the magnitudes, which are altered in some smooth way.

This seems to have the effect of producing smooth results without violent oscillations, and without the introduction of extraneous detail (which random phase changes would effect).

Another important reason, of course, that the uncertainty principle is so important to our study of the physical world is the basically wavelike nature of the universe on its most fundamental level, as revealed by studies in quantum mechanics. The momentum of the particle, by de Broglie's relation, has a closely associated wavelength (which is the reciprocal of the spatial frequency). If we substitute this mathematical relation into Eq. (5.41), we will get the form of the uncertainty principle that we usually associate with Heisenberg.

5.7. The Discrete Fourier Transform

A. GENERAL

As with the continuous Fourier transform, we could treat the equations for the discrete Fourier transform (DFT) as completely independent, derive all the required theorems for them, and work entirely within this "closed system." However, as the data from which the discrete samples are taken are usually continuous, some discussion of sampling error is warranted. Furthermore, the DFT is inherently periodic, and the limitations and possible errors associated with this should be discussed.

The discrete Fourier transform is defined as

$$C_n \equiv \frac{1}{N} \sum_{K=0}^{N-1} f(k) \exp\left(-i\frac{2\pi}{N}nk\right) = F(n) \tag{5.42}$$

and its companion, the inverse discrete Fourier transform, is defined as

$$f(k) \equiv \sum_{n=0}^{N-1} C_n \exp\left(i\frac{2\pi}{N}nk\right) \tag{5.43}$$

where N is the number of sample points and n and k are integers.

The Fourier series and the DFT are actually special cases of the Fourier transform. The Fourier series has a discrete spectrum, but a periodic spatial function (note that an equally spaced discrete spectrum necessarily implies a periodic function with a finite period given by the wavelength of the lowest frequency). See Bracewell (1978) to see how the explicit form of the Fourier series may be obtained from the Fourier transform. We may arrive at the final form for the DFT by taking equally spaced samples over one period of the series (e.g., see Howard, 1978). Conceptually, though, it would be just as easy to consider the DFT as a special case of the Fourier transform directly.

With the DFT, then, both domains must obviously be periodic as well as discrete.

B. LIMITATIONS OF A PERIODIC REPRESENTATION

Addressing first the limitations of a periodic representation, such as with the DFT or Fourier series, it is evident that these forms are adequate only to represent either periodic functions or data over a finite interval. As data can only be taken over a finite interval, this is not in itself a serious drawback. However, under convolution, as the function represented over the interval repeats indefinitely, serious overlapping with the adjacent periods could occur. This is generally true for deconvolution also, as it is simply convolution with the inverse filter, $\mathcal{F}^{-1}\{1/G(\omega)\}$. If the data go to zero at the endpoints, one way of minimizing this type of error is simply to pad more zeros to one or both endpoints to minimize overlapping. Making the separation across the endpoints between the respective functions equal to the effective width of the impulse response function is usually sufficient for most practical purposes.

Another problem with a discrete periodic representation is that it is very difficult to represent functions that are not equal at their endpoints. The abrupt discontinuity across the endpoints of a periodic representation causes a considerable amplification of the high frequencies, which, in general, are very difficult to work with. Also, unless the sampling interval is taken very fine, this function can not be adequately represented by the DFT. However, this problem can be treated by extending each endpoint in a smooth curve that joins smoothly with the next period so as to yield an overall periodic function that is reasonably smooth. This is a valid operation as it is only necessary that the function be adequately represented over the interval of interest. The advantage of a smooth curve is that the high frequencies are now much smaller, and the overall numerical problem much more tractible.

With convolution and deconvolution, one must be careful to avoid endpoint error with this type of function. Convolution with the function beyond the endpoint of the data will extend inside the interval containing the data about half the length of the impulse response function, so the error will extend about half the length of the impulse response function also (assuming the impulse response function is approximately symmetrical). To minimize this error, the function extending beyond the endpoints should approximate the true function if anything is known about it. However, simply extending a very smooth curve across the endpoints is usually sufficient for most practical purposes. A good discussion of the endpoint error involved in the deconvolution of molecular scattering data is provided by Sheen and Skofronick (1974). Incidentally, a discrete function to extend that data in a usually very satisfactory manner is provided in a very versatile spline-fitting computer program developed by de Boor (1978). It minimizes the curvature by minimizing the second derivative of the discrete data function. Weights can be assigned to particular points, such as the endpoints, to assure small deviations there, and small weights can be assigned to the points beyond the endpoints so as to have sufficient flexibility to allow the discrete function there to form a very smooth curve. This program is also very useful for smoothing and base-line fitting.

C. SAMPLING ERROR

Next, we discuss sampling error. Fortunately, Fourier analysis is one of the few disciplines that provides a quantitative treament of this. As discussed earlier, sharp corners, discontinuities, and fine detail require the highest frequencies to represent them adequately. Smooth data may usually be adequately represented by a lower frequency band. On sampling with a coarse interval, it is evident that all fine detail is missed. This error enters into the Fourier expression of the data as an impersonation, or *aliasing,* of the lower frequencies by the higher frequencies; that is, for every low frequency in the Fourier expression, there is a set of high-frequency components that exhibit exactly the same behavior under the Fourier transform. From the sampled data alone, it would be impossible to determine how much of the lower frequency is present or how much of any of the other frequencies in the higher frequency set is present. All one would know is their sum. However, if all the higher frequencies were absent, that is, if the data were *band-limited,* then a complete recovery of the continuous function would be allowed by the discrete samples.

One procedure for recovering the continuous (band-limited) function exactly is provided by the *Whittaker–Shannon sampling theorem:*

$$f(x) = \sum_{n=-\infty}^{\infty} f\left(\frac{n}{2\Omega}\right) \text{sinc}(2\Omega x - n) \tag{5.44}$$

In words, this formula tells us that when the data are band-limited with $\omega = \Omega$ the highest frequency present, the spacing of the sampling interval may be as much as $\Delta x = 1/(2\Omega)$ and yet allow a complete recovery of the original continuous function. A proof of the sampling theorem may be found in Hamming (1962) and Papoulis (1962). An interesting discussion of sampling and aliasing error in terms of the comb function is provided by Bracewell (1978). For further discussion of aliasing and other error in the DFT, as well as a good coverage of digital filtering, the interested reader should peruse the series of articles in Rabiner and Rader (1972), especially the one by Bergland (1969).

The DFT representation, however, will allow a more convenient and faster interpolation of periodic data. To see how this can be, we write a few terms of the inverse DFT, which is a discrete Fourier series:

$$f(k) = \sum_{n=0}^{N-1} C_n \exp\left(i\frac{2\pi}{N}nk\right)$$

$$= C_0 + C_1 \exp\left(i\frac{2\pi}{N}k\right) + \cdots$$

$$= A_0 + A_1 \cos\frac{2\pi}{N}k + B_1 \sin\frac{2\pi}{N}k + A_2 \cos\frac{2\pi}{N}2k + \cdots \quad (5.45)$$

Note that we could let k be a continuous rather than a discrete variable, and we would then obtain a continuous function,

$$f(x) = A_0 + A_1 \cos\frac{2\pi}{N}x + B_1 \sin\frac{2\pi}{N}x + A_2 \cos\frac{2\pi}{N}2x + \cdots \quad (5.46)$$

where the continuous variable x has replaced k. This is the same functional form as the continuous Fourier series with the period $L = N$:

$$f(x) = a_0 + a_1 \cos\frac{2\pi}{L}x + b_1 \sin\frac{2\pi}{L}x + a_2 \cos\frac{2\pi}{L}2x + \cdots \quad (5.47)$$

The continuous function consisting of just N terms can only at best approximate the most general (continuous) function, for as we know, the Fourier series of the most general periodic function requires an infinite number of terms. However, if the particular periodic function under examination is made up of only N terms or less of its Fourier series, that is, if it is band-limited, then, because of the linear independence of the sinusoidal terms, the coefficients of the DFT are exactly the same as those of the Fourier series

$$A_0 = a_0, \quad A_1 = a_1, \quad B_1 = b_1, \quad A_2 = a_2, \quad \cdots \quad (5.48)$$

and the continuous function with the DFT coefficients produces exactly the same continuous function as the Fourier series. No information is lost on taking the Fourier transform. For an interesting proof of this and other important theorems for the DFT, see Bracewell (1978). Therefore, the N sample points obtained by taking the inverse DFT of these coefficients completely represent the original DFT coefficients, and hence the continuous function formed from them. Stated in another way, if the continuous periodic function is band-limited, with the number of discrete spectral components being N or less, then taking N equally spaced samples over the period is sufficient for perfect interpolation between the points. This may be done by constructing a continuous series from the DFT coefficients. Note that only N samples are necessary because one cycle is fully characteristic of the periodic function. For an interesting derivation of the relationship between the coefficients of the Fourier series and DFT, see Hamming (1962), whose explicit expression shows exactly which set of coefficients alias a particular given coefficient.

Closely associated with sampling error is the question of to what extent the information given in the DFT, which is a finite number of discrete samples or spectral components, is capable of representing the continuous function (or spectrum) over an infinite interval. A periodic function is certainly capable of being represented by a finite number of discrete samples. In the preceding paragraphs we have discussed how this is possible. For the nonperiodic function, though, even if it is band-limited and the sampling interval is sufficiently small, a finite number of samples is insufficient to represent the continuous function correctly. The sampling theorem tells us that an infinite number of samples is required. There is an aspect of a finite band, though, that we have not yet considered in these problems. This is that the finite-extent property of the band may be used as a constraint, as discussed earlier, to extrapolate the sampled function. We would hope that an infinite number of sample points might be obtained this way and that they would be unique. Unfortunately, this is not the case. It has been pointed out by Fiddy and Hall (1981) and Schafer et al. (1981) that, given a finite number of samples of a function, the constraints of square integrability and band limitation are not sufficient to determine that function uniquely. A family of functions is the best that may be determined.

With experimentally obtained data, which always contain random noise, such questions as uniqueness, are to be sure, academic. With noise, an exact solution is impossible to obtain, and the best that one may do, in a statistical sense, is to find the solution that is most probable. And even a solution that is most probable (overall) is not always what is desired. A unique solution is forced by the criterion or method of the solution adopted, such as minimizing the sum of squares or minimizing the maximum deviation. Each of these criteria produces a solution that is optimal in some sense. Various aspects of the error will be minimized in each of these slightly differing solutions. We may want to choose the criterion that minimizes some aspect of this error (or emphasizes some other aspect of the restoration). However, we may want to choose some particular criterion simply because it lends itself to more convenient mathematical manipulation or faster numerical calculation. Except for special cases, the differences among the restorations produced by the various criteria are usually small and inconsequential. In a gross sense, the restorations produced by the methods mentioned in this section that apply many of the most effective constraints usually are much closer to the original undistorted function, even in the presence of moderate to high noise levels. Thus the primary objective in initiating these restoration procedures is largely accomplished.

D. CONCLUDING REMARKS

For the representation of almost all experimental data and their restorations over an interval, the DFT has been found to be very adequate and useful. The errors peculiar to the DFT representation, such as those due to periodicity and a finite number of samples, are usually small compared to the errors due to noise. Restoration operations, such as deconvolution, are usually adequately performed within the DFT formulation.

As discussed earlier, the information-containing components of the Fourier spectrum of experimental data (even after restoration) become smaller with increasing frequency and merge into the noise at the high-frequency portion of the spectrum. Taking the DFT of experimental data, it is found that the informational spectrum is represented in most cases by a quite small number of discrete components. The information-bearing components that are aliased would necessarily be very small and would contribute negligible error. However, the noise spectrum decays very slowly (if at all) and is still significantly large at the higher frequencies, and the highest of the noise frequencies would be aliased (for any sampling interval). Taking a finer sampling interval minimizes this aliasing. With a finer sampling interval, more of the high-frequency-noise spectral components that were previously aliased now show up in the Fourier spectrum (that they are now present in the Fourier spectrum implies that they are certainly not aliased). So taking increasingly finer sampling intervals further minimizes the aliasing of the low-frequency informational components by the high-frequency-noise components. The reader should be aware that this has little effect on the low-frequency noise, though. Note that this reduction of the aliasing with a finer sampling interval closely corresponds to minimization of the error in the data in a statistical sense, in that simply "getting more points" on the data allows a reduction of the error by least-squares calculations.

The preceding discussion also suggests a way of "tightly packing" the data, that is, a way of representing the significant information in the data by a much smaller number of points. Truncating the Fourier spectrum at some point before the noise assumes a significant fraction of the magnitude and saving this much smaller number of discrete components constitute a procedure that usually preserves all the important information in the data.

5.8. Extrapolation of Discrete Fourier Spectra

A. INTRODUCTORY REMARKS

The discrete Fourier spectrum, as given by the DFT, comprises the coefficients of a complex Fourier series. The inverse DFT is, of course, this series:

$$f(k) = \sum_{n=0}^{N-1} C_n \exp\left(i\frac{2\pi}{N}nk\right) = C_0 + C_1 \exp\left(i\frac{2\pi}{N}k\right) + \cdots$$

$$= A_0 + A_1 \cos\frac{2\pi}{N}k + B_1 \sin\frac{2\pi}{N}k + A_2 \cos\frac{2\pi}{N}2k$$

$$+ B_2 \sin\frac{2\pi}{N}2k + \cdots + A_{N-1} \cos\frac{2\pi}{N}(N-1)k \qquad (5.49)$$

The coefficients of the sines and cosines will be real for real data. Restoring a high-frequency band of c (unique complex) discrete spectral components to a low-frequency band of b (unique complex) spectral components will be the same (when transformed) as forming the discrete Fourier series from the high-frequency band and adding this function to the series formed from the low-frequency band. When applying the constraints in the spatial domain, the Fourier series representation will be used. In all restorations treated in this research, the series formed from the low-frequency band is held fixed, and the series formed from the high-frequency band varies by allowing the coefficients to vary until the particular constraint or constraints are satisfied. The reader will recall that we discussed the general (continuous) case involving the application of constraints to these two bands earlier. With discrete variables, $u(k)$ would denote the series expression obtained from the low-frequency band and $v(k)$ the series expression obtained from the high-frequency band. The explicit Fourier series expression for each would be

$$u(k) = A_0 + A_1 \cos\frac{2\pi}{N}k + B_1 \sin\frac{2\pi}{N}k$$

$$+ A_2 \cos\frac{2\pi}{N}2k + \cdots + B_{b-1} \sin\frac{2\pi}{N}(b-1)k \qquad (5.50)$$

$$V(k) = A_b \cos\frac{2\pi}{N}bk + B_b \sin\frac{2\pi}{N}bk + A_{b+1} \cos\frac{2\pi}{N}(b+1)k$$

$$+ \cdots + B_{b+c-1} \sin\frac{2\pi}{N}(b+c-1)k \qquad (5.51)$$

The restored function, as discussed earlier, is given by the sum $u(k) + v(k)$, where the coefficients in $v(k)$ vary to satisfy the constraints. As $u(k)$ is constant for all restoration problems, no useful purpose will be served by writing out its Fourier series expression, and so the series representation will always be suppressed.

Let the discrete spectrum (which are the coefficients) of $u(k)$ and $v(k)$ be denoted by $U(n)$ and $V(n)$, respectively. The low-frequency spectral components $U(n)$ are most often given by those most noise-free spectral components that have undergone inverse filtering. $V(n)$ for these cases would then be the restored spectrum. However, for Fourier transform spectroscopy data, $U(n)$ would be the finite number of samples that make up the interferogram. For these cases $V(n)$ would then represent the interferogram extension.

As mentioned earlier, the sum of the squared error is found to be the most convenient measure of the error, as much of the calculation may be done analytically. Let us now see what form the sum of squares will take for the constraint of finite extent.

B. Constraint of Finite Extent

1. *Theory*

This constraint applies to data that exist only over a finite interval and have zero values elsewhere. Let $N1$ and $N2$ denote the nonzero extent of the original undistorted data. The restored function, $u(k) + v(k)$, should then have no deviations from zero outside the known extent of the data. So we should minimize the sum of these squared deviations from zero of the function $u(k) + v(k)$ for those sample points outside the known extent of the data to find the coefficients in $v(k)$ that will best satisfy this constraint. Actually, recovering only a band of frequencies in $v(k)$ implies the additional constraint of holding all higher frequencies above this band to zero. This is necessary for stability and is an example of one of the smoothing constraints discussed earlier. We minimize the expression

$$\sum_{\substack{k<N1 \\ k>N2}} [u(k) + v(k)]^2 = \sum_{\substack{k<N1 \\ k>N2}} \left[u(k) + A_b \cos\frac{2\pi}{N} bk + B_b \sin\frac{2\pi}{N} bk \right.$$

$$+ A_{b+1} \cos\frac{2\pi}{N}(b+1)k + \cdots$$

$$\left. + B_{b+c-1} \sin\frac{2\pi}{N}(b+c-1)k \right]^2 \qquad (5.52)$$

The standard procedure for finding the minimum of a function of several variables is to take the partial derivative with respect to each variable and set the result to zero. Taking the derivative with respect to each unknown coefficient and setting the result equal to zero will give (the summation interval is suppressed)

$$\frac{\partial}{\partial A_b} \sum [u(k) + v(k)]^2 = 0$$

$$\frac{\partial}{\partial B_b} \sum [u(k) + v(k)]^2 = 0$$

$$\frac{\partial}{\partial A_{b+1}} \sum [u(k) + v(k0)^2 = 0 \qquad (5.53)$$

$$\vdots$$

$$\frac{\partial}{\partial B_{b+c-1}} \sum [u(k) + v(k)]^2 = 0$$

Considering in detail the derivative with respect to A_b, we have

$$\sum \frac{\partial}{\partial A_b} \left[u(k) + A_b \cos \frac{2\pi}{N} bk + \cdots \right]^2 = 0$$

$$= 2 \sum [u(k) + v(k)] \cos \frac{2\pi}{N} bk = 0 \qquad (5.54)$$

The other derivatives are calculated in a similar manner, and we have for the complete set of equations

$$\sum [u(k) + v(k)] \cos \frac{2\pi}{N} bk = 0$$

$$\sum [u(k) + v(k)] \sin \frac{2\pi}{N} bk = 0$$

$$\sum [u(k) + v(k)] \cos \frac{2\pi}{N} (b + 1)k = 0 \qquad (5.55)$$

$$\vdots$$

$$\sum [u(k) + v(k)] \sin \frac{2\pi}{N} (b + c - 1)k = 0$$

Because of aliasing, the total number of coefficients solved for should not be greater than N. We have a set of $2c$ linear equations for the $2c$ unknown coefficients. A number of standard methods are available for solving a set of linear equations. The Gauss–Jordan matrix reduction method may be used for solving these. However, there are important advantages to iterative methods when the number of equations to solve is large. Once the coefficients have been obtained, they may be converted to complex form and added to the original spectrum. Taking the inverse DFT would then yield the restored function. However, if the number of solved coefficients are small, it may be quicker simply to substitute the coefficients into the series representation of $v(k)$ and add this series to $u(k)$.

The methods developed here are very general and may apply to many research fields. The artificial data treated in this chapter could represent data from a diversity of research areas. The restorations produced in this chapter could also be representative of any of these areas. The abscissa on these plots would then represent what the recorded quantity is being measured against and could be time, linear distance, angle, wave number, etc. The experimental data treated in this chapter will always be IR spectral lines in the 3-μm wavelength region, and the abscissa will always represent the wave number in units of centimeter^{-1}. The ordinate, then, would represent electromagnetic intensity.

2. Applications

a. Artificial Data.   To illustrate the effectiveness of the finite-extent constraint, the restoration of two merged, almost completely noise-free Gaussian peaks is shown in Fig. 5.2. These data, as do all data to which the finite-extent constraint is applied, make up a 256-point data field. The original peaks are shown in Fig. 5.2a. The Fourier spectrum truncated after the seventh (complex) coefficient is shown in Fig. 5.2b. The restoration of Fig. 5.2c was accomplished by restoring 16 complex coefficients to the Fourier spectrum with the summation region being over the last 128 points of the data field of Fig. 5.2b. Note that an almost perfect restoration was accomplished. The Fourier spectrum of a Gaussian function is also a Gaussian and dies out very quickly, so restoring only 32 coefficients (16 unique complex) produced a very good approximation to the original data. It was found that when the minimization procedure involved only the last quarter of the data field (64 data points), a good restoration was nevertheless obtained. The solved coefficients were almost the same as in the previous case. Even with the summation being over only one-eighth of the data field (32 points), a crude approximation to the first few coefficients after the

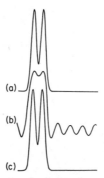

FIG. 5.2. Restoration of the Fourier spectrum of almost completely noise-free data. (a) Original two Gaussian peaks. (b) Same peaks with the spectrum truncated after the seventh (complex) coefficient. (c) Peaks of (b) with 16 (complex) coefficients restored.

truncation frequency was obtained. However, the higher frequency components were much larger than their true size.

It is important to note that these data are not completely error free, and that some approximations are involved. There are several sources of small error, computational roundoff probably being dominant. Also, a Gaussian function never dies out exactly to zero. However, its values are very small after even two or three standard deviations away from its maximum value. If the noise and other error are very much larger than this, however, severe computational difficulties ensue. Figures 5.3–5.6 illustrate the effect of moderate amounts of noise on the restoration.

The effects of a measured amount of Gaussian noise on the deconvolution of a single Gaussian peak are given in Fig. 5.3 to enable a more quantitative discussion of the results. The original Gaussian function is given in Fig. 5.3a. The deconvolution of this function (with another Gaussian) is given in Fig. 5.3b, which shows that the correctly restored result should be Gaussian in form and have a width about half that of the original function. Note that inverse filtering is sufficient for the restoration if the data are largely noise free. We soon see, however, that even relatively small amounts of noise necessitate truncation of all but a few coefficients of the Fourier spectrum. Fig. 5.3c is the same function as in Fig. 5.3a, with Gaussian noise of rms one-twentieth of the amplitude of the peak superimposed, a rather high level. Upon deconvolution of this noisy function, it was found that meaningful results could not be obtained unless the spectrum of the inverse-filtered result was truncated after the sixth (complex) coefficient. The reason for this is quite apparent when the spectrum of the noise in the inverse-filtered result is examined. Figure 5.4 illustrates this problem. Figure 5.4b is the magnitude of the first nine Fourier spectral components of the noise in

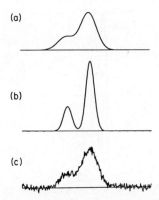

FIG. 5.3. Deconvolution of a single Gaussian peak. (a) Noise-free Gaussian peak. (b) Inverse filtering of the peak of (a) with another Gaussian function. The resulting peak is also Gaussian in form. This is what the restoration from the noisy data will be compared with. (c) Peak in (a) with Gaussian noise of rms one-twentieth of the amplitude of the Gaussian peak superimposed.

the original data, Fig. 5.3c. Figure 5.4a is the magnitude of these same spectral components after inverse filtering. From examining Fig. 5.4a, it is evident that keeping more than six (complex) coefficients in the inverse-filtered result would contribute unacceptably large noise error into the restoration. Even when only six coefficients or fewer are kept, the high noise level contributes considerable instability into the solution, which is especially apparent when the summation interval is decreased.

For Figs. 5.5 and 5.6, the extent of the summation interval, which is the

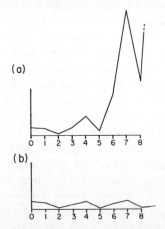

FIG. 5.4. Fourier spectrum of the noise that was superimposed on the Gaussian peak of Fig. 5.3c. (a) Spectrum of the noise after inverse filtering. It is evident that the noise error increases considerably after the sixth complex coefficient. (b) Spectrum of the noise in the original peak.

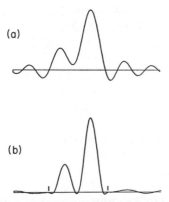

FIG. 5.5. Restoration by inverse filtering of the low-frequency band followed by spectral restoration of the high-frequency band with the constraint of finite extent. (a) Inverse filtering of the peak in Fig. 5.3c with 6 (complex) coefficients retained in the Fourier spectrum produced this result. (b) Restoration of 16 (complex) coefficients to the spectrum with the constraint of finite extent applied to the region indicated by the tick marks yields this improved function.

region to which the constraint is applied, is indicated by the tick marks on the graphs. Figure 5.5a shows the inverse-filtered function with only 6 coefficients kept in its Fourier spectrum. Recall that the broadened peak and the ringing around the peak, characteristics of a function with a truncated spectrum, come from the theoretical interpretation of convolution of the original function with the sinc function. Letting the summation interval

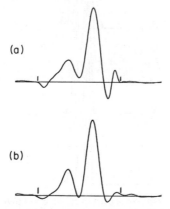

FIG. 5.6. Restoration of the inverse-filtered result shown in Fig. 5.5a with the required summation for the constraint of finite extent taken over the interval indicated by the tick marks. (a) Restoration of 16 (complex) coefficients to the inverse-filtered estimate. (b) Restoring only 3 (complex) coefficients to the inverse-filtered estimate produced this restored function.

include the first negative sidelobe on each side of this function and solving 32 coefficients (16 complex) produced the result shown in Fig. 5.5b, which is a reasonably good result. However, by taking the summation interval further away from the peak, as in Fig. 5.6, a highly erroneous result is obtained. For the summation interval defined by the tick marks, restoring 16 (complex) coefficients produced the result shown in Fig. 5.6a, a very unsatisfactory result. To yield any improvement for this summation interval, no more than 6 (3 complex) coefficients were allowed to be recovered. This is shown in Fig. 5.6b. As stated earlier, recovering only a small band of frequencies is an additional constraint that is necessary in many cases of strongly error-laden data.

  b. Experimental Data. The experimental data chosen for improvement were two merged IR spectral lines, shown in Fig. 5.7a. These were methane spectral lines taken with a two-pass Littrow-type diffraction grating spectrometer. These data are (as are all the grating spectrometer data discussed herein) isolated sets of IR lines excerpted from data recorded and described by Hunt *et al.* (1978). To improve the resolution, inverse filtering was first performed.

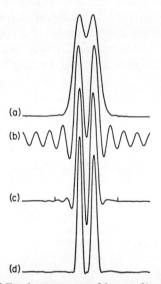

FIG. 5.7. Restoration of Fourier spectrum of inverse-filtered noisy IR peaks with the constraint of finite extent. (a) Two merged IR peaks. (b) Inverse-filtered IR peaks with the spectrum truncated after the tenth coefficient. (c) Spectrum restored by applying constraint outside the marked region. Five (complex) coefficients were restored. (d) Spectrum restored with constrained region including the first negative sidelobes and dip between peaks, as well as all other regions outside the peaks. Sixteen (complex) coefficients were recovered.

A Gaussian function was chosen as the impulse response function, which reasonably approximates the true impulse response for these lines (Jansson, 1968). The Fourier spectrum of a Gaussian usually suitably approximates most impulse response functions at their lower frequencies. However, as this spectrum dies out so quickly, the approximation is usually poor at higher frequencies. If inverse filtering is not followed by spectral restoration and if more higher frequencies are retained, probably a better approximation to the correct impulse response is needed. The author became aware of this behavior of the Gaussian impulse response function as he was trying to reduce the effects of the rapidly ascending noise term in the inverse-filtered result by "supersmoothing" the experimental data. It was hoped that this would reduce the magnitudes of the noise in the higher frequencies sufficiently to take a truncation point for the inverse-filtered result further into the higher frequencies. However, the Gaussian spectrum died out so quickly that the spectrum of the inverse-filtered result did not descend any further toward zero than it did without the smoothing, and no improvement was gained by this method.

Getting back to the data shown in Fig. 5.7, to minimize the error due to the noise in these methane lines, the inverse-filtered result was truncated after the tenth (complex) coefficient. This is shown in Fig. 5.7b. To restore the spectrum after the tenth coefficient, the summation interval was chosen to be over the first 65 and the last 64 data points, as it is evident from examining the original data that no information exists in these regions. Attempting to restore 32 coefficients produced highly erroneous results. A much narrower band of frequencies must be attempted if a reasonable result is to be obtained. Solving for 10 (5 unique complex) coefficients produced the restored peaks shown in Fig. 5.7c. A considerable improvement in resolution is obtained. The constraint ensured that the base line would be straight in the summation region, as it should be. However, the first negative sidelobes around the peaks are still rather large, and the function dips strongly negatively between the peaks. More of the function will have to be constrained for improvement. Extending the summation region to include the first negative sidelobe on each side of the peaks and most of the negative dip between the peaks produced the restoration in Fig. 5.7d, which has a much improved appearance. However, this operation is of questionable validity, as we are not sure that information does not exist in these included regions. For further improvement, without assumptions, additional constraints are needed. We find later that the constraint of minimum negativity will yield a better result for the restoration of these IR lines.

In data-point units, the original IR peaks were about 34 units wide (FWHM). This corresponds to an actual width of approximately 0.024 cm^{-1}. The impulse response function was about 25 units wide. After inverse filtering and restoration of the Fourier spectrum, the resolved peaks were 11 and 14 units wide, respectively. This is close to the Doppler width of these lines.

C. Constraint of Minimum Negativity

1. *Theory*

The constraint of minimum negativity applies to data for which it is known that the correctly restored function should be all positive. For our formulation, we want to find the coefficients of $v(k)$ that best satisfy this constraint, which will be those that minimize the negative deviations in the total function, $u(k) + v(k)$. The sum of the squared values of the negative deviations is given by

$$\sum_{k=0}^{N-1} \{H[-u(k) - v(k)][u(k) + v(k)]\}^2$$

where $H(y)$ is the unit step function and is defined for an arbitrary argument y as

$$H(y) \equiv \begin{cases} 0, & y < 0 \\ \tfrac{1}{2}, & y = 0 \\ 1, & y > 0 \end{cases} \tag{5.56}$$

The set of coefficients in $v(k)$ that minimize the expression with the step function is the desired solution. However, we cannot carry out the minimization procedure with this expression. We cannot take the partial derivatives with respect to this function as it is not continuous. However, consider the alternative expression

$$\sum_{k=0}^{N-1} \left(\frac{1}{1 + \exp\{K[u(k) + v(k)]\}} [u(k) + v(k)] \right)^2$$

where K is a variable parameter. Note that $1/[1 + \exp(Ky)]$ approaches $H(-y)$ as $K \to \infty$ for an arbitrary y. Thus, as K in the above summation approaches infinity, the entire expression approaches arbitrarily close to the original expression with the step function. Now we have an expression in closed form that consists entirely of analytic functions. We may now carry out the minimization procedure by taking the derivatives with respect to the unknown coefficients and setting the results equal to zero. For simplification let

$$w(k) = 1/(1 + \exp\{K[u(k) + v(k)]\})$$ (5.57)

Then we will have for the resulting set of equations:

$$\frac{\partial}{\partial A_b} \sum_{k=0}^{N-1} \{w(k)[u(k) + v(k)]\}^2 = 0$$

$$\frac{\partial}{\partial B_b} \sum_{k=0}^{N-1} \{w(k)[u(k) + v(k)]\}^2 = 0$$

$$\frac{\partial}{\partial A_{b+1}} \sum_{k=0}^{N-1} \{w(k)[u(k) + v(k)]\}^2 = 0$$ (5.58)

$$\vdots$$

$$\frac{\partial}{\partial B_{b+c-1}} \sum_{k=0}^{N-1} \{w(k)[u(k) + v(k)]\}^2 = 0$$

Considering in detail the derivative with respect to A_b, we have

$$\sum_{k=0}^{N-1} \frac{\partial}{\partial A_b} \left(\frac{1}{1 + \exp\{K[u(k) + v(k)]\}} [u(k) + v(k)] \right)^2$$

$$= 2 \sum_{k=0}^{N-1} \cos \frac{2\pi}{N} bk \left(\frac{u(k) + v(k)}{1 + \exp\{K[u(k) + v(k)]\}} \right)$$

$$\times \left(\frac{1}{1 + \exp\{K[u(k) + v(k)]\}} - K \exp\{K[u(k) + v(k)]\} \right.$$

$$\times \left. \frac{1}{1 + \exp\{K[u(k) + v(k)]\}} \right) = 0$$ (5.59)

The second term in the rightmost set of large parentheses approaches zero as $K \to \infty$, so that for K large, we have to a good approximation,

$$\sum_{k=0}^{N-1} \frac{u(k) + v(k)}{(1 + \exp\{K[u(k) + v(k)]\})^2} \cos \frac{2\pi}{N} bk = 0$$ (5.60)

The other derivatives are calculated in a similar manner, and we have for the complete set of equations

$$\sum_{k=0}^{N-1} w^2(k)[u(k) + v(k)] \cos\frac{2\pi}{N}bk \qquad = 0$$

$$\sum_{k=0}^{N-1} w^2(k)[u(k) + v(k)] \sin\frac{2\pi}{N}bk \qquad = 0$$

$$\sum_{k=0}^{N-1} w^2(k)[u(k) + v(k)] \cos\frac{2\pi}{N}(b + 1)k \quad = 0 \qquad (5.61)$$

$$\vdots$$

$$\sum_{k=0}^{N-1} w^2(k)[u(k) + v(k)] \sin\frac{2\pi}{N}(b + c - 1) = 0$$

where $b + c < N/2$.

Because the unknown coefficients are also in the exponentials, these equations are nonliner in the coefficients and would ordinarily be difficult to solve. However, certain iterative techniques that not only yield a converging solution but also bring about considerable simplification in the equations may be applied. A form of the method of successive substitutions was developed for this research. The Newton–Raphson method also shows promise. However, as a matrix square in the number of equations, $2c$, must be solved on each iteration, the Newton–Raphson method may not be appropriate when c is very large. However, the Newton–Raphson method converges faster than the method of successive substitutions (e.g., see Hildebrand, 1965).

The particular iterative method chosen for this research is now discussed in detail. First, each of the equations is solved for one of the unknown coefficients within the first set of brackets. There are a number of ways of doing this. However, a reduction in the number of calculations results from solving for the coefficient associated with the multiplicative sinusoidal factor in each equation. Only the first equation of the resulting set is written, as it illustrates all the salient features:

$$A_b = -\frac{\displaystyle\sum_{k=0}^{N-1} \frac{u(k) + v(k) - A_b \cos(2\pi/N)bk}{(1 + \exp\{K[u(k) + v(k)]\})^2}\cos\frac{2\pi}{N}bk}{\displaystyle\sum_{k=0}^{N-1} \frac{\cos^2(2\pi/N)bk}{(1 + \exp\{K[u(k) + v(k)]\})^2}} \qquad (5.62)$$

Next, the initial values of the coefficients are substituted into the right-hand sides of the equations. Zeros are substituted if no better initial values are known. The substantial advantage of this approach now becomes apparent. For K sufficiently large, if the function $u(k) + v(k)$ is negative by even the smallest amount, the exponential will by extremely small, and the factor $1/(1 + \exp\{K[u(k) + v(k)]\})^2$ is approximately unity. If $u(k) + v(k)$ is positive by even the smallest amount, the factor $1/(1 + \exp\{K[u(k) + v(k)]\})^2$ essentially vanishes. These approximations approach exactness as $K \to \infty$. Thus the equations may be expressed essentially as follows:

$$A_b = -\frac{\sum_{k=0}^{N-1} [u(k) + v(k) - A_b \cos(2\pi/N)bk] \cos(2\pi/N)bk}{\sum_{k=0}^{N-1} \cos^2(2\pi/N)bk}$$

$$B_b = -\frac{\sum_{k=0}^{N-1} [u(k) + v(k) - B_b \sin(2\pi/N)bk] \sin(2\pi/N)bk}{\sum_{k=0}^{N-1} \sin^2(2\pi/N)bk}$$

$$A_{b+1} = -\frac{\sum_{k=0}^{N-1} [u(k) + v(k) - A_{b+1} \cos(2\pi/N)(b + 1)k] \cos(2\pi/N)(b + 1)k}{\sum_{k=0}^{N-1} \cos^2(2\pi/N)(b + 1)k}$$

$$\vdots \qquad\qquad (5.63)$$

$$B_{b+c-1} = -\frac{\sum_{k=0}^{N-1} [u(k) + v(k) - B_{b+c-1} \sin(2\pi/N)(b + c - 1)k] \sin(2\pi/N)(b + c - 1)k}{\sum_{k=0}^{N-1} \sin^2(2\pi/N)(b + c - 1)k}$$

for $u(k) + v(k) < 0$. That is, take the summation only over those data points for which the function $u(k) + v(k)$ is negative. The considerable computational time saved by not having to calculate the exponentials is evident. Note that the negative values of $u(k) + v(k)$ change in each iteration as the new values of the coefficients are determined, so that a different summation is made in each iteration. For this reason it is necessary to test $u(k) + v(k)$ for its negative values before summing over them.

Although this procedure was developed from the constraint of minimum negativity, it is found that it will easily accommodate other constraints as well, with only slight modification. Note that if the summation is not over a different set of data points each iteration, but is over a fixed set of points, the summation need only be taken once, as $u(k)$ and the sinusoids are constant for each value of the variable k. This is the case for the constraint of finite extent, as the summation is taken over the fixed interval outside the known extent of the data. The form of the preceding equations would be the same as that taken by the equations of finite extent when the method of successive substitutions is used. The constant summation interval of finite extent yields the constant coefficients (not to be confused with the coefficients being solved for) of the set of linear equations in the unknowns. The form of the method of successive substitutions for a set of linear equations is known as the Gauss–Seidel or The Jacobi method, respectively, depending on whether each new unknown determined was used in improving the unknown in the succeeding equation, or whether every new unknown was determined from all the old ones before another iteration was begun. That both constraints result in very similar equations under the method of successive substitutions strongly suggests that both constraints could probably be included in one formulation to yield the optimum resolution for a given set of data. It is found in practice that all that is necessary to implement both constraints successfully on the same set of data is to take the summation over all data points outside the known extent of the data (for the constraint of finite extent), while summing the negative values only over all other intervals (for the constraint of minimum negativity).

The more mathematically inclined reader may want to provide greater rigor to this loose development by formulating the sum-of-squares expression to include both constraints. Carrying out the minimization procedure and the other simplifications would result in the same numerical operations to obtain the solution as in the preceding.

Further, if the data have an upper bound as well as a lower bound, this additional constraint may also be applied by summing over the data points above the upper bound [after subtracting the upper bound value from $u(k) + v(k)$], as well as over those below the lower bound. Although this additional constraint has been successful in minimizing values above the upper bound, it has resulted in little overall improvement in the restoration.

The modified procedure just discussed can successfully accommodate any of the constraints, or any combination of them, in a relatively uncomplicated way. Applying all the constraints simultaneously produces a result much more likely to be correct than the result obtained by applying each constraint separately. The general procedure developed permits great versatility.

There are two different procedures by which the iteration may be carried out. One may substitute each improved coefficient, along with all the others, into the succeeding equation. Alternatively, all the unknown coefficients in all the equations may be determined using only the set of coefficients determined from the previous iteration. Converging solutions for the latter case were seldom obtained, however, and its use was abandoned early in the research. The former procedure converges almost always when the tolerance is not chosen exceedingly small.

The tolerance determines when the iteration is stopped. The iterations continue until the maximum change in any of the coefficient values over its value in the previous iteration is less than the chosen tolerance. With this procedure, convergence is quick to a large tolerance and much slower to a smaller tolerance. For almost all cases in this research the tolerance was taken to be about one-hundredth of the average of the values close to the truncation point. With this tolerance, most of the restorations shown in this work usually required from 10 to 50 iterations. However, convergence for some data was very slow, and occasionally a data run would take several hundred iterations. If the processing and restoration of data becomes a routine procedure in the laboratory, tolerances larger than the one discussed here would probably be preferable. Tolerances several times larger have produced very satisfactory results.

2. Applications

a. Artificial Data. The procedure to implement the constraint of minimum negativity, as given in the preceding paragraphs, is first applied to the deconvolution of the artificial data shown in Fig. 5.3. This is done in order to permit a better comparison of the effectiveness of this constraint with that of finite extent. Figure 5.8a shows the result of inverse-filtering the Gaussian peak shown in Fig. 5.3c with 6 (complex) coefficients retained in its spectrum, and is the same function as that shown in Fig. 5.5a. Restoration of 32 (16 complex) coefficients produced the result shown in Fig. 5.8b. This is slightly better than the result obtained with the constraint of finite extent, in which the summation interval included the first negative sidelobes around the peak, shown in Fig. 5.5b. It is vastly better, though, than the result obtained with the summation interval taken further away from the peak, as

FIG. 5.8. Restoration by inverse filtering of the low-frequency band followed by spectral restoration of the high-frequency band with the constraint of minimum negativity. (a) The same inverse-filtered result as that shown in Fig. 5.5a. Six coefficients are retained. (b) Restoring 16 (complex) coefficients to the Fourier spectrum by applying the constraint of minimum negativity.

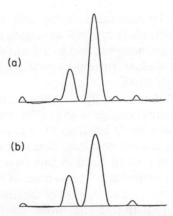

FIG. 5.9. Effect on the spectral restoration of choosing a different truncation point for inverse filtering of the peak shown in Fig. 5.3c. (a) Seven (complex) coefficients were retained in the inverse-filtered result. Restoring 16 coefficients to the spectrum produced this restored function. This illustrates the effect of retaining too many error-laden coefficients in the inverse-filtered result. (b) Five (complex) coefficients were retained in the inverse-filtered result. Restoring 16 coefficients to the spectrum produced this restored function.

shown in Fig. 5.6. It has been found to be generally true that the constraint of minimum negativity produces much superior results to those obtained from the constraint of finite extent.

Figure 5.9 shows the constraint of minimum negativity applied to the same deconvolution as that shown in Fig. 5.8, but with different truncation points on the Fourier spectrum. Figure 5.9a shows restoration to the inverse-filtered estimate with 7 (complex) coefficients retained, and illustrates the distortion occurring when too many noise-laden coefficients are retained in the Fourier spectrum. From Fig. 5.4a it is evident that the seventh coefficient contains a large amount of noise error. Figures 5.9b shows restoration to the inverse-filtered result with only 5 complex coefficients retained in the Fourier spectrum. It differs little from the restoration with only 6 coefficients retained in the inverse-filtered estimate shown in Fig. 5.8b. For both cases shown in Fig. 5.9, 16 complex coefficients were restored.

b. Experimental Grating Spectroscopy Data. Figures 5.10 and 5.11 illustrate the application of the constraint of minimum negativity to restore inverse-filtered IR spectral lines. A Gaussian function was chosen as an approximation to the impulse response function, and 32 (16 unique complex) coefficients were restored in each case. Both sets of data make up a 256-point field.

The first two plots in Fig. 5.10 are the same as the first two plots of Fig. 5.7, and permit a comparison of the constraints of minimum negativity and

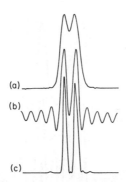

FIG. 5.10. Restoration of Fourier spectrum to the inverse filtering of two noisey IR peaks using constraint of minimum negativity. (a) Two merged IR peaks. (b) Inverse filtering of IR peaks with spectrum truncated after the tenth coefficient. (c) Spectrum restored by minimizing the sum of the squares of the negative regions of the inverse-filtered result. Sixteen (unique complex) coefficients were restored.

finite extent for experimental data. Figure 5.10c is the restoration using the constraint of minimum negativity. It is evidently far superior to the restoration given in Fig. 5.7c, which was obtained from the constraint of finite extent. In Fig. 5.10c the base line is quite straight in the regions outside the immediate vicinity of the peaks and is correct there, as an examination of Fig. 5.10a reveals that no information exists in these regions. If, however, too many coefficients that are contaminated by a high proportion of noise are retained in the deconvolution, false detail will begin to show up in these regions. An examination of the base line away from the peaks in the original data thus provides us with a crude measure of the error involved in restoration, especially that caused by retaining too many error-laden high-frequency coefficients.

The data illustrated in Fig. 5.11a are methane absorption lines (0.02 cm^{-1} in width) observed with a four-pass Littrow-type diffraction grating spectrometer. The data were taken at low pressure, so that Doppler broadening is the major contributor to the true width of the lines. The straightforward inverse-filtered estimate with 15 (complex) coefficients retained is given by Fig. 5.11b. Figure 5.11c is the restored function. The positions and intensities of the restored absorption lines agree well with other independent studies. In data-point units, the original peaks were approximately 19 units wide (FWHM). The restored peaks are about 8–9 units wide, or close to the expected Doppler width. The Gaussian impulse response function is approximately 16.5 units wide.

It is noted for both Figs. 5.10 and 5.11 that the negative values of the restored functions are very small.

Figures 5.12–5.18 illustrate restoration in the presence of a drifting base

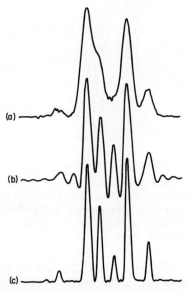

FIG. 5.11. Restoration of Fourier spectrum of inverse-filtered, strongly merged IR peaks using constraint of minimum negativity. (a) Noise IR data. (b) Inverse filtering of IR data with spectrum truncated after fifteenth coefficient. (c) Spectrum restored by minimizing the sum of the squares of the negative regions of the inverse-filtered result. Sixteen (complex) coefficients were restored.

line. These data are methane absorption lines taken with a four-pass Littrow-type diffraction grating spectrometer. For these data 2048 data points were taken. The impulse response function was approximated by a Gaussian.

The original data are shown in Fig. 5.12. A spline fit has been made to the curved base line. These data are adjusted to a zero base line in accordance with the transmittance relation

$$T_m = U(\sigma)/U_0(\sigma) \tag{5.64}$$

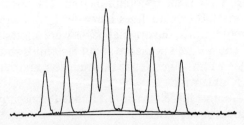

FIG. 5.12. Noise IR data (2048 sample points) with spline fit to curved base line.

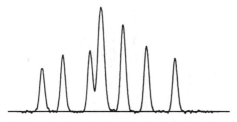

FIG. 5.13. Data of Fig. 5.12 adjusted to a function with zero base line according to the transmittance relation.

where T_m is the measured transmittance, $U_0(\sigma)$ is the unabsorbed intensity, $U(\sigma)$ is the observed intensity after absorption by the gas in the sample, and σ denotes wave number. The corrected data are shown in Fig. 5.13. Figure 5.14 illustrates inverse filtering of these corrected data with the Fourier spectrum truncated after the thirty-fifth coefficient. The Gaussian impulse response function had a FWHM of 39 (data-point) units. Restoring 32 (16 unique) coefficients to the truncated spectrum by minimizing the sum of the square of the negative values of the function shown in Fig. 5.14 produces the improved IR lines shown in Fig. 5.15.

Figure 5.16 shows the result of inverse filtering with a Gaussian impulse response function of FWHM 46 units. The Fourier spectrum was truncated after the thirtieth coefficient. Note that the broader impulse response function should result in narrower restored peaks. Restoring 62 (31 unique) coefficients to the Fourier spectrum of the inverse-filtered result of Fig. 5.16 by minimizing the sum of the squares of the negative deviations produces the result shown in Fig. 5.17. Note that these peaks are narrower than those of Fig. 5.15, which implies a broader Fourier spectrum. This necessitates recovering more spectral components in order to obtain reasonable results. Restoring 74 (37 unique) coefficients to the Fourier spectrum of the inverse-filtered result shown in Fig. 5.16 with the application of the constraint of

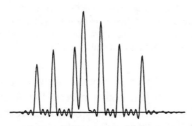

FIG. 5.14. Result of inverse-filtering the corrected data of Fig. 5.13 with the Gaussian impulse response function of FWHM = 39 units. The Fourier spectrum was truncated after the thirty-fifth (complex) coefficient.

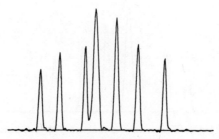

FIG. 5.15. Restoring 32 (16 complex) coefficients to the inverse-filtered spectrum of the function shown in Fig. 5.14 by minimizing the sum of the squares of the negative deviations produces this result.

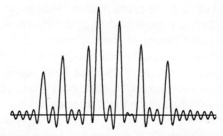

FIG. 5.16. Inverse-filtering the corrected data of Fig. 5.13 with a Gaussian impulse function of FWHM = 46 units produced this result. The Fourier spectrum was truncated after the thirtieth coefficient.

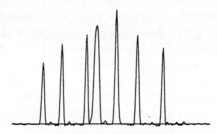

FIG. 5.17. Restoration of 62 (31 complex) coefficients to the inverse-filtered spectrum of the function shown in Fig. 5.16 with the constraint of minimum negativity produced this result. Note that the broadened spectrum of these narrower peaks necessitates recovering more spectral components in order to obtain reasonable results.

minimum negativity produces the result shown in Fig. 5.18. Increased resolution is noted for all the peaks except the fourth one. A stronger deconvolution shows that this peak may be further resolved into three lines. The result shown in Fig. 5.18 is close to the expected Doppler width. We may interpret the deconvolution with the narrower impulse response function physically as a removal of only part of the distortion.

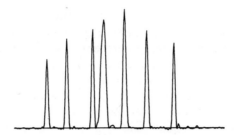

FIG. 5.18. Restoration of 74 (37 complex) coefficients to the inverse-filtered spectrum of the function shown in Fig. 5.16 by minimizing the sum of the squares for the negative deviations produced this result.

D. FOURIER TRANSFORM SPECTROSCOPY DATA

1. *Introductory Remarks*

The treatment of Fourier transform spectroscopy (FTS) IR data involves application of essentially the same techniques that apply to the other IR data.[1] However, sufficient difference exists in practice to warrant a separate discussion. In grating spectroscopy, the data recorded are the IR lines, with random noise superimposed. The data recorded in Fourier transform spectroscopy form what is known as the interferogram, and the Fourier transform is taken of the interferogram to obtain the IR spectral lines. It is evident, then, for FTS data, that the Fourier spectrum of the interferogram and the electromagnetic spectrum are the same. The restoration problem is slightly different for each of these cases. It is seldom possible to obtain the entire nonzero extent of the interferogram experimentally, as this generally requires a very large optical path difference. So for FTS data the purpose is to restore the interferogram function by applying constraints to its transform, the IR spectral lines. For grating spectroscopy, restoration comes from the (general) deconvolution operation. Here it is the inverse-filtered transform that is extended, extrapolated from a function that is truncated because of the ascending noise. In practice FTS data seldom undergo inverse filtering, unless the original lines have undergone considerable broadening.

In the operating mode customarily used, which is to determine the existence, location, and intensity of the spectral lines, the interferometer produces an interferogram that is symmetric about the zero displacement position. If the zero displacement position (the maximum point on the "central fringe") is taken as the origin of the interferogram function, the Fourier transform of this will produce an IR spectrum that is real and symmetric about its origin. Note that for this case it does not matter whether

[1] For a different treatment of FTS data, see Chapter 4 in this volume.

the forward or inverse Fourier transform is used, as the same result will be obtained. If the one-sided interferogram is given, it is usually symmetrically extended about the origin. An improvement in the efficiency of the required calculations is afforded by a real and symmetric function. See Chapter 17 in Bell (1972) for a detailed discussion of the fast Fourier transform in efficient calculational schemes of interferometric data. However, for illustration, only one side of the interferogram and its spectrum is shown, usually the function of the positive spatial and spectral variable. In other operating modes of the interferometer, asymmetric interferograms that have a complex Fourier transform are produced. Asymmetric interferograms are not treated in this work. For a more complete discussion of Fourier transform spectroscopy, the reader should consult Bell (1972), Mertz (1965), Steel (1967), Vanasse and Sakai (1967), Vanasse and Strong (1958), the *1970 International Conference on Fourier Spectroscopy, Aspen, Colorado* (Vanasse *et al.*, 1971), and the two volumes of *Spectrometric Techniques* (Vanasse, 1977, 1981). Further interesting historical development, not included in these references, may be found in Connes (1969), which also contains many important contributions by the author. A brief historical sketch is also provided by Loewenstein (1966).

The incomplete interferogram that is recorded could be represented by the complete interferogram function multiplied by the rect function. The transform, of course, is the convolution of the IR lines with the sinc function, which is the origin of the oscillatory artifacts that alternate positively and negatively about the base line around the peaks. The complete interferogram should yield a set of IR spectral lines that are all positive, so that the constraint of minimum negativity could appropriately be applied here. If all IR frequencies outside the band of interest are filtered out before reaching the interferogram, then the constraint of finite extent could also be applied. In practice, however, this constraint is often awkward to apply, as the filters never terminate a spectrum abruptly.

For FTS data, artifact removal is a consideration that is as important as resolution improvement for most researchers in this field. Interferogram continuation methods are not as yet widely known in this area. Methods currently in widespread use that are effective in artifact removal involve the multiplication of the interferogram by various window functions, the operation called *apodization*. A carefully chosen window function can be very effective in suppressing the artifacts. However, the peaks are almost always broadened in the process. This can be understood from the uncertainty principle. A window that reduces the function most strongly closest to the endpoints will have a transform that must be broader than it was originally. Alternatively, we may employ the convolution theorem, which states that the multiplication of the interferogram by the window is the same as convolution of the IR lines with the Fourier transform of the window. One window function widely used for apodization is the triangular window, which is very effective in removing negative artifacts. However, as its transform is the sinc^2 function, the small positive sidelobes characteristic of this function show up around sharp peaks in the spectrum.

For most data it is seldom possible to effect a complete restoration of the interferogram. Upon recovering even a relatively few additional data points, though, a considerable improvement in resolution is usually obtained. However, the artifacts in most cases are still appreciably large. It has been found that multiplying the interferogram by an appropriate window function, one that does not go to zero at the endpoints, will effect, upon extending the interferogram, a removal of almost all of the artifacts, as well as an improvement in resolution over the lines of the original interferogram. However, it is noted that the ultimate resolution obtained with this window is not as good as that obtained with the straightforwardly extended interferogram in the absence of the window. The use of these windows essentially involves a trade-off between artifact removal and resolution improvement.

For FTS data, then, the general procedure for improvement is first to determine the number of additional points on the interferogram that can be recovered, then to multiply the (unrestored) interferogram by one of a class of window functions appropriate to the number of points to be recovered, and finally to restore the additional points to the interferogram using as many of the applicable constraints as possible. The Fourier transform of the interferogram is almost always computed with the DFT in order to take advantage of the speed of the FFT computational algorithm. We may therefore borrow almost all of the DFT formulation of the restoration problem for application to FTS data. Actually, deconvolution with a symmetric impulse response function is the same as multiplying the interferogram by a high-pass filter, as the Fourier transform of a real, symmetric impulse response function is also a real, symmetric function and would produce no phase shifts. So convolution and inverse filtering would then be only special cases of multiplying the interferogram by a certain class of window functions before its continuation.

2. Simulated FTS Data

For a more quantitative analysis of the errors involved, artificial data are addressed first. To see the effects of truncation and restoration on a single spectral line, we first consider a monochromatic electromagnetic source. Figure 5.19 could represent such a source. Of course, an entirely monochromatic source is physically impossible, but there are many wave trains in nature whose total lengths are very long compared to their wavelengths, and

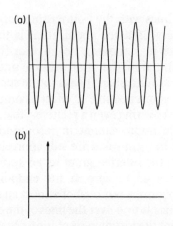

FIG. 5.19. Interferogram and spectrum of a monochromatic source. (a) The interferogram is a cosine function that extends indefinitely; (b) its Fourier transform, the Dirac delta function.

which would therefore yield very sharp spectral lines. The case we have illustrated could closely approximate many aspects of such a source. Figure 5.19a could be a segment of an interferogram of a monochromatic source. Its Fourier transform, given in Fig. 5.19b, is a single sharp spectral line (two lines actually, symmetric about the origin). Theoretically, the Fourier transform of a monochromatic source of finite intensity is two Dirac delta functions, and each would be infinitely high and have zero width.

Figure 5.20 illustrates a more realistic case, that of a finite interferogram. Figure 5.20a could be the finite interferogram of an approximately monochromatic source. Its Fourier transform, the sinc function, is shown in Fig. 5.20b. This much broadened spectral line with the ringing around it closely

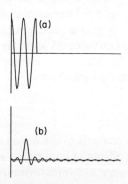

FIG. 5.20. Simulation of a monochromatic source with a finite arm displacement of the interferometer. (a) The truncated cosine function (30 discrete data points); (b) its Fourier transform, the sinc function, which simulates the IR spectral line.

approximates the lines obtained in practice from the interferograms of approximately monochromatic sources. For improvement of these spectral lines we would like to remove the artifacts, as well as increase the resolution. Most presently used methods only remove the artifacts by the process of apodization. Nearly all of these window functions employed for apodization have the property of going smoothly to zero at the endpoint of the interferogram. One window function widely used is the triangular window function. This function is shown in Fig. 5.21d. Multiplying the interferogram of Fig. 5.20a by this window function produces the altered interferogram shown in Fig. 5.22a. The Fourier transform of this is shown in Fig. 5.22b. It is important to note that the negative artifacts have been completely removed. The small positive sidelobes remaining are not nearly so prominent as in the original spectral line. This spectral function, incidentally, is the sinc² function, which is the Fourier transform of the triangle function. This operation has been very effective in reducing the artifacts, but a heavy price has been paid. The spectral line has been considerably broadened, as is evident from comparing the widths of the lines in Figs. 5.20b and 5.22b.

If increasing the resolution is the only consideration, then we may simply extend the interferogram function by the methods discussed earlier. The constraint of minimum negativity is only used in Figs. 5.23–5.58. The straightforward extension of the interferogram of Fig. 5.20a by minimizing the negative values of the function shown in Fig. 5.20b produces the restored spectral line shown in Fig. 5.23b, if the interferogram is extended by the amount shown in Fig. 5.23a. A considerable improvement in the resolution

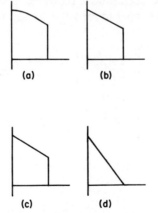

FIG. 5.21. Four window functions that are used to multiply the interferogram. (a) Gaussian window. (b) Triangular window. (c) Triangular window of greater slope than (b). (d) Triangular window that tapers to zero at the endpoint of the interferogram. This window is used for apodization.

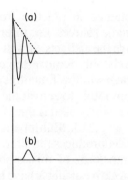

FIG. 5.22. Apodization, which is the reduction of artifacts in the spectral line by the multiplication of the interferogram by a window that tapers to zero at the endpoint of the interferogram. (a) The cosine interferogram multiplied by the triangular window function of Fig. 5.21d. (b) Resulting spectral line, the sinc² function.

of the spectral line has been achieved. However, as is evident from examining the remaining function around the peak of Fig. 5.23b, the artifacts are still rather large. Figure 5.24 is shown to illustrate the effectiveness of the restoration algorithm. The considerably improved spectral line of Fig. 5.24b shows what may be achieved with only *one* iteration.

To increase the resolution *and* reduce the artifacts simultaneously, the interferogram must be multiplied by the proper window function before extension, as discussed earlier. A variety of functional forms for the window function that will bring about, to some degree, the simultaneous achievement of both goals have been found. However, they all share the common property that they do *not* taper to zero at the endpoint of the interferogram.

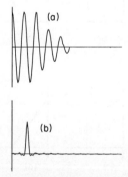

FIG. 5.23. Straightforward extension of the interferogram by minimizing the negative values of the spectrum of Fig. 5.20b. (a) Interferogram (of 30 data points) which has been extended 40 more points. (b) Restored spectral line, which exhibits a considerable increase in resolution.

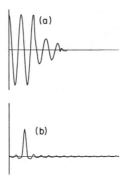

FIG. 5.24. Same situation as in Fig. 5.23 but showing the improvement that may be obtained with only one iteration. (a) Interferogram extended 40 data points. (b) Improved spectral line, illustrating the improvement in resolution obtained with only one iteration.

Consider the triangular window shown in Fig. 5.21c. Multiplying the interferogram of Fig. 5.20a by this window function and extending the interferogram to the point where the triangle function would cross the spatial axis yields the result shown in Fig. 5.25a. The extent of the original interferogram is denoted by x_c on the plot. The considerably improved spectral line, with negative values almost nonexistent, is shown in Fig. 5.25b. Note that the resolution is improved over the original spectral line of Fig. 5.20b, and that the artifacts have been almost completely removed, with only small positive sidelobes remaining. However, note also that the resolution is not quite so good as the extended interferogram of Fig. 5.23b, which has not been multiplied by a window. This comparison illustrates the trade-off between

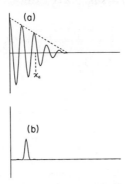

FIG. 5.25. Graph illustrating the effectiveness in removing the artifacts from the spectrum by multiplying the interferogram by the proper window function before extending the interferogram by a finite number of points. (a) Cosine interferogram premultiplied by the triangular window function shown in Fig. 5.21c before extending 40 more data ponts. (b) Restored spectral line.

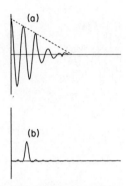

FIG. 5.26. Same situation as in Fig. 5.25 but showing the improvement obtained with only one iteration. (a) Altered interferogram extended 40 more points. (b) Spectral line showing improvement in resolution and artifact reduction.

resolution and artifact removal brought about by the use of a window function. When restoring a given number of points to the interferogram, the researcher should choose the appropriate window function to emphasize whichever of the two aspects he deems most important. Incidentally, to display the improvement that may be obtained with only one iteration, Fig. 5.26 is shown. The interferogram and window are the same as in Fig. 5.25.

The researcher should also be careful to choose a window that yields maximum improvement. The choice of an inappropriate window function is illustrated in Fig. 5.27. The same window and interferogram as in the previous example are used, but more points on the extended interferogram are recovered. The resulting interferogram is shown in Fig. 5.27a. The restored spectral line shown in Fig. 5.27b exhibits very little, if any, improve-

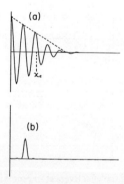

FIG. 5.27. Illustration of the poor result obtained when an inappropriate choice of window function is used to multiply the interferogram before extending a given number of data points. (a) Same window and interferogram as in Fig. 5.25, but with the interferogram extended 50 more points. (b) Restored spectral line showing no improvement over that of Fig. 5.25b.

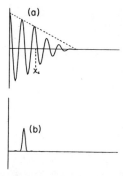

FIG. 5.28. Illustration of extension by the same number of points as in Fig. 5.27, but with premultiplication of the interferogram by a more appropriate window function. (a) Interferogram extended 50 more points after multiplication by the window function of Fig. 5.21b. (b) Restored spectral line.

ment over the line of Fig. 5.25b. When restoring more points to the interferogram, a window of less taper is needed. Multiplying the same interferogram by the triangular window shown in Fig. 5.21b and extending by the same amount as in Fig. 5.27 produce the restored interferogram shown in Fig. 5.28a. Figure 5.28b is the improved spectral line with nearly all the artifacts removed. It is important to note that the resolution is improved over that of Fig. 5.25b, which illustrates the general result that the more points recovered on the extended interferogram, the better the resolution, if the entire spectrum is not recovered.

To see the effects that noise would have on a single spectral line, consider the interferogram of unity amplitude shown in Fig. 5.29a, for which Gaus-

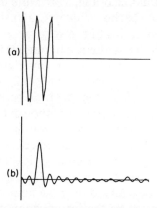

FIG. 5.29. Same interferogram as in Fig. 5.20, but with added Gaussian noise of rms 0.1. (a) Cosine interferogram of unity amplitude with random noise of rms amplitude 0.1 superimposed. (b) Single spectral line with the oscillatory artifacts.

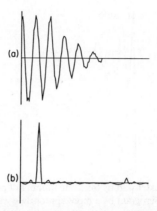

FIG. 5.30. Straightforward extension of the noisy interferogram of Fig. 5.29a by minimizing the negative values of the distorted spectral line of Fig. 5.29b. (a) Interferogram extended 50 data points. (b) Restored spectral line.

sian noise of rms amplitude 0.1 is added. It is evident that this high noise level considerably distorts the interferogram function. Figure 5.29b is the resulting spectral line. The amplitude of this spectral line is arbitrarily chosen to be slightly larger than that of the noise-free case. Note that it is quite smooth, which is not exactly what we would expect considering the high noise level in the interferogram. The smoothness comes about because the noise extends only over part of the data field — the part over the finite interferogram.

By minimizing the negative values of this function, we get the restored interferogram and spectral line of Fig. 5.30. Note that all cases of restoring this interferogram that will be shown involve extension by this same number of points. The resolution of this line is very much the same as that of the noise-free case. However, let us attempt to remove the debris from the base line by reducing the artifacts due to a finite interferogram. Multiplying this interferogram by the triangular window of Fig. 5.21b and then extending, we get the interferogram shown in Fig. 5.31a. The restored spectral line is shown in Fig. 5.31b. Surprisingly, the resolution of the spectral line is almost the same as that of the noise-free case. However, many low-level artifacts have been introduced. Multiplying the interferogram by the Gaussian window shown in Fig. 5.21a and extending yield the interferogram of Fig. 5.32a and the restored spectral line of Fig. 5.32b. Again, the resolution of the spectral line has been little changed over the noise-free instance. The main effect of the noise seems to be the introduction of many low-amplitude features scattered randomly about the base line.

Considering more complicated spectra, we see in Fig. 5.33 the (noise-free)

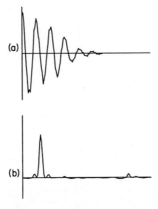

FIG. 5.31. Interferogram of Fig. 5.29a multiplied by a triangular window before extension in an attempt to remove the artifacts. (a) Interferogram premultiplied by the triangular window of Fig. 5.21b before extending 50 additional points. (b) Resulting spectral line.

interferogram and spectral lines for the superposition of two closely spaced frequencies. This example demonstrates the ability of the constraint of minimum negativity to separate these two closely spaced spectral lines. Figure 5.34a is the finite interferogram. Figure 5.34b is the spectrum. Note that the lines for this finite interferogram are completely merged. Extending the interferogram by the amount shown in Fig. 5.35a by minimizing the sum of the squares of the negative values of the merged spectral lines effectively separates these two lines, as Fig. 5.35b demonstrates.

Considering increasingly more realistic examples, for the superposition of

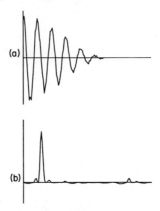

FIG. 5.32. Interferogram of Fig. 5.29a multiplied by a Gaussian window before extension in an attempt to remove the artifacts. (a) Interferogram premultiplied by the Gaussian window of Fig. 5.21a before extending 50 additional points. (b) Restored spectral line.

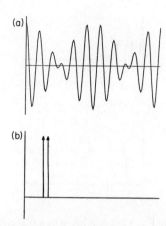

FIG. 5.33. Interferogram (noise-free) and spectrum of two monochromatic sources that differ slightly in wave number. (a) Interferogram, which is understood to repeat indefinitely. (b) The two closely spaced spectral lines.

six monochromatic sources of varying intensity, we have the interferogram and six spectral lines shown in Fig. 5.36. The interferogram for a finite path displacement is shown in Fig. 5.37a. The spectral lines for this finite interferogram are shown in Fig. 5.37b, which are now broadened and merged. Straightforwardly extending this interferogram by the amount shown in Fig. 5.38a by minimizing the negative values of the lines in Fig. 5.37b produces the restored lines shown in Fig. 5.38b. All the lines are completely resolved, and the result suggests that there is not that much interaction among the peaks on restoration; that is, the restored lines are

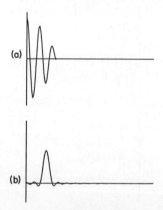

FIG. 5.34. Interferogram of the two monochromatic sources that would be obtained for a finite maximum path difference of the interferometer. (a) The finite interferogram. (b) The recorded spectrum. Note that the two lines are completely merged into one.

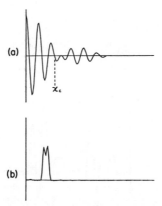

FIG. 5.35. Interferogram of Fig. 5.34a extended by minimizing the negative values of the spectrum of Fig. 5.34b. (a) Interferogram extended 50 additional points. (b) Restored spectrum. Note that the lines have been effectively resolved.

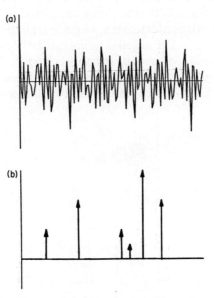

FIG. 5.36. Interferogram (noise-free) and spectrum of the superposition of six monochromatic sources. (a) Interferogram—the superposition of six cosine functions of differing amplitudes and wave numbers. (b) Fourier transform of the interferogram—six Dirac delta functions.

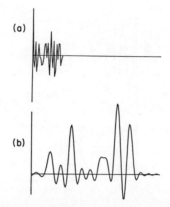

FIG. 5.37. Finite interferogram and resulting spectrum for the six monochromatic sources of Fig. 5.36. (a) Interferogram of 30 data points. (b) Broadened and merged lines and oscillatory artifacts due to a finite interferogram.

very much like what one would get by restoring each line separately and then superimposing them. It is also noted that the degradation and restoration operations affect each spectral line the same way, regardless of its wavelength. Although the resolution of the lines is good, quite large artifacts still remain in the restoration. If the interferogram is multiplied by the triangular window of Fig. 5.21b before extension, we get the interferogram and spectral lines shown in Fig. 5.39. The negative artifacts have been almost completely removed. Yet some loss of resolution has occurred.

For another example with several frequencies present, consider the interferogram of Fig. 5.40a, which corresponds to the superposition of four

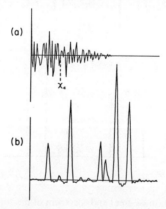

FIG. 5.38. Extended interferogram and restored spectrum resulting from minimizing the negative values of the distorted spectrum of Fig. 5.37(b). (a) Interferogram extended 50 additional points. (b) Restored spectrum.

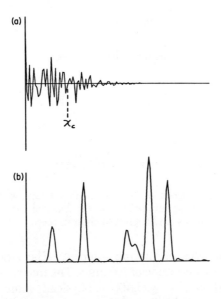

FIG. 5.39. Interferogram of Fig. 5.37a multiplied by the triangular window of Fig. 5.21b before extension so as to bring about artifact reduction. (a) Altered interferogram extended 50 additional points by minimizing the negative values of its Fourier transform. (b) Restored spectrum.

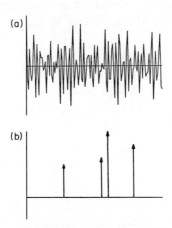

FIG. 5.40. Interferogram and spectrum of the superposition of four monochromatic sources. (a) Noise-free interferogram. The magnitude of the largest of the four cosine functions is 1.6 units. (b) The spectrum—four Dirac delta functions.

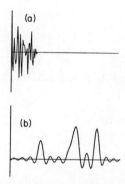

FIG. 5.41. Finite interferogram of the four monochromatic sources of Fig. 5.40 with Gaussian noise of rms 0.02 superimposed and the resulting degraded spectral lines. (a) Interferogram of 30 data points. (b) Merged and distorted spectral lines.

monochromatic sources of varying intensity. The largest cosine in the interferogram has an amplitude of 1.6 units. The four sharp spectral lines of this spectrum are shown in Fig. 5.40b. A physically more realistic case, that of a finite interferogram with Gaussian noise of rms amplitude 0.02 added, is shown in Fig. 5.41a. Its spectrum, the much broadened lines with large oscillations shown in Fig. 5.41b, bears a close resemblance to many spectral lines observed in practice. By minimizing the negative values of this spectrum, we get the restored interferogram and spectrum shown in Fig. 5.42. The restored spectral lines shown in Fig. 5.42b do not differ appreciably from those of the noise-free case. However, let us attempt to remove the debris from the base line to see what remains after reducing the artifacts due to a finite interferogram. Multiplication by the triangular window of Fig.

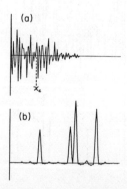

FIG. 5.42. Extended interferogram and restored spectrum obtained by minimizing the negative values of the spectrum of Fig. 5.41b. (a) Interferogram extended 50 data points. (b) Restored spectral lines.

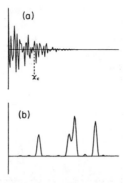

FIG. 5.43. Multiplying the interferogram of Fig. 5.41a by the triangular window of Fig. 5.21b before extending to remove the artifacts. (a) Interferogram extended 50 points. (b) Restored spectral lines.

5.21b and determination of the extended interferogram function produce the restored interferogram and spectral lines shown in Fig. 5.43. The restored spectrum here also looks very much like the noise-free instance, with the exception of very small artifacts randomly located along the base line.

Thus far, the discussion has been restricted to triangular window functions. However, it has been discovered that windows of many other functional forms are capable of bringing about improvement in the spectral lines. In this research the author has found that the window of Gaussian shape has produced the best overall results. With the same interferogram and extension by the same amount as in the previous example, premultiplication by the Gaussian window shown in Fig. 5.21a produced the restored interferogram shown in Fig. 5.44a. The restored spectral lines shown in Fig.

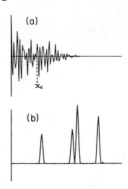

FIG. 5.44. Interferogram of Fig. 5.41a multiplied by the Gaussian window of Fig. 5.21a before extension to remove the artifacts due to a finite interferogram. (a) Interferogram extended 50 more data points. (b) Restored spectrum.

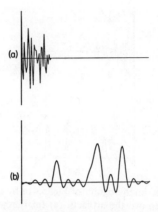

FIG. 5.45. Finite interferogram and resulting spectrum of the same four monochromatic sources of Fig. 5.40a, but now with Gaussian noise of rms 0.1 superimposed on the interferogram. (a) Finite interferogram of 30 data points. (b) Merged and distorted spectral lines.

5.44b have a resolution much improved over that of Fig. 5.43b, where the triangular window was used, and yet the artifacts are no worse. The researcher should explore the various functional forms of the window function to find the one best suited for his particular data.

When we consider more general examples, Fig. 5.45a shows the interferogram of the same four monochromatic sources illustrated in the previous example, but with Gaussian noise of rms amplitude 0.1 added. The degraded spectral lines are shown in Fig. 5.45b. Minimizing the negative values of this spectrum produces the extended interferogram and restored

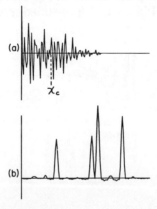

FIG. 5.46. Extended interferogram and restored spectral lines resulting from minimizing the negative values of the distorted spectrum in Fig. 5.45b. (a) Interferogram extended 50 additional points. (b) Restored spectral lines.

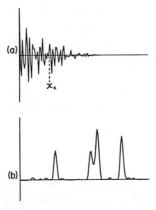

FIG. 5.47. Interferogram of Fig. 5.45a multiplied by the triangular window of Fig. 5.21b before extension. (a) Interferogram extended 50 additional data points. (b) Restored spectral lines.

spectral lines of Fig. 5.46. As noted earlier, the noise seems to have little effect on the resolution. To remove the artifacts, the interferogram is multiplied by the triangular window before extending. Figure 5.47 shows the restored interferogram and spectral lines for this case. As noted with the earlier examples, the main effect of the noise seems to be the introduction of small artifacts randomly located about the data field. The best overall results are obtained by premultiplying the interferogram by the Gaussian window of Fig. 5.21a before extension. These results are shown in Fig. 5.48. The spectral lines of Fig. 5.48b are better resolved than those of Fig. 5.47b, and

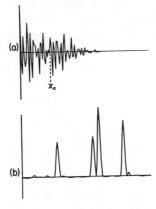

FIG. 5.48. Premultiplying the interferogram of Fig. 5.45a by the Gaussian window of Fig. 5.21a before extension. (a) Interferogram extended 50 additional data points. (b) Restored spectrum.

yet the artifacts are no worse. As for all the earlier cases mentioned, the resolution seems little affected by the noise.

The major effect of the noise for all cases seems to be the introduction of randomly located low-amplitude artifacts (over and above those obtained for the noise-free instance). Even with the rms 0.1 noise level, very little interaction among the peaks is observed. However, even though this is generally true, occasionally a restoration will show wide divergence from this, especially when the noise level is high.

3. Experimental FTS Data

Finally, experimental FTS data are now addressed. For further discussion and description of the experimental data and the experimental conditions under which the data were taken, see Toth et al. (1981). Given the interferogram, the Fourier transform must be computed to obtain the spectral lines, as the constraints are applied to the spectrum. We may attempt to restore the entire spectrum or isolated sets of spectral lines. The iterative method developed here seems adequate for restoring a large spectrum consisting of many data points. The method of successive substitutions used is capable of accommodating a large set of equations. Attention here, though, is restricted to isolated sets of lines. As we are not sure at what spectral frequencies the information exists for these causes, only the constraint of minimum negativity can be validly applied for improvement. For a small set of spectral lines with only a few data points, it is usually unnecessary to multiply the interferogram function by a window before extending, as the entire interferogram is recovered in most cases. This is because real spectral lines have a nonzero width, unlike the Dirac delta function lines used in the artificial data.

The experimental data illustrated here are methane absorption lines observed in the 3-μm-wavelength IR spectral region. The narrow Lorentzian lines due to the molecular transitions are broadened by Doppler effects to produce a final line shape that is approximately Gaussian. A two-sided interferogram that extends 50 cm on each side of the central fringe is taken. As 50 cm does not extend to the "wash-out" point (where the signal becomes comparable to the noise) on the interferogram, the line shape recorded will be the convolution of the above-mentioned line shape with the sinc function. Minimizing the negative values of this final spectral function is expected to produce a reasonable approximation to the complete interferogram and to the true line shape. A very-low-frequency sinusoid was superimposed on these spectral lines because of *channeling*. This comes about by reflections from the window surfaces that contain the sample gas. A spike is often produced on the interferogram, which results in a superimposed sinusoid on transforming. Instead of the sinusoid being removed from the entire data set, a smooth curve was fit to each isolated set of lines treated.

There are three major sources of error in these particular data. There is, of course, the noise. Then there is the inevitable error due to the base line fit of this strongly varying function. Third, it is impossible to obtain completely isolated lines. As the data are convolved with the sinc function, the peaks die out slowly, and an isolated set of lines never dies out exactly to zero. Some adjustment of the endpoints of this type of data is almost always necessary in order to make the data go smoothly to zero there. In spite of these errors, reasonably good restorations were obtained for all three of the data sets treated here.

The simplest case, that of two large IR lines, is shown in Fig. 5.49a. A smooth curve is fit to the base line, as shown. A spline-fitting computer program developed by de Boor (1978) was used to obtain this fit very conveniently. After the fit was obtained, the data were adjusted to a flat base line, as shown in Fig. 5.49b and the data field was extended by padding with zeros to yield an overall data field of 256 points. Taking the Fourier transform, the interferogram function shown in Fig. 5.50 was obtained (even though it was not obtained directly from the interferometer as recorded data, we refer to this function as the interferogram function to avoid the introduction of new and possibly confusing terminology). Note that, as expected, the interferogram function does have a rather sharp cutoff point. The residual low-amplitude interferogram extended beyond the cutoff point is due to the errors discussed in the preceding paragraph. The amplitude of

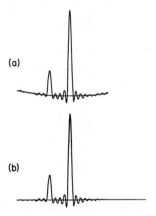

(a)

(b)

FIG. 5.49. Experimentally obtained methane absorption lines in the IR spectral region. (a) Two isolated methane spectral lines. A smooth curve is fit to the base line. (b) All points on this smooth curve are assigned the value of zero, and all values on the spectral lines are adjusted accordingly. The replotted line is shown on this graph.

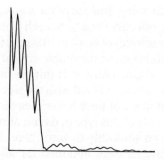

FIG. 5.50. Interferogram function for the set of spectral lines of Fig.5.49b.

this extended interferogram function provides a crude measure of this error. This residual extended interferogram function is cleanly truncated to yield a smooth noise-free set of spectral lines to which to apply the constraints. The IR spectral lines given by this truncated interferogram function are shown in Fig. 5.51a. Note that by the definition of the Fourier spectrum presented here, which we have given as the Fourier transform of the function or data under consideration, we may consider the interferogram function to be the "Fourier spectrum" for these IR lines. Although we usually call the forward transform the spectrum, it would make little difference on application to the symmetric FTS data treated here. Recall that earlier we refer to the Fourier transform of the experimentally obtained interferogram as the Fourier spectrum.

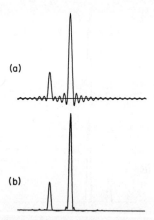

FIG. 5.51. Set of spectral lines and restoration yielded by truncating the interferogram function of Fig. 5.50 just before its sharp drop-off, keeping 27 data points. (a) The smooth set of lines obtained from this truncation. (b) Restored IR spectral lines produced by minimizing the negative values of (a) and extending the interferogram 60 more points.

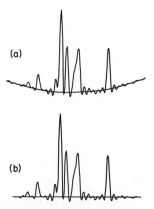

FIG. 5.52. Methane absorption lines in the IR spectral region. (a) An isolated set of IR spectral lines. A smooth curve is fit to the base line. (b) Result obtained by taking the differences from the curved base line drawn and replotting.

Truncating the residual interferogram is not an absolutely necessary step, as the computer program written for restoration will restore a band of Fourier spectral components for any given real function, regardless of whether or not the Fourier spectrum (which is the interferogram in this case) has been truncated. However, (additional) error will occur for an interferogram that is not truncated if the index of the furthermost nonzero point is greater than the highest index in the band of points of the restored interferogram function.

Minimizing the negative values of the lines in Fig. 5.51a produces the restored lines shown in Fig. 5.51b. Both lines show an increase in resolution. The origin of the two small "wings" on each side of the larger peak is

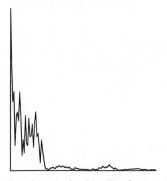

FIG. 5.53. Interferogram function obtained by Fourier transforming the spectral lines of Fig. 5.52b.

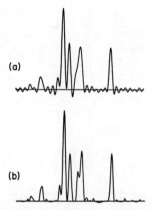

FIG. 5.54. Truncating the interferogram function of Fig. 5.53 just before its sharp drop-off, keeping 28 data points, yields the smooth spectrum to be restored. (a) Smooth spectrum. (b) Restored IR lines resulting from minimizing the negative values of (a). The interferogram was extended 60 more points.

unexplained. However, they occur in the restoration of many lines of this data run.

A more complicated set of spectral lines is shown in Fig. 5.52a. A spline fit is made to the base line, as shown, which allows adjustment to a flat base line. This is shown in Fig. 5.52b. Taking the Fourier transform of this yields the interferogram function shown in Fig. 5.53. Truncating this function after the sharp drop-off that signals the end of the interferogram, the Fourier transform is taken to yield the much smoother set of spectral lines shown in Fig. 5.54a. Applying the constraint of minimum negativity to these lines

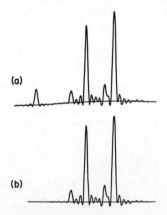

FIG. 5.55. Isolated set of IR absorption lines in the IR spectral region. (a) Isolated set of IR lines with a smooth curve fit to the base line. (b) Adjusted to zero base line.

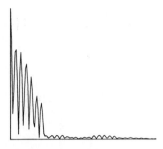

FIG. 5.56. Interferogram function resulting from Fourier-transforming the spectrum of Fig. 5.55b.

yields the restored lines of Fig. 5.54b. All the lines show an improvement in resolution. Note that the merged peaks in the original data separate into two distinct lines in the restoration. As mentioned with the previous example, two of the Fourier transforms involved here are not absolutely necessary. We could directly apply the constraint of minimum negativity to the data of Fig. 5.52b if they were relatively error free.

For the final example, we have the set of spectral lines shown in Fig. 5.55a. Fitting a smooth curve to the base line and adjusting it to zero base line give Fig. 5.55b. Taking the Fourier transform produces the interferogram function shown in Fig. 5.56. Choosing a truncation point in the sharp drop-off of this function and transforming produce the smooth set of spectral lines shown in Fig. 5.57a. Minimizing the negative values of these spectral lines produces the restored IR spectrum shown in Fig. 5.57b. Increased resolution is noted. Figure 5.58 is shown to emphasize that a good restoration is not

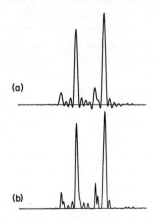

(a)

(b)

FIG. 5.57. Fourier transform of the truncated interferogram of Fig. 5.56 yields this smooth set of spectral lines to be restored. (a) Smooth spectrum. (b) Restored IR lines resulting from minimizing the negative values of (a).

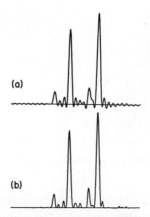

FIG. 5.58. Spectral lines resulting from Fourier-transforming the truncated interferogram of Fig. 5.56, but retaining one data point less in the interferogram than in Fig. 5.57. (a) Smooth spectrum. (b) Restored IR lines resulting from minimizing the negative values of (a).

obtained every time with this restoration procedure. By truncating the interferogram function of Fig. 5.56 and retaining one point less than for the previous figure, the Fourier transform shown in Fig. 5.58a is produced. Restoration from·this function produces the restored lines of Fig. 5.58b. This restoration is not exactly what is expected from the original data and is generally considered inferior to the restoration of Fig. 5.57b.

Let us conclude this section with a few remarks on practical restoration with the DFT. Often we obtain FTS data that are "tightly packed"; that is, only the minimum number of points needed to represent them are given. If the spectral lines are given, the density of points representing them will be very sparse. The finite interferogram function for this case will extend over all (or nearly all) of the discrete points of the DFT. For the restoration, however, we find that there is little or no interferogram function to extend with this number of points. For further improvement, it is necessary to pad more zeros onto the end of the interferogram function to double the total number of data points, which brings the number up to the next integral power of two. (This is using the efficient base 2 FFT calculational algorithm. Other algorithms for computing the DFT may be used.) Upon transforming, it will be found that the density of points on the spectral lines has doubled. Applying the constraints will then restore the spectrum and extend the interferogram function. Greater resolution will be obtained for the spectral lines, which implies that more information is now carried by the data points. Many find this result surprising, that is, that the additional data points included actually may bring more information with them. Yet this property may be amply verified in practice with both artificial and experimental data.

Also, if further extension of the interferogram is needed, more zeros may be simply padded onto it.

5.9. Conclusion

Directions for future research in the area of experimental data restoration may be broadly defined. We want to find as many of the physical constraints (generally, any prior information) as possible, and to develop efficient computational procedures for applying them to the general restoration problem.

The final restoration method adopted in this research is capable of accommodating four constraints easily, and lends itself to further inclusion of other constraints of fixed limits. The iterative procedure is able to manage large data sets quickly and yields an improved result even in the presence of considerable noise in the data. However, much room for improvements still exists.

For deconvolution from the general convolution model, restoration in two distinct spectral bands lends itself to very fast calculational algorithms. It is still not optimal, though, because of the residual error in the low-frequency band of spectral components used as a region of support. Perhaps the requirement that the inverse-filtered low-frequency spectrum (or equivalently, its corresponding spatial function) be held constant for the restoration could be relaxed to allow small variations in those low-frequency spectral components closest to the truncation point. This could effect an improved solution that better satisfies the concerned constraints.

All the restoration techniques used in this research could be generalized straightforwardly to two (or more) dimensions. The three constraints, finite extent, minimum negativity, and recovery of a finite spectral band, for example, are appropriate for picture processing. The finite-extent constraint would apply to medical images. However, other constraints peculiar to these data and the unique geometry of the particular apparatus would need to be developed.

Finally, we conclude this chapter with a few practical remarks on calculation of the inverse-filtered spectrum. In this research the Fourier transform of the data was divided by the Fourier transform of the impulse response function for the low frequencies. Letting $\hat{f}$ denote the inverse-filtered estimate, we would have for the inverse-filtered spectrum

$$\hat{F}(n) = H(n)/G(n) \tag{5.65}$$

For the cases where G is very small or zero at certain frequencies, the indeterminate discrete Fourier spectral components corresponding to these values of n may be determined along with the high-frequency band when the Fourier spectrum is continued. It is necessary to make sure that these coefficients, along with their associated sine and cosine terms, are included in the resulting equations that enforce the constraints.

Data are often normalized so that the area under the curve is preserved. This area is given by the dc spectral term, that is, for $n = 0$. To preserve the area in the discrete inverse-filtered result, every term should be multiplied by the dc spectral component of the impulse response function (if the impulse response function has not been earlier normalized). We would have then for $\hat{F}$

$$\hat{F}(n) = [H(n)/G(n)]G(0) \qquad (5.66)$$

If unity for the area is to be preserved throughout, then each term of the inverse-filtered result should be multiplied by $G(0)/H(0)$. Note that spectrum continuation, as it does not involve the dc term, does not change the area under the data curve.

In the discussion of inverse filtering and filters given in Section 5.4, it is implicitly assumed that all calculations were performed in the Fourier domain. However, inverse filtering (and all other filtering operations as well) does not necessarily have to be performed entirely in the Fourier domain. By the convolution theorem, multiplication by the inverse filter in the Fourier domain would be a convolution with its transform in the spatial domain; that is,

$$f(k) = \mathcal{F}^{-1}\{H(n)[1/G(n)]\} = h(k) * \mathcal{F}^{-1}\{1/G(n)\} \qquad (5.67)$$

For much data of interest, the transform of the inverse filter (and many other associated filters as well) may be suitably approximated by a number of data points that is much smaller than the number in the data field. Where this is the case, the number of calculations to be performed in the spatial domain is often less than the number performed in the Fourier domain. Generally, when the number of data points is large, the calculational efficiency is greater in the Fourier domain when the impulse response function is broad. However, the calculational efficiency for each individual case depends heavily on such factors as the functional form of the impulse response function, as well as its width, the number of data points, the sharpness of the truncation of the Fourier spectrum, the approximations involved, and the noise level. Broad generalizations, thus, could not be made on the superiority of one computational procedure over the other.

Convolution with the transformed inverse filter generally does not result in a sharp cutoff of the Fourier spectrum. This comes from the diffuse filtering effect due to the approximations involved in going to a smaller number of points.

However, this would not be a serious drawback for the restoration methods developed here. The algorithms developed for Fourier spectrum continuation in this research may be employed only to "improve" a degraded spectrum, rather than always to restore a sharply truncated one.

Appendix A

The equations for the coefficients of the sines and cosines in the frequency spectrum to be restored have been derived for the two-dimensional case. The general expression for these coefficients for a square array is illustrated in the following two equations:

$$
A_{p,q} = - \frac{\sum_{x=0}^{N-1} \sum_{y=0}^{N-1} \left[u_{x,y} + v_{x,y} - A_{p,q} \cos \frac{2\pi}{N}(px + qy) \right] \cos \frac{2\pi}{N}(px + qy)}{\sum_{x=0}^{N-1} \sum_{y=0}^{N-1} \cos^2 \frac{2\pi}{N}(px + qy)}
$$

(A.1)

$$
B_{p,q} = - \frac{\sum_{x=0}^{N-1} \sum_{y=0}^{N-1} \left[u_{x,y} + v_{x,y} - B_{p,q} \sin \frac{2\pi}{N}(px + qy) \right] \sin \frac{2\pi}{N}(px + qy)}{\sum_{x=0}^{N-1} \sum_{y=0}^{N-1} \sin^2 \frac{2\pi}{N}(px + qy)}
$$

(A.2)

for $u_{x,y} + v_{x,y} < 0$, where $x, y, p, q = 0, 1, 2, \ldots, N - 1$, and N is the number of rows or columns. The discrete spatial variables are denoted by x and y and the corresponding spectral variables by p and q. The functions $A_{p,q}$, $B_{p,q}$, $u_{x,y}$, and $v_{x,y}$ are the two-dimensional counterparts of the one-dimensional functions discussed in the text.

If one is looking at the discrete Fourier spectrum of real data with the dc component centered at $(N/2, N/2)$, one wishes to recover a band of frequencies within the desired spectral range in the first quadrant, including the zero frequencies (corresponding to sinusoids oriented along the x or y axes). In addition, a corresponding band with one negative spectral variable should be included (exclusive of the zero frequencies). This is necessary in order to obtain a complete set of waveforms. This additional spectral band could either be in the second or fourth quadrant. The choice is completely arbitrary. No other frequencies are required. The reader will recall that the complex coefficients in the other two quadrants are the complex conjugates of those in the two quadrants chosen.

Appendix B. An Efficient Program for Continuing the Fourier Spectrum Using the Minimum-Negativity Constraint

Program MINEG uses the constraint of minimum negativity for continuation of the discrete Fourier spectrum. Recovering a finite spectral band of arbitrary extent is an additional constraint implicit in the procedure. The additional constraints of finite extent and upper bound may be applied, together with the preceding two constraints, with only slight modification of the program.

This program reads in the band-limited data and their associated low-frequency Fourier spectral components (coefficients), restores an additional Fourier spectral band and corresponding spatial function according to the constraint of minimum negativity, and outputs the total spectrum (sum of the two bands) and improved spatial function. Reading in and outputting the Fourier spectrum, actually, are optional. The restoration is made to the spatial function; that is, it is the region of support. The coefficients of the restored band and the (total) improved spatial function are all generated in each iteration. The parameters that the programmer needs to read in or adjust in the program are the number of data points, the number of additional Fourier coefficients to recover, the index of the next complex coefficient beyond the truncation point of the Fourier spectrum of the band-limited data, the initial values of the coefficients to be recovered, the maximum number of iterations, and the desired tolerance.

The role of the tolerance is discussed in the text. The tolerance is used to convey some idea of the accuracy of the result. If restoration of the experimental data becomes a routine procedure in the laboratory, though, the programmer would probably only want to perform a set number of iterations. The errors remaining after performing only 5 or 10 iterations are usually fewer than those due to noise, anyway. If the programmer wants to perform only a fixed number of iterations, in the program MAX is set to this integral value and TOL to a very small value or zero.

This program performs restorations very efficiently for the constraint of minimum negativity. For example, the central processing time for performing 17 iterations in recovering 32 (16 unique complex) coefficients is 1.67 sec on CDC's CYBER 760. The computer memory requirements are not large. When the data field is composed of M samples, the memory requirements are seldom more than $7 \times M$ words. If the Fourier spectrum is not desired, then it is seldom that more than $5 \times M$ words are needed.

When this program is used to implement the finite-extent constraint, however, the programmer may want to modify it somewhat so that the summation is taken over the required interval (outside the known extent of the object) only once. With the minimum-negativity constraint, the summation interval varies and must be taken on every iteration.

Finally, the researcher may want to combine this program with the one used for inverse filtering, so that the entire restoration procedure (that is, for both spectral bands) may be done in one continuous operation. Before this can be done automatically, though, the researcher needs to know the processing bandwidth of the inverse-filtered result that will produce the best overall restoration. The research would need to know the rms magnitude of the noise and signal, and the normalized magnitudes of the transfer function components, in order to determine the truncation point with sufficient accuracy. The latter two items may be easily calculated from the data and impulse response function. For some data sets, the rms of the noise also may be determined without too much difficulty. For example, for some data sets a smooth curve can be fit to the data, and the rms deviations of the recorded data from this smooth curve can be computed to produce reasonable results.

```
Program MINEG

C   THIS PROGRAM IS COMPATIBLE WITH THE FAST FOURIER TRANSFORM ALGORITHM.
C   IT WAS WRITTEN FOR CDC COMPUTERS. MINOR CHANGES MAY BE NEEDED TO BE
C   COMPATIBLE WITH OTHER SYSTEMS.
C
C   WRITTEN BY            SAMUEL J. HOWARD
C
        PROGRAM MINEG(DECON,SPECTR,RESCO,NONEG,CMT,TAPE5=DECON,TAPE6=RESCO,
       +TAPE7=SPECTR,TAPE8=NONEG,TAPE9=CMT)
C
C   GIVEN DISCRETE DATA FOR WHICH THE HIGH-FREQUENCY PORTION OF THE
C   FOURIER SPECTRUM IS MISSING OR IN ERROR, THIS PROGRAM RESTORES THIS
C   SPECTRUM IN SUCH A WAY THAT THE SUM OF THE SQUARE OF THE NEGATIVE
C   VALUES OF THE RESULTING FUNCTION IN THE SPATIAL DOMAIN IS MINIMIZED
C   (IF FTS DATA ARE UNDER CONSIDERATION, IT IS THE INTERFEROGRAM FUNCTION
C   THAT IS EXTENDED BY MINIMIZING THE SUM OF THE SQUARED VALUES OF THE
C   RESULTING SPECTRUM). THE BAND-LIMITED DATA ARE FOUND IN FILE DECON AND
C   ITS TRUNCATED SPECTRUM (CALCULATED BY THE FFT) IS FOUND IN FILE SPECTR
C   THESE TWO FILES ARE READ IN, THE RESTORED COEFFICIENTS ARE CALCULATED
C   AND ADDED TO THOSE GIVEN BY SPECTR, AND THE COMPLETE SPECTRUM IS
C   OUTPUTTED IN FILE RESCO. THE RESTORED FUNCTION IS OUTPUTTED IN FILE
C   NONEG. COMMENTS ARE OUTPUTTED IN FILE CMT.
C   (NOTE: THIS PROGRAM RESTORES TO ANY FUNCTION IN THE SPATIAL DOMAIN.
C   TO READ IN AND OUTPUT THE DISCRETE FOURIER SPECTRUM (THE COEFFICIENTS)
C   ARE OPTIONAL.)
C   DIMENSION DATA, CS, CSQ, AND IND TO NDP, SP TO 2*NDP, AND COEF TO N.
C
        REAL DATA(256),SP(512),CS(256),CSQ(256),COEF(32),CSUM,DIFF,C,DCO
        INTEGER S,IND(256)
        READ(5,22) DATA
     22 FORMAT(4(E21.15))
        READ(7,50) SP
     50 FORMAT(4(E21.15))
C
C   SET NDP TO THE NUMBER OF DATA POINTS IN THE ENTIRE FIELD.
C
        NDP=256
C
C   SET N TO THE NUMBER OF ADDITIONAL COEFFICIENTS DESIRED. THE NUMBER
```

```
C    OF UNIQUE COMPLEX COEFFICIENTS IS GIVEN BY N/2 (N MUST BE AN
C    EVEN NUMBER).
C
       N=32
C
C    SET L TO THE INDEX OF THE NEXT (COMPLEX) COEFFICIENT AFTER THE POINT
C    OF TRUNCATION OF THE SPECTRUM. FOR FTS DATA THIS WOULD BE THE INDEX
C    OF THE NEXT POINT ON THE ONE-SIDED INTERFEROGRAM.
C    (IF M (UNIQUE) COEFFICIENTS ARE GIVEN FROM THE TRUNCATED SPECTRUM,
C    SET L EQUAL TO M+1.)
C
       L=7
C
       N2=N/2
       FAZ=NDP/4*3+1
       C=6.283185307179586/NDP
       DO 5 I=1,NDP
       CS(I)=COS(C*(I-1))
     5 CSQ(I)=(COS(C*(I-1)))**2
C
C    INITIALIZE COEFFICIENTS. SET THESE TO ZERO IF NO BETTER VALUES
C    ARE KNOWN.
C
       DO 66 I=1,N
    66 COEF(I)=0.0
C
C    SET MAX TO NUMBER OF ITERATIONS AND TOL TO DESIRED TOLERANCE.
C
       MAX=80
       TOL=.2
C
       DO 30 IJ=1,MAX
       DIFF=0.0
       DO 20 K=1,N
       SAVE=COEF(K)
       CSUM=0.0
       XSUM=0.0
       ADD=1
       K2=(K+1)/2
       IF(K2*2-K.EQ.0) ADD=FAZ
       KL2=K2+L-2
       ISUM=ADD-KL2
       DO 9 I=1,NDP
       ISUM=ISUM+KL2
       IF(ISUM.GE.NDP+1) ISUM=ISUM-NDP
       IND(I)=ISUM
C
C    IF THE ADDITIONAL CONSTRAINT OF FINITE EXTENT IS ALSO TO BE APPLIED,
C    INCLUDE THE STATEMENT "IF(I.LT.N1.OR.I.GT.N2) GO TO 88" AS THE NEXT
C    LINE IN THE PROGRAM. THE DATA POINTS N1 AND N2 DETERMINE THE
C    NON-ZERO EXTENT OF THE OBJECT.
C    FOR THIS CASE THE CONSTRAINT OF MINIMIZING ALL DEVIATIONS FROM THE
C    BASELINE OUTSIDE OF N1 AND N2 IS APPLIED TOGETHER WITH THE CONSTRAINT
C    OF MINIMIZING THE NEGATIVE REGIONS ONLY OVER THE NON-ZERO EXTENT
C    OF THE OBJECT TO ACHIEVE MAXIMUM RESOLUTION.
C
C    IF THE OBJECT HAS AN UPPER BOUND AS WELL AS A LOWER BOUND, THIS
C    ADDITIONAL CONSTRAINT MAY BE INCLUDED WITH ONLY SLIGHT MODIFICATION
C    OF THE PROGRAM. SUMMATION WOULD THEN BE TAKEN ABOVE THE UPPER BOUND
C    (AFTER SUBTRACTING THE UPPER BOUND VALUE FROM DATA) AS WELL AS
C    BELOW THE LOWER BOUND.
C
C    THE FOLLOWING IF STATEMENT ASSURES SUMMATION OVER THE NEGATIVE
C    REGIONS ONLY.
C
       IF(DATA(I).GT.0.0) GO TO 9
C
    88 CSUM=CSUM+CSQ(IND(I))
       XSUM=XSUM+DATA(I)*CS(IND(I))
```

```
    9 CONTINUE
      COEF(K)=COEF(K)-XSUM/CSUM
      DCO=COEF(K)-SAVE
      DO 12 I=1,NDP
   12 DATA(I)=DATA(I)+CS(IND(I))*DCO
      IF(DIFF-ABS(COEF(K)-SAVE)) 15,20,20
   15 DIFF=ABS(COEF(K)-SAVE)
   20 CONTINUE
      IF(TOL-DIFF) 30,40,40
   30 CONTINUE
      WRITE(9,201) TOL,MAX
  201 FORMAT(14H TOLERANCE OF ,E14.7,15H NOT MET AFTER ,I4,12H ITERATIONS.)
      GO TO 54
   40 WRITE(9,202) IJ
  202 FORMAT(21H TOLERANCE MET AFTER ,I4,12H ITERATIONS.)
C
C   IN THE FOLLOWING THE COEFFICIENTS ARE CONVERTED TO COMPLEX FORM
C   AND ADDED TO THE ORIGINAL SPECTRUM (OPTIONAL).
C
      DO 51 I=1,N
      S=I+2*(L-1)
   51 SP(S)=SP(S)+.5*COEF(I)*(-1)**(I+1)
      DO 52 I=1,N2
      S=2*NDP+5-2*(L+I)
      SP(S)=SP(S)+.5*COEF(2*I-1)
      S=2*NDP+6-2*(L+I)
   52 SP(S)=SP(S)+.5*COEF(2*I)
      WRITE(6,33) SP
   33 FORMAT(4(E21.15,X))
C
C   THE RESTORED FUNCTION IS PRINTED OUT HERE.
C
      WRITE(8,44) DATA
   44 FORMAT(4(E21.15,X))
   54 STOP
      END
```

Appendix C

Recent investigations have been made into the computational efficiency of the restoration methods discussed here in Chapter 5. Rewriting Eqs. (5.63), (A.1), and (A.2) in different forms to find perhaps a form that involved fewer computations was explored. Means to bring about a more rapid convergence of these equations were also investigated. The two-dimensional equations are addressed in the following discussion, although most of the techniques mentioned also apply to the one-dimensional situation.

The summation over the squared sines and cosines, respectively, in the denominator of Eqs. (A.1) and (A.2) essentially acts as a weighting function applied to each Fourier coefficient. Calculating these summations for the coefficients restored over several iterations, the author observed that this weighting function generally varied very slowly over the Fourier frequencies and iterations. This strongly suggested that for the numerical calculations involved, this function could be replaced by a constant value:

$$\left[\sum_x \sum_y \cos^2 \frac{2\pi}{N} (px + qy) \right]^{-1} \approx \left[\sum_x \sum_y \sin^2 \frac{2\pi}{N} (px + qy) \right]$$

$$\approx \text{constant} = S \qquad \text{(C.1)}$$

Replacing all the weighting functions by a single constant value in the numerical calculations for several test data sets resulted in little significant change in the image over the first few iterations. A considerable reduction in the number of computations results from the use of the constant factor.

To reduce the calculational burden further, an attempt was made to separate the variables. To see how this may be implemented, let us consider Eq. (A.1), which enforces the minimum negativity constraint. Note that it may also be written

$$A_{p,q} = - \frac{\displaystyle\sum_x \sum_y (u_{x,y} + v_{x,y}) \cos(2\pi/N)(px + qy)}{\displaystyle\sum_x \sum_y \cos^2(2\pi/N)(px + qy)} + A_{p,q} \qquad \text{(C.2)}$$

for $u_{x,y} + v_{x,y} < 0$. Replacing the summation by the constant discussed in the preceding paragraph and denoting $u_{x,y} + v_{x,y}$ by $h(x, y)$, we have

$$A_{p,q} = A_{p,q} - S \sum_x \sum_y h(x, y) \cos \frac{2\pi}{N} (px + qy) \qquad \text{(C.3)}$$

for $u_{x,y} + v_{x,y} < 0$. The $A_{p,q}$ term on the right-hand side of Eq. (C.3), as for Eqs. (5.63), is understood to be the old value of this coefficient. The $A_{p,q}$ term on the left-hand side is the new (hopefully improved) value of this coefficient after the current iteration. Finally, the summation over the negative values is equivalent to multiplying $h(x, y)$ by a mask that zeros all but the negative values of this band-limited function. This mask is unity over the negative values and zero elsewhere. It would be a rect function in one dimension. In two dimensions, though, it could have many varied patterns. Denoting this mask by $m(x, y)$ we now have

$$A_{p,q} = A_{p,q} - S \sum_x \sum_y h(x, y) m(x, y) \cos \frac{2\pi}{N} (px + qy) \qquad \text{(C.4)}$$

The finite-extent constraint may easily be included in this formulation by simply letting the nonzero extent of the mask additionally include all values of the data field outside the limited extent of the object.

We may include the coefficient for the sine corresponding to any given frequency by writing the coefficients in complex form:

$$A_{p,q} + iB_{p,q} = A_{p,q} - S \sum_x \sum_y h(x, y)m(x, y) \cos \frac{2\pi}{N} (px + qy)$$

$$+ iB_{p,q} - iS \sum_x \sum_y h(x, y)m(x, y) \sin \frac{2\pi}{N} (px + qy)$$

$$= A_{p,q} + iB_{p,q} - S \left\{ \sum_x \sum_y h(x, y)m(x, y) \right.$$

$$\times \left[\cos \frac{2\pi}{N} (px + qy) + i \sin \frac{2\pi}{N} (px + qy) \right] \right\}$$

$$= A_{p,q} + iB_{p,q} - S \left\{ \sum_x \sum_y h(x, y)m(x, y)e^{i(2\pi/N)(px+qy)} \right\} \quad \text{(C.5)}$$

The complex exponential separates into factors involving only a single variable. Lumping the constant S with the mask, we now have for the correction term

$$A_{p,q} + iB_{p,q}$$

$$= A_{p,q} + iB_{p,q} - \sum_x e^{i(2\pi/N)px} \sum_y h(x, y)m(x, y)e^{i(2\pi/N)qy} \quad \text{(C.6)}$$

This separation of the variables allows a vast reduction in the number of calculations. This savings becomes more significant as the number of data points increases. Further, note that the final summation in Eq. (C.6) is in the form of a one-dimensional Fourier transform. This implies that the considerable calculational advantage of the fast Fourier transform (FFT) algorithm may be used here. The entire summation may be performed by repeated application of the one-dimensional FFT. This implies that for any data set for which it is practical to apply the FFT, it would be practical to apply the nonlinear constraints for improvement also.

There is one important disadvantage stemming from variable separation and use of the FFT, however. One is limited to the use of the "point simultaneous" procedure in the determination of the coefficients. That is, all the coefficients must be computed in an iteration before they can be substituted back into the iterative equations. With the "point successive" method, the improved coefficient determined by one equation is substituted in the succeeding equation to render additional improvement. In the author's experience with one-dimensional data, the point simultaneous method seldom yielded converging solutions, whereas the point successive method almost always did. With the two-dimensional data treated by the author, it was found that both methods yielded converging solutions, but the point simultaneous procedure converged much more slowly than the point successive method. It is quite apparent that a more thorough investigation, both theoretical and experimental, into the convergence properties of these equations is needed.

The application of the point simultaneous procedure to two-dimensional equations yields adequate restorations for many interesting two-dimensional data. However, faster convergence is clearly desirable. Two techniques have been developed so far by the author that have proved successful in bringing about more rapid convergence. One method involves the use of a "reblurring factor" that yields corrections to add back to the improved spectrum. The other procedure involves the use of more or less *ad hoc* multiplicative factors that produce spectral values closer to the original by a product with the spectrum determined from the iteration.

To understand how the reblurring factor produces improved results, a brief review of Fourier theory is necessary. For the first iteration, what we would desire is that spatial function produced by the *high frequencies* (beyond cutoff) only, that cancels out the negative values of the given band-limited spatial function (produced by the low-frequency spectral band). Multiplying this function by the mask, then, would produce the spatial function that is the *negative* of the given (low-frequency) band-limited function multiplied by the mask. The convolution theorem tells us that multiplication by the mask in the spatial domain results in convolution with the Fourier transform of the mask in the frequency domain. This gives us another interpretation for the Fourier spectrum produced by the iteration. It would be the convolution of the Fourier transform of the mask with the (original) low-frequency spectrum. Alternatively, it could be considered the convolution of the Fourier transform of the mask with the *negative* of the high-frequency spectrum that produces the spatial function that cancels the negative values of the band-limited function.

Interpreting the degradation as a convolution of the desired high-frequency spectrum with the mask transform suggests the use of deconvolution procedures to restore the spectrum. Inverse filtering would not apply with this type of response function. The constraint of minimum negativity could not appropriately be applied because the spectral components are generally both positive and negative. The constraint of finite extent could appropriately be applied because all values in the low-frequency range could be interpreted as lying outside the extent of the high-frequency range. Because the spectrum we are considering is the Fourier transform of the negative values of the original spatial function, the correct spatial function that lies outside the range of these negative values should produce a Fourier transform that zeros all frequencies lying in the low-frequency spectral range. To implement this constraint numerically, we now apply the mask in the *spectral* domain, in a reversal of the usual procedure, to zero those frequencies that lie outside the low-frequency range. (The high-frequency band is saved, of course.) Taking the inverse Fourier transform of this low-frequency band, we multiply the resulting spatial function by the negative image of the original spatial mask, which passes only those values outside the extent of the original negative region, zeroing all others. Taking the Fourier transform of this spatial function, the resulting spectral values are added back to the saved high-frequency spectrum to yield the corrected high-frequency band. Finally, the *negative* of this high-frequency band is joined to the original correct low-frequency band to produce the entire improved Fourier spectrum. Taking the inverse Fourier transform of this, we are ready to begin another iteration.

This correction to the spectrum that we have just discussed was originally designated as a "reblurring factor" because it was originally obtained by "reblurring" or convolving the high-frequency spectrum again with the Fourier transform of the mask that passed only the negative values. This reblurring was accomplished in the transformed domain because the inverse transform of the high frequencies was multiplied by the mask and the resulting function then transformed back to the frequency domain. These spectral values were then subtracted from the original high-frequency band in an attempt to produce some approximation to the original spectrum before the first convolution. The motivation for applying these corrections, of course, was that as the high-frequency band obtained from the transform of the negative regions is considered a reasonable first approximation to the restored high-frequency spectrum, a reblurring should yield at least a crude approximation to the changes produced by the first convolution. Adding the negative of these changes to the spectrum should produce a high-frequency band closer, overall, to the original. Reblurring produces essentially the same corrections as applying the finite-extent constraint in the frequency domain, for, if one follows the development closely, it is discovered that one set of corrections is the negative of the other. Regardless of the interpretation given these corrections, it has proved for a variety of test data to bring about significant improvement in the resulting images. However, because two additional FFTs are involved in the generation of these corrections, very little overall reduction in computational time is presently being achieved.

It has also been discovered that a variety of simple multiplicative factors applied to the high-frequency spectrum during an iteration have been successful in bringing about more rapid convergence of the equations. The primary motivation for applying these was the observation that the largest spectral components immediately beyond cutoff that were restored in the first few iterations were usually considerably smaller than the original components, but that their signs were nearly all correct. Any simple positive factor that rises slightly above unity for those values immediately beyond cutoff should produce spectral values closer to the original. In practice, a wide variety of factors have shown to produce improvement. In the test data sets the author used, values of factors from unity to slightly above 2 could be applied without serious distortion in the image. For the larger factors, however, tapering window functions applied to the Fourier spectrum were needed to reduce the spurious high-frequency components that were occasionally generated. With the test data treated by the author, a window of Lorentzian form that tapered gradually from values of 2 for the high-frequency spectrum immediately beyond cutoff slowly to the higher frequencies produced the best combination of rapid and distortionless restorations. This window was gradually lifted as more of the higher frequencies were restored. The factor of 2 for the lower frequencies was altered only slightly, however, because it was noted that the correction to the spectrum generated on each iteration by the method was always underestimated.

REFERENCES

Andrews, H. C., and Hunt, B. R. (1977). "Digital Image Restoration." Prentice-Hall, Englewood Cliffs, New Jersey.
Bell, R. J. (1972). "Introductory Fourier Transform Spectroscopy." Academic Press, New York.
Bergland, G. D. (1969). *IEEE Spectrum* **6**, 41.
Bevington, P. R. (1969). "Data Reduction and Error Analysis for the Physical Sciences." McGraw-Hill, New York.
Biraud, Y. (1969). *Astron. Astrophys.* **1**, 124.
Blass, W. E., and Halsey, G. W. (1981). "Deconvolution of Absorption Spectra." Academic Press, New York.
Bracewell, R. N. (1978). "The Fourier Transform and Its Applications," 2nd ed. McGraw-Hill, New York.
Bracewell, R. N., and Roberts, J. A. (1954). *Australian J. Phys.* **7**, 615.
Burg, J. P. (1967). Maximum entropy spectral analysis. *37th Annu. Soc. Explor. Geophys. Meet.*
Connes, P. (1969). "Lasers and Light." Freeman, San Francisco, California.
Cooley, J. W., and Tukey, J. W. (1965). *Math. Comput.* **19**, 297.
de Boor, C. (1978). "A Practical Guide to Splines." Springer-Verlag, Berlin and New York.
Fiddy, M. A., and Hall, T. J. (1981). *J. Opt. Soc. Am.* **71**, 1406.
Fienup, J. R. (1980). *Opt. Eng.* **19**, 297.
Fienup, J. R., Crimmons, T. R., and Holtsztvnski, W. (1982). *J. Opt. Soc. Am.* **72**, 610.
Frieden, B. R. (1971). *Prog. Opt.* **9**, 311.
Frieden, B. R. (1972). *J. Opt. Soc. Am.* **62**, 511.
Frieden, B. R. (1975). *In* "Picture Processing and Digital Filtering" (T. S. Huang, ed.), Chapter 5. Springer-Verlag, New York.
Frieden, B. R. (1981). *J. Opt. Soc. Am.* **71**, 294.
Friedman, B. (1956). "Principles and Techniques of Applied Mathematics." Wiley, New York.

Gerchberg, R. W. (1974). *Opt. Acta* **21**, 709.

Goldman, S. (1953). "Information Theory." Dover, New York.

Gonzalez, R. C., and Wintz, P. (1977). "Digital Image Processing." Addison-Wesley, Reading, Massachusetts.

Goodman, J. W. (1968). "Introduction to Fourier Optics." McGraw-Hill, New York.

Hadley, G. (1962). "Linear Programming." Addison-Wesley, Reading, Massachusetts.

Hall, E. L. (1979). "Computer Image Processing and Recognition." Academic Press, New York.

Hamming, R. W. (1962). "Numerical Methods for Scientists and Engineers." McGraw-Hill, New York.

Harris, J. L. (1964). *J. Opt. Soc. Am.* **54**, 931.

Harris, J. L. (1966). *J. Opt. Soc. Am.* **56**, 569.

Helstrom, C. W. (1967). *J. Opt. Soc. Am.* **57**, 297.

Hestenes, M. (1980). "Conjugate Direction Methods in Optimization." Springer-Verlag, New York.

Hildebrand, F. B. (1965). "Introduction to Numerical Analysis," pp. 450, 451. McGraw-Hill, New York.

Howard, S. J. (1978). M.S. Thesis, University of Southern Mississippi, Hattiesburg.

Howard, S. J. (1981a). *J. Opt. Soc. Am.* **71**, 95.

Howard, S. J. (1981b). *J. Opt. Soc. Am.* **71**, 819.

Howard, S. J., and Rayborn, G. H. (1980). *NASA [Contract. Rep.]CR* **NASA CR-3229**.

Huang, T. S., ed. (1975). "Picture Processing and Digital Filtering." Springer-Verlag, New York.

Hunt, R. H., Brown, L. R., and Toth, R. A. (1978). *J. Mol. Spectrosc.* **69**, 482.

Ioup, G. E. (1981). *Bull. Am. Phys. Soc.* **26**, 1213 (abstr.).

Jansson, P. A. (1968). Ph.D. Dissertation, Florida State University, Tallahassee.

Jansson, P. A., Hunt, R. H., and Plyler, E. K. (1970). *J. Opt. Soc. Am.* **60**, 596.

Kawata, S., and Ichioka, Y. (1980a). *J. Opt. Soc. Am.* **70**, 762.

Kawata, S., and Ichioka, Y. (1980b). *J. Opt. Soc. Am.* **70**, 768.

Lawson, C. L., and Hanson, R. J. (1974). "Solving Least-Squares Problems." Prentice-Hall, Englewood Cliffs, New Jersey.

Lighthill, M. J. (1970). "Introduction to Fourier Analysis and Generalized Functions." Cambridge Univ. Press, London and New York.

Loewenstein, E. V. (1966). *Appl. Opt.* **5**, 845.

Maeda, J., and Murata, K. (1982). *Appl. Opt.* **21**, 2199.

Mammone, R., and Eichmann, G. (1982a). *Appl. Opt.* **21**, 496.

Mammone, R., and Eichman, G. (1982b). *J. Opt. Soc. Am.* **72**, 987.

Marks, R. J., II, and Smith, M. J. (1981). *Opt. Lett.* **6**, 522.

Mertz, L. (1965). "Transformations in Optics." Wiley, New York.

Montgomery, W. D. (1982). *Opt. Lett.* **7**, 54.

Morrison, J. D. (1963). *J. Chem. Phys.* **39**, 200.

Morton, D. C., and Rayborn, G. H. (1979). *J. Chem. Phys.* **70**, 2450.

Papoulis, A. (1962). "The Fourier Integral and Its Applications." McGraw-Hill, New York.

Papoulis, A. (1968). "Systems and Transforms with Applications in Optics." McGraw-Hill, New York.

Papoulis, A. (1977). "Signal Analysis." McGraw-Hill, New York.

Pratt, W. K. (1978). "Digital Image Processing." Wiley, New York.

Rabiner, L. R., and Rader, C. M., eds. (1972). "Digital Signal Processing." IEEE Press, New York.

Rosenfeld, A., and Kak, A. C. (1975). "Digital Picture Processing." Academic Press, New York.

Rushforth, C. K., and Frost, R. L. (1980). *J. Opt. Soc. Am.* **70**, 1539.

Rushforth, C. K., Crawford, A. E., and Zhou, Y. (1982). *J. Opt. Soc. Am.* **72**, 204.

Sabri, M. S., and Steenaart, W. (1978). *IEEE Trans. Circ. Syst.* **CAS-25**, 74.

Sato, T., Norton, S. J., Linzer, M. J., Ikeda, U., and Hirama, M. (1981). *Appl. Opt.* **20**, 395.

Savitzky, A., and Golay, M. J. E. (1964). *Anal. Chem.* **36**, 1627.

Schafer, R. W., Mersereau, R. M., and Richards, M. A. (1981). *Proc. IEEE* **69**, 432.

Schell, A. C. (1965). *Radio Electron. Eng.* **29**, 21.

Severcan, M. (1982). *Appl. Opt.* **21**, 1073.

Shannon, C. E., and Weaver, W. (1949). "The Mathematical Theory of Information." Univ. of Illinois Press, Urbana.

Sheen, S. H., and Skofronick, J. G. (1974). *J. Chem. Phys.* **61**, 1430.

Slepian, D., and Pollak, H. O. (1961). *Bell Syst. Tech. J.* **40**, 43.

Stark, H., Cahana, D., and Webb, H. (1981). *J. Opt. Soc. Am.* **71**, 635.

Stark, H., Cruze, S., and Habetler, G. (1982). *J. Opt. Soc. Am.* **72**, 993.

Steel, W. H. (1967). "Interferometry." Cambridge Univ. Press, London and New York.

Tam, K. C., and Perez-Mendez, V. (1981). *J. Opt. Soc. Am.* **71**, 582.

Toth, R. A., Brown, L. R., Hunt, R. H., and Rothman, L. S. (1981). *Appl. Opt.* **20**, 932.

Vanasse, G. A., ed. (1977). "Spectrometric Techniques," Vol. 1. Academic Press, New York.

Vanasse, G. A., ed. (1981). "Spectrometric Techniques," Vol. 2. Academic Press, New York.

Vanasse, G. A., and Sakai, H. (1967). *Prog. Opt.* **6**, 259.

Vanasse, G. A., and Strong, J. D. (1958). *In* "Classical Concepts of Optics" (J. D. Strong, ed.), Appendix F. Freeman, San Francisco, California.

Vanasse, G. A., Stair, A. T., Jr., and Baker, D. J., eds. (1971). *Aspen Int. Conf. Fourier Spectrosc. [Proc.], 1970* AFCRL-71-0019, Spec. Rep. No. 114.

van Cittert, P. H. (1931). *Z. Phys.* **69**, 298.

van de Hulst, H. C. (1946). *Bull. Astron. Inst. Neth.* **10**, 75.

Wolter, H. (1961). *Prog. Opt.* **1**, 155.

Youla, D. C. (1978). *IEEE Trans. Circ. Syst.* **CAS-25**, 694.

Zhou, Y., and Rushforth, C. K. (1982). *Appl. Opt.* **21**, 1249.

Index